THE PROBLEM OF
INDUCTIVE LOGIC

*Proceedings of the International Colloquium
in the Philosophy of Science, London, 1965,
volume 2*

Edited by

IMRE LAKATOS

Reader in Logic, University of London

1968

NORTH-HOLLAND PUBLISHING COMPANY
AMSTERDAM

THE PROBLEM OF INDUCTIVE
LOGIC

STUDIES IN LOGIC

AND

THE FOUNDATIONS OF MATHEMATICS

NORTH-HOLLAND PUBLISHING COMPANY
AMSTERDAM

PREFACE

This book constitutes the second volume of the Proceedings of the 1965 International Colloquium in the Philosophy of Science held at Bedford College, Regent's Park, London, from July 11th to 17th 1965. The Colloquium was organised jointly by the British Society for the Philosophy of Science and the London School of Economics and Political Science, under the auspices of the Division of Logic, Methodology and Philosophy of Science of the International Union of History and Philosophy of Science.

The Colloquium and the Proceedings were generously subsidised by the sponsoring institutions, and by the Leverhulme Foundation and the Alfred P. Sloan Foundation.

The members of the Organising Committee were: W. C. Kneale (Chairman), I. Lakatos (Honorary Secretary), J. W. N. Watkins (Honorary Joint Secretary), S. Körner, Sir Karl R. Popper, H. R. Post, and J. O. Wisdom.

The Colloquium was divided into three main sections: *Problems in the Philosophy of Mathematics*, *The Problem of Inductive Logic*, and *Problems in the Philosophy of Science*. The full programme of the Colloquium is printed in the first volume of the Proceedings.

This second volume of the Proceedings, *The Problem of Inductive Logic*, contains revised, and at times considerably expanded, versions of the seven papers presented in this field at the Colloquium. Some of the participants in the debates were invited to submit discussion notes based on the revised versions of the papers; thus they too differ, sometimes greatly, from the original comments made during the discussions. The authors' replies are in their turn based on these reconstructed discussion notes. The Editor imposed no restriction upon the length of contributions; happily no contributor abused this policy except for the author of the last essay.

The Editor regrets an omission from these Proceedings. In the discussion of Professor Carnap's paper Mr. David Miller presented a paradox of information which was discussed extensively. However, this paradox was published immediately after the Colloquium in *The British Journal for the Philosophy of Science* (Vol. 17, May 1966), and a discussion ensued in subsequent issues.

The Editor wishes to thank all the contributors for their kind cooperation. He is also grateful to his collaborators – above all, to Donald Gillies, David Miller and Alan Musgrave for their efficient editorial assistance, and to Miss Phyllis Parker for her conscientious secretarial and organisational help.

THE EDITOR

London, September 1967

CONTENTS

REALISTIC MODELS IN PROBABILITY

HANS FREUDENTHAL

Utrecht University

The subject of a science is never well circumscribed and there is little use sharpening its definition. However, nobody will deny that physics deals with nature and sociology with human society in some of their aspects. With logic, it is another matter. Logic is usually understood nowadays as a study of certain formal systems, though in former times there were philosophers who held that the subject matter of logic was the formal rules of human thought. In the latter sense it would be an empirical rather than a formal science, though its empirical subject matter would still be fundamentally different from that of psychology of thinking. One interpretation of logic does not exclude the other. Formal approaches are often easier than empirical ones, and for this reason one can understand why logic as a study of formal systems has till now made more progress than logic as a study of the formal rules of thought, even if restricted to scientific thought.

The case of methodology is analogous though less clear. Nobody would object to the subject of methodology being science, or some specified science. On closer inspection, however, this agreement is no more than a verbal coincidence. It rests on what is meant by science, as reported as a subject of methodology. In fact the subject methodologists call science is more often than not different from what scientists call science. Methodologists are inclined to consider a science as a linguistic system whereas the scientist would only admit that his science has a language, not that it is a language. Even if the methodologist's approach is less formal, his subject matter will most often be not an existing science but a construct. This is quite natural since research is always adapting its subject to the available methods. However, if this adaptation goes too far, and such a thing can happen in methodology, the result of the

1

transformation will be a fancy subject which does not exist anywhere but in the mind of its creator.

Of course this is a quite extreme situation but there are less extreme ones. A methodologist may feel obliged to rewrite a scientific subject during analysis or as a presupposition of analysis, as for instance Reichenbach did with relativity, but then his task with respect to this point is rather that of a textbook writer, not that of a reformer of the science. In any case in so far as a methodologist is rebuilding his subject matter, science, he has to be judged not as a methodologist but as someone working in that field of science. To give an example, Carnap's or Kyburg's approach to probability ought not to be evaluated as an analysis of existing probability theories, which it is not, but as a probability theory on its own; in practice this means considering whether it is a good or a bad theory of probability, whether it is consistent, whether problems of the old probability theory can be formulated and solved in the new system, and whether the new system is as good as, or even better than, the old one.

Axiom and axiomatics are more difficult notions in this respect. Probability is a mathematical notion, whereas axiom and axiomatics are metamathematical ones. Axiomatics means a particular way of organising a field of knowledge, and the particulars of this organisation can be understood in different ways by different people, though no one person need be completely right. Physicists, from the time of Gibbs onwards, call a presentation of a subject axiomatic, if the blackboard is covered with mathematical formulae, which, as it happens, are not related to a physical reality or otherwise motivated. The mathematician may be distressed about what he feels is a misuse of the term 'axiomatic', but he cannot prove that the physicist is wrong. Neither would the mathematician be pleased with the methodologist's use of the word 'axiomatics' for what is really formalisation, namely translating part of a textbook into a fully formalised language. But though this is not what axiomatics mean in mathematics, the mathematician has to recognize the fact that 'axiomatics' is not well-defined enough for monopolisation.

What axiomatics in its relation to reality has meant from

Hilbert's *Grundlagen* onwards, and what has been emphasized by Einstein with a formulation that has become classical, is the sharp separation between mathematical form and realistic contents. It is well known that this separation is carried out by means of implicit definition, an outstanding feature of axiomatics. For geometry it meant cutting the bonds with physical space, and thus the elimination of ontological questions, which had disturbed the peace of mind of the geometrician and the peace among geometricians during centuries; for instance, it resolved the old question whether a point is, by definition, something that has no parts, or whether it is the end of a line.

Though axiomatics was invented for the complete description of one particular field, viz. geometry, it soon took another turn. The enormous success of axiomatics and its all-pervading presence in today's mathematics is due to abstracting axiomatics, by the method of analysing several, often quite distant, fields of mathematical knowledge with respect to their common features in order to combine them into one field by means of a common axiomatic system.

Finally it has to be stressed that this activity of axiomatisation as understood by the mathematician, is not merely descriptive and conservative with respect to some state of science, but genuinely productive. Axiomatic systems are invented to be useful, and this means that profound reasoning is practically possible, not only about the system, but within it.

In these respects, axiomatics as conceived by mathematicians may differ from what some methodologists call axiomatics. The most notable difference, however, is the stress laid by methodologists on formalisation, which means the conscious organisation of the language in which something sayable is expressed. Most axiomatic mathematical systems are poorly formalised. What matters is the organisation of the subject matter, not of the language in which it is expressed. By accident the subject may itself be a language, and then of course formalisation will play a role in axiomatisation. But in most cases language is of secondary importance, and no mathematician would think of expressing some part of mathematics in a fully formalised language with the sole aim of calling it axiomatics.

Mathematical axiomatics has not made too much progress outside mathematics. Axiomatising physical space and probability have been important events, though they were comparatively easy subjects. Physics proper has been a less accessible subject, though there are now indications that at some time in the near future there will exist an axiomatic system of mechanics comparable to genuine mathematical axiomatics. The most outstanding feat has probably been the axiomatisation of thermodynamics; not of course Caratheodory's system, which is not axiomatic at all, but the more recent one of Giles, which might prove to be a paradigm of how physics ought to be axiomatised.

Probability, however, has not been as great a success as geometry was. An important feature of the axiomatisation of geometry I mentioned before was the complete elimination of ontological or quasi-ontological questions such as, 'What is a point?'. In probability theory the victory of axiomatics has been less complete. The old questions are still heard, and this, of course, means that there are people who try to answer them.

There is some reason why this has happened. Cutting the ontological bonds of geometry with space does not mean that geometry is never again applied to reality. So the problem of investigating how the axiomatic system of geometry is applied to reality, still subsists, whether somebody dares to tackle it or not. The same is true of probability. After Boole's failure, Keynes was the first to try a true axiomatisation of probability, and he was followed by Kolmogorov. Keynes used propositional calculus as an infrastructure, while Kolmogorov used set theory. Keynes' system, if duly completed, and Kolmogorov's, are equivalent. Kolmogorov's axiomatic system has been generally accepted by probabilists and statisticians, because it is the simplest and most practical solution anyone could ever imagine, but accepting one or other of these axiomatic systems does not imply how probability is put into practice. One may wonder why there are so few (if any) people who ask how axiomatic geometry is applied to nature, but many more who do so with respect to probability. The reason, I think, is that everybody believes that this problem is ever so simple in geometry, but highly sophisticated in probability (whereas it might turn out to be just the other way round).

After probability has become a mathematical notion, the question, 'What is probability?', still makes sense, at least if it is not asked as an analogue of questions like, 'What is a point?', 'Does the infinite plane exist?', 'How can a point move around a circle?', but rather as 'How is mathematical probability applied to reality?'.

In order to answer the question how probability is applied, one has first to *look* at how probability is applied, at least if one accepts the postulate that methodology is an empirical science. Probability invites oversimplification. Nobody believes that kicking a football tells him enough about the application of the mechanical notion of force, but probability seems so close to common sense (and so it is) that inventing an example on rolling a die seems to be a solid empirical basis on which to build a whole theory.

This is not to belittle the scientific level in methodology of probability. The literature is vast, the thought is often sophisticated, and sometimes even profound; it may be interesting too, except that often its subject is neither probability nor its actual applications. Expositions with the much more modest goal simply of explaining what probabilists and statisticians are doing, such as that in Braithwaite's *Scientific Explanation,* are usually much closer to the actual theory and application of probability.

The relative vastness of the literature on methodology of probability has had the awkward effect that struggling through it takes such an enormous effort that in the end the reader simply accepts that his empirical basis is broad enough. This is just not true. A bibliography of works on methodology of probability consists of works on methodology of probability. John von Neumann, who in this century contributed the most to methodology of probability, though he never wrote an explicit word on methodology, is barely mentioned. Methodology of probability has become a closed shop, where only methodologists buy and sell, and though I admit that precious things are bought and sold in this shop, I am not sure that probability as understood by probabilists is among them.

At the start of this lecture I dwelt on axiomatics because probability is just a point where axiomatics is understood in different ways by mathematicians and methodologists. To the methodologist the implicit definition of probability looks like shirking a duty. This explains the numerous attempts at defining probability explicitly. I think that the most remarkable amongst them, that of von Mises, has definitely proved why these attempts are condemned to failure.

The strongest testimony of the wide gap that has opened between methodology of probability and probability as a science, is the discussion on frequentism and subjectivism, a discussion that began more than a century ago. The discussion petered out in scientific circles when the new axiomatic theory of probability was accepted, though it is still alive in the methodological literature. Probabilists and statisticians are astonished to read in this literature that they are divided into frequentists and subjectivists, though they have never heard of these parties, and on reading the appropriate definitions, and perhaps understanding them, they reach the conclusion that they belong to none of these categories. Later on I shall come back to this point. In any case it is clear that if there is any sense in the question of what probability is, it cannot involve a difference in axiomatic approach, but can only mean that there are two different ways to apply mathematical probability, one frequentist and one subjectivist. But were this to be true, it would be a strange thing, if there were probabilists who insisted on applying probability in one way only and refused to apply it in the other way: in fact it would be unbelievable.

The methodological problem of how mathematical tools are applied to reality has actually not attracted the attention it deserves. Yet one fundamental fact has become clear, namely that mathematics is not applied directly to reality, but rather through an intermediate model. This fact is well-known to scientists, particularly to physicists, but it has not been recognised sufficiently by methodologists, mainly, I think, because in the last few years the term 'model' has been monopolised by model theorists. Here the terminologies of mathematicians, particularly logicians, and scientists again diverge. What a physicist means by a model is best illustrated by the history of this term, in which planetaria as models of the solar system, and the Rutherford–Bohr model as a description of the interior of the atom played a role. In mathematics the term 'model' originally indicated something analogous. I do not mean of course gypsum models of algebraic surfaces, but, rather, things like the well-known Cayley–Klein model of the non-Euclidean plane. Like the models of the physicists this was not a model of an axiomatic system (which did not exist for non-Euclidean geometry at that time), but a model of some reality. Of course there is already some difference, since the models of the physicist are meant as simplifying and also idealising patterns of nature, whereas the Cayley–Klein model is intended as a truthful representation within an intuitive Euclidean plane of something that is less intuitive.

In any case the notion of model has changed, and this is why I speak about *realistic* models of probability, in order to indicate that I do not mean a model of an axiomatic system, but a model of reality to which, thanks to suitable conventions, probability can be applied.

If really there can be different answers on the question, 'What is probability?', I think this question must mean, 'Are there essentially different models to which probability is applied?' Without further investigation one would suppose that the answer is yes. Probability is applied in physics in one way, and quite differently in statistics. Of course the physicist counting clicks of a Geiger–Müller counter behaves as a statistician proper, as long as he does not claim to be doing anything more than measuring a decay probability or the half-life of a radioactive material. But in a more profound sense the physicist applies probability as he applies Calculus or Fourier transforms, on the basis of a non-trivial physical theory. Probability as applied in gas theory is preceded by physical terms such as mechanical system, Hamiltonian, loose interaction, energy, canonical transformation, whereas the statistics of clicks does not presuppose much more theory than does counting sheep.

On the contrary the statistician proper applies probability to a material that has not yet been transformed by means of a profound theory. If I remember rightly, it was Laplace who defined probability as common sense pronounced in mathematical language. Indeed probability in statistics is that part of mathematics which

applies immediately to nature without any previous physical theory. It is comparable in this respect only to elementary arithmetic. Of course, if I predict that two rods of three feet each are six feet when put together, I apply mathematics to real things in the most straightforward way that can be imagined. But applications of probability in statistics are hardly less direct, though the mathematical tools there used are rather profound. We cannot apply potential theory or integral equations to reality without a highly developed intermediate physical theory, working with sophisticated physical models, whereas in statistics proper all specific models can be dispensed with. I will confine myself to this case of applied probability, because the common model of all statistics can be better studied in a case where this model is not tied up with a specific physical model. No scientist is as model minded as is the statistician − in no other branch of sciences is the word 'model' as often and as consciously used as in statistics.

No statistician present at this moment will have been in doubt about the meaning of my words when I mentioned the common statistical model. It must be a stochastic device producing random results. Tossing coins, or dice, or playing at cards is not flexible enough. The most general chance instrument is the urn filled with balls of different colours or with tickets bearing some ciphers or letters. This model is continuously used in our courses as a didactic tool, and in our statistical analyses as a means of translating realistic problems into mathematical ones. In statistical language 'urn model' is a standard expression. Innumerable times in courses or lectures I have asked the audience to imagine an urn containing red, white and blue balls in a given ratio; or black and white ones in an unknown ratio; or an urn containing the waist measurements of all Dutch women, from which I constructed a new urn containing all possible means over 5001 numbers out of the preceding urn; or two urns, one containing white and black balls in the ratio 3 : 1, and the other containing the same kind of balls in the inverse ratio, the problem being to guess from which urn some given sample of balls had been drawn. I never dreamt of bringing with me such an urn, or even of drawing the picture of such an urn on the blackboard, as a physicist would do when dealing with a gas in a vessel or the classical atomic model of hydrogen. Though I guess that none of my listeners has ever seen monstrosities like those urns, I am pretty sure that all of them grasp the meaning of my words with more ease than does the student of solid geometry who is asked to imagine a dodecahedron or even a cube. Sometimes I add that before drawing a ball, the urn is to be shaken, but even if I forget, I take it for granted that the student will shake it, as soon as he happens to work with such an urn.

The urn model is to be the expression of three postulates: (1) the constancy of a probability distribution, ensured by the solidity of the vessel, (2) the random character of the choice, ensured by the narrowness of the mouth, which is to prevent visibility of the contents or any consciously selective choice, and (3) the independence of successive choices, whenever the drawn balls are put back into the urn. Of course in abstract probability and statistics the word 'choice' can be avoided and all can be done without any reference to such a model. But as soon as the abstract theory is to be applied, random choice plays an essential role.

When we want to define 'random choice' we are committed to reality and realistic models, because no purely formal, that is to say, mathematical definition of random choice has so far been given, and because it is extremely improbable that such a definition will ever be found. In statistical practice random choice is made by using a table of random numbers, or so-called Tippett numbers. The first Tippett numbers were produced by means of a stochastic device. So they still reflect the urn model. On the other hand a number sequence produced by a causal machine (a Turing machine) can never be random; in fact it observes the law by which it is defined. It is true that in statistical practice number sequences produced by causal machines can serve as though they were random. The sequence of powers $a^m \bmod 10^{10}+1$ of a natural number a is a striking example. If the period of this sequence of digits is long enough, they behave in statistical practice as random numbers, because the underlying number-theory law is not likely to be met in natural material such as analysed by a statistician. But this does not provide any formal definition of random numbers, random choice, and disorder. It may be taken for granted that any

attempt at defining disorder in a formal way will lead to a contradiction. This does not mean that the notion of disorder is contra-
dictory. It is so, however, as soon as I try to formalize it. In order
to say, what is disorder or random choice, I am committed to
appeal to some real structure such as the urn model.

Probability theory has arisen from games. For two centuries
statistical problems were analysed according to the model of a
fair game. It has been the aim of the statistician to make some
statement about the contents of an urn. Under the same conditions
this could be a rough, and very reliable, statement or a more
refined, but less reliable one. There are a great many statistical
behaviour rules. No choice is possible as long as I do not account
for their individual consequences. This obvious truth has been
disguised (and it is still disguised) by the acceptance of conventional
rules with respect to the level of reliability of statistical decisions,
such as the 95 % rule of 'fingers and toes statistics'. (I allow for
the loss of one finger or toe.) In fact any good statistician will
account for the consequences of wrong or right decisions. In Wald's
theory this is done systematically. Wrong and right decisions are
to correspond to numerical losses and gains. In quality control
and drug testing it is not difficult to settle the gain and loss table.
But even in scientific work this is not as impossible as it seems.
A statement like, 'The elementary charge is $(4.803 \pm 0.005)\, 10^{-11}$
E.S.U.' aims at a statistical decision. It tells me the reliability
with which I can assert that the elementary charge is situated
within two bounds. As long as its value is an abstract magnitude,
no statistical problem will arise. But if my behaviour is essentially
different according to whether the value is $\geq 4.85 \times 10^{-11}$ or
$\leq 4.75 \times 10^{-11}$, I must be able to estimate numerically the losses
or gains caused by a wrong or right decision.

In order to exclude unselfish games, I will speak of a bet, if I
allude to Wald's statistical model. In applied probability, especially
in statistics, the bet model may be expected to supersede the pure
urn model, though at present practical statisticians are not yet
sufficiently bet-model-minded. In statistical evaluations of scientific
results, and generally in all cases where the gain and loss table is
not evident, the role of the bet model is not yet clear enough.

I think that the situation has been obscured by Wald's saying that in those cases the work of the statistician is a struggle against Nature. I think this is not more than a witticism that does not contribute in any way to the solution of the problem. I am sure that the bet model is correct in those cases too, but I do not believe in an interpretation where Nature should be assigned as a betting partner.

In our context the bet model is not as fundamental as the urn model. Once the urn model has been accepted, the bet model is no more than a refinement. I have stressed the informal character of the urn model: it cannot be replaced by a formal, purely mathematical device. It represents the appeal to reality that is needed as soon as mathematical probability is to be applied. Bets, however, can be formally defined on the basis of the urn model. It is true that a bet includes an agreement about what payments should be made if a ball of some colour is drawn out of the urn. But in order to understand the bet, we need not be told what the word 'payment' means. The only thing that matters is the minimax behaviour rule and this can be given in purely mathematical terms. We must be told that every bet partner will try to maximise his gain (or to minimize his loss) under the most unfavourable conditions. So after the urn model has been accepted, there is no need for new informal devices in order to establish the notion of a bet.

I am sure you will have got the impression from my exposition that the urn model is indispensable if mathematical probability is to be applied. This was my own conviction until, a few years ago, I realised that it is not correct. There is a quite different model that can serve as well as the urn model. I noticed this when I tried to develop a language in which we might communicate with human-like beings not acquainted with any one of our natural languages, not even with our mathematical mode of expression. This lecture is not the place to give details of that project. It will suffice to mention in this connection that so far four chapters have been developed dealing with respectively: 'Mathematics', 'Time', 'Behaviour' and 'Space, Motion, Mass'. It is a noteworthy fact that many features of human behaviour could be shown and named before the introduction of any notion from the material world, any notion of mechanics. At a certain point in the chapter, 'Behaviour', I was struck by the possibility of introducing probability, not as an abstract mathematical notion, but in its applied form. This could be done without any appeal to the material world, at a moment when there was not the slightest opportunity of speaking about urns that could be shaken, coins that could be tossed, or any other material devices whatsoever.

I introduced two actors playing some game like matching pennies. In its usual form this game is played by two persons A and B who simultaneously show a penny. If the shown result is two heads or two tails, A wins the bet; if it is one head and one tail, B wins.

Owing to von Neumann's work the theory of games has become a favourite topic of research nowadays, but even if you have never heard of this theory, you will have no difficulty in discovering the essential features of a game. Of course when playing it, you will try to increase your chance, but the only way to do it is to discover regularities in the actions of your opponent, and to avoid such regularities in your own behaviour. As soon as one of the players falls into some regularity, the other player can take advantage of it. But there is one minimax strategy for both players, that is to say a strategy that is the best under the worst circumstances. The minimax strategy consists in the random choice of head and tail of the coin, each side having the probability $\frac{1}{2}$. In order to realize this strategy, players should avail themselves of some stochastic device, like an unbiased coin that tells which side of the coin should be shown. Otherwise it would not be easy not to betray oneself. People who are asked to reel off numbers will quickly fall into repetitions. A skilled player can read them like a book. So does Shannon's machine that scores 60 % when playing matching pennies against human partners.

In Shannon's and my own version the game of matching pennies is played by choosing simultaneously one of the numbers 1 and 2. If both choose 1 or both choose 2, A wins, otherwise B wins. Any human-like intelligent being who understands human behaviour and the rules of this game will discover the minimax strategy, especially if illustrated by a few examples. The complete strategist playing against another complete strategist is a minimax strategist, and the minimax strategist in matching pennies is equivalent to an urn producing two events with equal probabilities. This means that in all applications such an urn can be replaced by a human being, a complete strategist playing matching pennies against another complete strategist. It is evident that this is not a special feature of urns containing white and black balls in the same ratio; it is easy to find out a game that corresponds to a given urn, so that the complete strategist of this game, considered as a stochastic device, is equivalent to the given urn.

It does not matter how the complete strategist actually ensures his completeness. Eventually this might be done by using a mechanical chance device, but in a definition of the complete strategist the special means of realisation need not be unveiled. So you will understand that in the earlier mentioned context it was possible to introduce probability and probabilistic notions like random choice at a stage when no appeal to material reality was possible. Instead we used what are essentially features of human behaviour.

I think it is a noteworthy result that the seemingly indispensable urn model can be dispensed with in applied probability. In the bet model the material chance device can be replaced by a complete strategist playing against another complete strategist. Of course the model of the complete strategist equivalent to an urn is as little formal as is the urn. It is not a mathematical device. In order to define it we must appeal to reality, though not to the material reality of an urn, but to that of human behaviour.

After all, this is not to be wondered at. Historically probability and probabilistic notions like disorder and random events have their roots in such important instances of human behaviour as games. In this respect disorder and chance do not differ from order and law which are not less deeply rooted in human behaviour as it is unveiled in human society.

Coming back to our original question, whether there are essentially different ways in which mathematical probability is applied, that is, whether there are essentially different realistic models for applying probability, I would say there are: the urn

model and the model of the complete strategist, the one related
to what in former times was called the frequentist approach, and
the other to what could be rightly understood by the term 'subjectivism' – and these are not exclusive, but complementary approaches to applied probability.

DISCUSSION

P. SUPPES: *Some remarks on the application of probability and the concept of model.*

I would like to express several points of agreement and some points of disagreement with Professor Freudenthal. Certainly I agree with his remarks about the difficulties that beset many methodological discussions of probability, and one way I would like to put it, related to some of our discussions of set theory, is this. A criticism of classical theories of probability is that they are categorical theories, and it is precisely the problem of application that probability theory not be categorical. In spirit the Laplacean conception of probability, the relative-frequency view, and the early work in confirmation theory lead to categorical theories. In practice, of course, everybody knows that you cannot have a categorical theory. Take, for example, Laplace. In the introduction to his famous treatise, after stating in Principle 1, the well-known classical definition of probability, Principle 2 asserts that in cases where we do not have a division into equally possible cases we must proceed otherwise. The classical definition of probability in terms of the ratio of favourable cases to equipossible cases has always been only a suggested definition and not one that could be taken seriously in application. I am very much in agreement with Freudenthal's remarks in this connection.

My second point is concern for the reasons behind the gap between the conception of probability and statistics held by mathematicians and statisticians, on the one hand, and methodologists and philosophers on the other. It seems to me that the difference is not so much that the two groups are working on really different problems but that the techniques of approach are so different. Philosophers have traditionally worked on probability theory in the context of elementary logic. Now it is very easy to show that the most elementary problems of statistics cannot be handled in a satisfactory way when we restrict ourselves to this framework, and the

15

difficulty has been then that the discussions by philosophers of
the foundations of induction have not been able to make detailed
contact with modern theoretical statistics because the apparatus
being used is difficult to bring into close juxtaposition to the
apparatus and results of the statisticians.

A simple example is the standard treatment of the binomial
distribution in statistics, and the application of the law of large
numbers to problems about this distribution. It is not possible
directly to express many of the results obtained in terms of modern
confirmation theory.

My third point concerns the treatment of temporal dependencies.
Classical statistics was, to a very large extent, restricted to strong
assumptions of independence. Application of realistic probability
models to complicated physical phenomena bring to the fore the
necessity to use the concepts and techniques of stochastic processes.
The dependency of what happens at a given time on what happened
at an earlier time is one of the most general observations of common
sense and experience, but it cannot be emphasized too strongly
that the fact of this dependency is extremely difficult to express
in any of the contemporary theories of probability discussed by
methodologists and philosophers mainly concerned with confirmation theory and the foundations of induction. In this sense then
we have an ever-widening gap between the realistic applications
of probability in the empirical sciences, and the methodological
issues being discussed by philosophers.

I now come to a point of disagreement with Freudenthal. I
cannot really accept his use of the word 'model'. I would say that
one of the characteristic things about the discussion of models in
statistics and in probability is that it is a completely straightforward
matter to formulate the models used in a set-theoretical fashion,
that is, these models have a clear formulation within the standard
set-theoretical framework.

Finally, two remarks about physics. I certainly agree with most
of what Freudenthal has said about physics. Certainly in the case
of physicists they don't look at distributions; they consider only
the expectation of an operator and look at such a large number
of observations that the law of large numbers applies in effect,

and no statistical methods are needed in order to analyse the data.

The second remark is that when we talk about models of probability it is in physics that we get as yet the only really striking and deep divergence from the standard methodology of probability and statistics. What I have in mind is the fact that if we look carefully at probability theory and quantum mechanics, then the standard tools of probability theory have to be handled with extreme care, and one can make quite a strong claim that probability theory itself must be modified in order to have an appropriately exact discussion of the nature of probability in quantum mechanics. What I have in mind is the fact that we do not have a joint distribution of conjugate random variables, for example, position and momentum, whereas the marginal distributions do exist. It seems a mistake to regard the underlying logic as the σ-algebra of sets; what in fact one has is a weaker structure which does not express, in which we cannot express, the joint distribution, for the very good reason that the joint distribution does not exist. What is interesting in this case about probability models is that for the first time, as far as I know, in the history of science, we have a new development, not about the nature of probability being subjective or objective, for example, but at a much deeper level, namely in terms of the formal properties of probability itself in the quantum mechanical setting. We have a sharp turning point in our actual formal conception of probability.

Y. BAR–HILLEL: *Freudenthal contra methodologos.*

1. *The professional hazards of the methodologist.* In his contributions to our conference, Professor Freudenthal continues to play his role as the methodologists' *advocatus diaboli*, a role which he has professed so successfully and helpfully for many years. I am sure that his injunctions against the loss of applicability that will be incurred by the methodologist if he indulges unselfcritically in his abstractions, extrapolations and idealizations are often to the point, and the methodologist will disregard them only to his own detriment. But I also think that Freudenthal has not been able

completely to avoid some of the dangers inherent in playing the
advocatus diaboli, in particular that of setting up a strawman to be
knocked down in some situations when no full-blooded opponent
is available.

It is true, presumably, that professional methodologists, when
they speak about science, have an idealized picture before their
mind. When Carnap, for instance, speaks about the axioms and
rules of correspondence of a science, he perhaps does not always
make it sufficiently clear that this is an idealizing assumption and
that no actual science has ever been presented in this form or
presumably ever will be. It is perhaps also the case that he, and
other methodologists, may on occasion themselves forget, or at
least not pay sufficient attention to, the idealizing nature of this
picture. But what Freudenthal apparently does not quite realize
is that this idealizing approach is *necessary*. For the methodologist,
any science in the investigation of whose methods he is engaged,
will always – and not only 'most often,' as Freudenthal has it –
'be not an existing science but a construct' and this is not only
'quite natural' but part and parcel of any scientific approach. That
such idealizations *may* result in a 'fancy subject' whose connection
with actual science is too slim to make the trouble worthwhile,
is one of the professional hazards of the methodologist, but he
shares these hazards with every other scientist. Have not innumer-
ably many theoretical scientists been accused, at various times, of
exactly the same transgression?

There is nothing wrong in pointing out once more the dangers
inherent in the pursuit of any theoretical activity, but by formulating this point as 'Methodologists are inclined to consider a
science as a linguistic system whereas the scientist would only
admit that his science has a language, not that it is a language',
a straw opposition is set up, with pretty clear emotional overtones
but little actual content. Which scientist has ever admitted 'that
his science has a language'? I myself do not recall ever having
come across this phrase and would not have been quite sure what
could have been meant by it, had I seen it. And which methodologist
has seriously – i.e. outside of prefaces, blurbs, provocative footnotes, and quick discussion remarks – claimed that 'science is a

language'? Since the methodologist Freudenthal must surely have often used the phrase 'the language of science' (or 'the language of (some particular science)') himself, how did he combine these *prima facie* – though by no means necessarily – incompatible usages?

Freudenthal similarly overplays the difference in the conception of axiomatics by the working mathematician and the methodologist. Of course, it is true that 'most axiomatic mathematical systems are poorly formalized' and that 'no mathematician would think of expressing some part of mathematics in a fully formalized language with the sole aim of calling it axiomatic', but Freudenthal does not seem to be aware of the fact that logicians and methodologists of mathematics do not at all identify axiomatization with formalization, and that Church, e.g., makes in his textbook very clear and careful, explicit distinctions between informal and formal axiomatization.

2.   *The deontologization of pure geometry.* I don't understand what Freudenthal means by his remark that 'the sharp separation between mathematical form and realistic contents' brought about by modern axiomatics starting with Hilbert and employed by Einstein, for instance, 'meant cutting the bonds with physical space, and thus the elimination of ontological questions, which had disturbed the peace of mind of the geometrician and the peace among geometricians during centuries'. What had actually happened was that the pure geometrician, by sheer division of labor, put himself in a position to produce, develop, axiomatize, and re-axiomatize his geometrical calculi without having to bother about possible interpretations. But the question of the bonds of these calculi with physical space was, of course, not thereby resolved or eliminated. It was only squarely put into the lap of the applied geometrician. *His* peace of mind continued to be disturbed by problems of interpretation, and *he* continued to feud with his fellow applied geometricians about these interpretations. The 'old question whether a point is, by definition, something that has no parts, or whether it is the end of a line' was indeed 'resolved' in certain pure geometries in which a point – or, rather, 'point' –

turned out to be a primitive term which had no definition. But
this move, of course, did not resolve the underlying real problem
of the interpretation of this term, or rather of the interpretation
of the whole calculus in which it occurred, through rules of correspondence, though it helped to sharpen this real problem and, as
a side-effect, to show the pointlessness (no pun intended) of the
original 'ontological' quarrels.

3. *The interpretational and ontological modes of questions.* I don't
see any important difference between the questions 'What is probability?' and 'What is a point?', after these two notions have both
'become mathematical notions', which probably means that they
occur in some calculus. Both kinds of questions can be understood
as having been posed in the 'interpretational mode' or in the
'ontological mode' ('external existence questions', in Carnap's
terminology), i.e. they both may be either meant as quests for
an interpretation of some probability or geometry calculus, respectively, or as quests for the clarification of the 'ontological
status' of probabilities and points, respectively. In both cases, the
second quest has to be rejected as pseudo.

I do not want to deny thereby that the interpretations of the
probability and geometry calculi could proceed in essentially
different ways. Under the relative-frequency interpretation (or
Freudenthal's 'urn model'), the atomic probability sentences turn
into (more or less) directly observable statements, and the notion
of probability receives a direct and complete interpretation.
Nothing of the kind is possible for the standard geometrical calculi.
Their (physical) interpretation is always provided through an
embedding in some physical theory, and the interpretation given
to 'point', for instance, will then turn out to be indirect and
incomplete.

4. *Random sequences and sequences of maximum degree of disorder.*
As Carnap has repeatedly pointed out (in conversation, though
not yet in print), the notion of 'random sequence', as ordinarily
understood, seems to refer to a sequence of elements produced by
certain kinds of physical devices ('random devices') and is therefore

not 'purely formal'. On the other hand, the notion of 'a sequence exhibiting maximum degree of disorder' can be purely formally defined, and Carnap himself, as well as Popper, for instance, have presented effective methods for the production of such sequences. The time has come to dissociate fully these two concepts whose fusion has created an inordinate amount of confusion. When this is accomplished, it will indeed be the case that 'in order to say, what is ... random choice, ... [one is] committed to appeal to some real structure such as the urn model' – though nobody would any longer be surprised by this finding – whereas this will not hold when 'random choice' is replaced by 'maximum degree of disorder', again, hopefully, to nobody's surprise.

5. *The contributions of professionals and amateurs to methodology of probability.* Just for the record – and I realize that this is not an argument – let me formally state that trying to think in terms of Freudenthal's 'urn model' and 'bet model' did not improve one bit my way of understanding the *Anwendungsproblem* of the probability concept beyond that amount of understanding I thought to have achieved by following Carnap's explications. This, though, may solely be due to the fact that my reading on methodology of probability consisted almost exclusively of 'professional' works on the methodology of probability (and not of mathematical, statistical or physical texts in which probability theory was applied as well as perhaps also 'amateurishly' discussed). I would be greatly indebted to Freudenthal if he could provide me with a (short) reading list of amateur texts where I could find additional enlightenment (in addition to von Neumann's contributions with which I am familiar).

I am quite ready to agree with Suppes that the 'logical foundations' provided for probability theory in all its generality by recent contributions to inductive logic and confirmation theory are still quite restricted in scope, and in particular are not yet able to deal satisfactorily with temporal dependencies, whether through having restricted themselves to the employment of elementary logic exclusively or through other self-restrictions. But I understand that investigations are in progress that could close this gap. I don't see how these investigations would profit from Freudenthal's remarks.

H. FREUDENTHAL: *Reply to Bar–Hillel.*

1. Idealizing his subject matter is not only the right but even the duty of the methodologist as it is of any scientist. I stressed it in my paper so there is no reason to guess that I did not realize it. But then indeed, it is the subject matter that has to be idealized, and not something else, be it objective material but outdated, or modern but of the methodologist's own invention. Since Bar–Hillel candidly admits that his own reading on the methodology of probability consists almost exclusively of 'professional' works on methodology, and not of mathematical, statistical, or physical texts, he can hardly measure the bewilderment a probabilist is seized with among methodologists – I mean the phenomenon of two different sciences which separated about half a century ago and have since moved steadily away from each other.

As for axiomatics, I think Bar–Hillel overstrains a play on words which I took the liberty to use. I agree that there are a few methodologists who know and respect the distinction between axiomatization and formalization, and there are several more who claim to know it. What I meant to assert was that carefully devised formal systems with a poor axiomatic background are more often the rule than the exception in methodological work. The evidence is so overwhelming that there is hardly any need to give details.

2–3. What Bar–Hillel writes about deontologization of geometry does not deviate in any way from what I said, perhaps in too condensed a form. Read my sentences, 'So the problem of investigating how the axiomatic system of geometry is applied to reality still subsists . . .', and ' . . . everybody believes that this problem is ever so simple in geometry but highly sophisticated in probability whereas it might turn out to be just the other way round.'

However, I have to take exception to Bar–Hillel's identifying the urn model with the 'relative-frequency interpretation'. I protest as strongly as I would if anybody called me an epicurean because I believed in atoms.

4. I agree with Bar–Hillel's warning against the confusion between randomness and disorder, though I have to add that the confused ones are not the probabilists but the methodologists. What is true is that, first, creating disorder is a common means of securing randomness; secondly, an orderly result may be an inducement statistically to doubt randomness; and thirdly, a disorderly result does not prove randomness, any more than an orderly one disproves it. Methodologists are still confused by von Mises's approach in which disorderly sequences play an important part. This concept may be interesting in itself (and to show it I would rather quote mathematical papers, such as Doerge's) but it has not anything to do with present probabilistic theory and practice.

5. It is by now generally accepted that to know what is geometry, one has to learn geometry. Even kings are not excepted, as Euclid maintained against Ptolemy. Since I am still less Euclid than Bar–Hillel is Ptolemy, I would answer his request: there is no '*probabilité sans larmes*' for the use of methodologists.

Reply to Suppes.

Suppes has added so much material and so much profoundness to my remarks that I would rather keep silent than prove myself ungrateful. The only objection I wish to make, is terminological. I like to use the word 'model' in the same sense as the maker of a planetarium speaks about a model of the solar system. In the same context Suppes would call the solar system a model of Newton's *Principia*. My objection against monopolizing 'model' to this use is that it leaves the maker of the planetarium without terminology. I can tell Suppes how and where this change of terminology took place. Klein's model of non-Euclidean geometry was a model in the first sense, since at that time non-Euclidean geometry was a reality though with a Platonic flavour. Non-Euclidean geometry in turning axiomatic just made a half-turn around 'model'. It is in this inverted relation that logicians found and adopted the 'model'.

THE JUSTIFICATION OF INDUCTIVE RULES OF INFERENCE *

WESLEY C. SALMON

Indiana University

Philosophers of very different persuasions agree that Hume conclusively demonstrated the impossibility of justifying induction, but they have drawn diverse morals. Professor Popper candidly concludes that inductive inference can play no role in science, if science is to retain intellectual respectability. He undertakes, quite appropriately I think, to reconstruct the logic of science without recourse to inductive logic [1]. Other philosophers, including Professor Ayer and Mr. Strawson, maintain that the impossibility of justifying induction shows that we had no need for any such justification in the first place. They seem to argue, by a kind of logic that frankly escapes me, that induction needs no defence because it is indefensible [2]. In contrast to both of these views, I claim that there is a crucial sense in which the logic of science is inescapably inductive, and that a justification of induction is essential to a full understanding of the logic of science [3]. I believe that the attempt to provide a pragmatic vindication of induction is, in spite of its

---

* The author wishes to express his gratitude to the National Science Foundation (USA) and the Minnesota Center for Philosophy of Science for support of research on inductive logic and probability.

[1] Karl R. Popper, *The Logic of Scientific Discovery*, New York, Basic Books Inc., 1959, § 1.

[2] A. J. Ayer, *The Problem of Knowledge*, Penguin Books, 1956, pp. 71–75; P. F. Strawson, *Introduction to Logical Theory*, London, Methuen & Co. Ltd., 1952, ch. 9.

[3] I have elsewhere argued in detail against various attempts to evade the problem of justification of induction; see, for example, Wesley C. Salmon, 'Should we attempt to justify induction?', *Philosophical Studies*, 8, 3, 1957; Wesley C. Salmon, Stephen F. Barker and Henry E. Kyburg Jr., 'Symposium on inductive evidence', *American Philosophical Quarterly*, 2, 4, 1965.

severe difficulties, the most promising approach. Since this approach must seem like a quixotic enterprise to those who accept either of the foregoing views, I shall begin by giving reasons for rejecting each of these appealing ways of avoiding the task of justification. I shall then discuss some of the serious issues attending the attempt to provide a pragmatic vindication.

1. *Deductivism.* If the logic of science can be explicated without reference to inductive inference we can cheerfully dispense with inductive logic and dismiss the problem of justification of induction. The first task is, therefore, to examine Popper's attempt to implement this program. In his effort to purge the logic of science of all inductive elements, Popper rejects induction by enumeration, and he rejects the hypothetico-deductive schema as a means for confirming hypotheses by positive results. He maintains instead that the schema is applicable only when negative results occur, and in this case it conforms to the deductively valid *modus tollens.* On the ground, then, that no finite set of positive instances can establish a general hypothesis while one negative instance can falsify it, he maintains that general hypotheses are amenable to falsification but not verification. The only mode of inference available for the acceptance or rejection of hypotheses is *modus tollens,* and it is obviously suitable for rejection only.

Hypothetico-deductive theorists and inductive probabilists maintain that positive instances tend to enhance the probability of the hypothesis or give it inductive support. With enough confirming instances of the appropriate sort the probability of the hypothesis becomes great enough to warrant accepting it as true – not, of course, with finality and certainty, but provisionally. With sufficient inductive support of this kind we are justified in regarding it as well-established. Popper, however, rejects the positive account, involving as it does the notion of inductive support. If a hypothesis is tested and the result is negative, we can reject it. If the result is positive, all we can say is that we have failed to falsify it. We cannot say that it has been confirmed or that it is more probable. Popper does admit a notion of corroboration, of course, but that is quite distinct from confirmation. I shall take up corroboration

shortly. For now, all we have are successful or unsuccessful attempts
to falsify; all we can say about our hypotheses is that they are
falsified or unfalsified. This is as far as inference takes us; according
to Popper, this is the limit of logic. The logic is entirely deductive.

This is where the trouble arises. Valid deductive inferences,
though truth-preserving, are nonampliative in character – that is,
the content of the conclusion is present implicitly or explicitly
in the premises. It is impossible to deduce from observation
statements alone any conclusions whose content exceeds that of
the observation statements themselves. If science consisted literally
of observation statements supplemented only by deductive inferences from them, then talk about theories, their falsifiability, and
their tests would be empty. The content of science would be
coextensive with the content of the statements used to describe
what we observe. There would be no general theories, no predictive
content, no inference to the remote past. Science would be barren.

Consider a couple of simple time-honored examples. Suppose
that the statement, 'All ravens are black', has been entertained
critically and subjected to every attempt at falsification we can
think of. Suppose it has survived all such attempts. What is the
scientific content of all this? We can say that 'All ravens are black'
has not been falsified, which is equivalent to saying that we have
not observed a non-black raven. This statement is even poorer in
content than a recital of our color observations of ravens. To say
that the hypothesis has not been falsified is to say less than is
given in a list of our relevant observation statements. Next, consider the generalization, 'All swans are white', which has been
falsified. What have we said when we say that it has been falsified?
We have said only that a non-white swan has been found. Again,
the information conveyed by this remark is less than we would
get from a simple account of our observations of swans.

Popper does not claim that falsification by itself can establish
scientific hypotheses. When one particular hypothesis has been
falsified many alternative hypotheses remain unfalsified. Moreover,
there is nothing unique about a hypothesis that survives without
being falsified. Many other hypotheses remain to explain the same
facts. Popper has readily admitted all this. If science is to amount

to more than a mere collection of statements describing our observations and various reformulations thereof, it must embody some other methods besides observation and deduction. Popper has supplied the additional factor: *corroboration*.

When a hypothesis has been falsified, it is discarded and replaced by another hypothesis that has not yet experienced falsification. Not all unfalsified hypotheses are on a par. There are principles of selection among unfalsified hypotheses. Again, falsifiability is the key. Hypotheses differ from one another with respect to the ease with which they can be falsified. Popper directs us to seek hypotheses that are as highly falsifiable as possible. A highly falsifiable hypothesis which is severely tested and survives the tests without actually being falsified becomes highly corroborated. The greater the severity of the tests – the greater their number and variety – the greater the corroboration of the hypothesis that survives them.

Popper makes it extremely clear that hypotheses are not to be regarded as true because they are highly corroborated. Hypotheses cannot be firmly and finally established in this or any other way. Furthermore, because of the inverse relation between falsifiability and probability, we cannot regard highly corroborated hypotheses as probable. To be sure, a serious attempt to falsify a hypothesis which fails does add to its corroboration, so there is some similarity between corroboration and confirmation as most hypothetico-deductive theorists think of it, but it would be a misinterpretation to suppose that increasing the corroboration is a process of accumulating positive instances to increase the probability of the hypothesis.

Nevertheless, Popper does acknowledge the need for a method of selecting from among the unfalsified hypotheses. He has been unequivocal in his emphasis upon the indispensability of far-reaching theory in science. Empirical science is not an activity of merely accumulating experiences; it is theoretical through and through. Although we do not regard any hypothesis as certainly true, we do accept them tentatively and provisionally. Highly corroborated hypotheses are required for prediction and explanation. From among the ever-present multiplicity of hypotheses compatible with the available evidence, we select and accept. There is just one point I want to make regarding all of this. Popper's theory is not properly characterized as *deductivism*. He has not succeeded in purging the logic of science of all inductive elements. My reason for saying this is very simple. Popper furnishes a method for selecting hypotheses whose content exceeds that of the relevant available observation statements. Demonstrative inference alone cannot accomplish this task, for valid deductions are nonampliative – i.e., their conclusions cannot exceed their premises in content. Furthermore, Popper's theory does not claim that basic statements plus deduction can give us scientific theory; instead, corroboration is introduced. Corroboration is, I think, a nondemonstrative kind of inference. It is a way of providing for the acceptance of hypotheses even though the content of these hypotheses goes far beyond that of the basic statements. *Modus tollens* without corroboration is empty; *modus tollens* with corroboration is induction.

If we ask, 'Why should we reject a hypothesis when we have accepted one of its potential falsifiers?' the answer is easy. The potential falsifier contradicts the hypothesis, so the hypothesis must be false if the potential falsifier holds. That is simple deduction. When we ask, 'Why should we accept from among all the unfalsified hypotheses one that is highly corroborated?' we have a right to expect an answer. An answer would be some kind of justification for the methodological rule – for the method of corroboration. Popper offers an answer to this question.

Popper makes it clear that his conception of the logic of science differs in important respects from the conceptions of many inductivists. I certainly have no desire to quibble over a word in claiming that Popper is, himself, a kind of inductivist. The issue is not a trivial verbal one. Popper has claimed that scientific inference is exclusively deductive. We have seen, however, that deductive inference is not sufficient to the task of providing a reconstruction of the acceptance – albeit tentative and provisional – of hypotheses. Popper realizes this and introduces a mode of nondemonstrative inference. It does not matter whether we call this kind of inference 'induction'. Whatever we call it, it is ampliative and nondemonstrative. With the same force and logic with which Hume raised questions about the justification of induction, we may and must raise problems about the justification of any kind of nondemonstrative inference. Hume's arguments are not peculiar to induction by enumeration or any other special kind of inductive inference; they apply with equal force to any inference whose conclusion might be false even when it has true premises. One cannot dismiss induction by enumeration on grounds of Hume's argument, and then accept some other nondemonstrative mode of inference without even considering how Hume's argument might apply to it.

I am not arguing that Popper's reconstruction is incorrect; I am not even arguing that he has failed in his attempt to justify his method of nondemonstrative inference. I am arguing that he has not avoided the problem of justification of induction raised by Hume. It seems to me that he is engaged in the same enterprise as many of his inductivist friends – namely, the task of providing some sort of justification for a mode of nondemonstrative inference. Many of us see this goal as a pragmatic vindication of induction.

2. *Dissolution.* If the foregoing argument is correct, some sort of nondemonstrative ampliative inference is an integral part of the logic of science. If this is so, we cannot avoid confronting the problem of justification of induction, more or less as posed by Hume. According to many philosophers, however, a careful analysis of the problem shows that it can be dissolved – that is, that induction plays its proper role in the logic of science (and common sense) and stands in no need of any special sort of justification or vindication. It is this attempt to show that a vindication of induction is superfluous that I wish to examine next.

Hume, it is often said, tried to find a way of proving that inductive inferences with true premises would have true conclusions. He properly failed to find any such justification precisely because it is the function of deduction to prove the *truth* of conclusions on the basis of true premises. Induction has a different function. Given true premises, the inductive inference establishes its conclusions as *probable*. Small wonder that Hume failed to find a justification of induction! He was trying to make induction into deduction, and he really succeeded only in proving the platitude that induction is not deduction.

The first crucial point in this approach hinges on the meaning of the term 'probable'. Clearly it cannot be construed in any frequency sense, for to do so would be to claim that inductive inferences with true premises often have true conclusions. Hume's argument has already shown that this claim cannot be substantiated. Long before Hume it was recognized that inductive inferences cannot be expected to lead to truth in all cases; the suggestion that Hume merely showed the fallibility of induction is a mistake [1]. Hume's argument shows not only that we cannot justify the claim that *every* inductive inference with true premises will have a true conclusion, but further that we cannot prove that *any* inductive inference with true premises will have a true conclusion. We can show neither that inductive inferences establish their conclusions as true nor that they establish them as probable in the frequency sense.

A more promising probability concept identifies probability with rational belief. To say that a statement is probable in this sense means that one would be rationally justified in believing it; the degree of probability is the degree of assent a person would be rationally justified in giving. To say that a statement is probable in this sense means simply that it is supported by evidence. Moreover, a statement that is the conclusion of an inductive inference with true premises *is* supported by evidence – by inductive evidence – and this is what it means to be supported by evidence. It follows immediately that the conclusion of an inductive inference is probable under this concept of probability. To ask, with Hume, if we should accept inductive conclusions is tantamount to asking if we should fashion our beliefs in terms of the evidence, and this, in turn, is tantamount to asking whether we should be rational. Once we understand clearly the meanings of such key terms as 'rational', 'probable', and 'evidence', we see that the problem arose out of deep linguistic confusion and resolves itself into the question of

---

[1] This error seems to be involved in Jerrold Katz, *The Problem of Induction and its Solution*, Chicago, University of Chicago Press, 1962, p. 115.

whether it is rational to be rational. Such tautological questions, if meaningful at all, demand affirmative answers.

Appealing as the foregoing kind of argument is, it does not, in my opinion, successfully demonstrate the dispensability of a justification of induction. Consider the concept of inductive evidence as it figures in the argument. The fundamental difficulty arises from the fact that the very notion of inductive evidence is determined by the rules of inductive inference. In order for a conclusion to be supported by inductive evidence it must be the conclusion of a correct inductive inference with true premises. Whether the inductive inference is correct depends upon whether the rule governing that inference is correct. The relation of inductive evidential support is inseparably bound to the correctness of rules of inductive inference. In order to be able to say whether a given statement is supported by inductive evidence we must be able to say which inductive rules are correct.

Suppose, for example, that a die has been thrown a large number of times and we have observed that the side two came up in one-sixth of the tosses. This is our 'evidence' e. Let h be the conclusion that, 'in the long run', side two will come up one-sixth of the times. Consider the following three rules:

(1) (Induction by enumeration). Given m/n of observed A are B, to infer that the 'long run' relative frequency of B among A is m/n.

(2) (*A priori* rule). Regardless of observed frequencies, to infer that the 'long run' relative frequency of B among A is $1/k$, where k is the number of possible outcomes – six in the case of the die.

(3) (Counter-inductive rule). Given m/n of observed A are B, to infer that the 'long run' relative frequency of B among A is $(n-m)/n$.

Under rule 1, e is positive evidence for h; under rule 2, e is irrelevant to h; and under rule 3, e is negative evidence for h. In order to say which conclusions are supported by what evidence, it is necessary to arrive at a decision as to what inductive rules are acceptable. If rule 1 is correct, the evidence e supports the conclusion h. If rule 2 is correct, we are justified in drawing the conclusion h, but this is entirely independent of the observational evidence e; the same conclusions would have been sanctioned by rule 2 regardless of observational evidence. If rule 3 is correct, we are not only prohibited from drawing the conclusion h, but also we are permitted to draw a conclusion h' which is logically incompatible with h. Whether a given conclusion is *supported by evidence* – whether it would be *rational to believe* it on the basis of given evidence – whether it is *made probable* by virtue of its relation to given evidence – depends upon selection of the correct rule or rules from among the infinitely many rules we might conceivably adopt.

The problem of induction can now be reformulated as a problem about evidence. What rules ought we to adopt to determine the nature of inductive evidence? What rules provide suitable concepts of inductive evidence? If we take the customary inductive rules to define the concept of inductive evidence, have we adopted a proper concept of evidence? Would the adoption of some alternative inductive rules provide a more suitable concept of evidence? These are genuine questions which need to be answered.

We find, moreover, that what appeared earlier as a pointless question now becomes significant and difficult. If we take the customary rules of inductive inference to provide a suitable definition of the relation of inductive evidential support, it makes considerable sense to ask whether it is rational to believe on the basis of evidence as thus defined rather than to believe on the basis of evidence as defined according to other rules. For instance, I believe that the *a priori* rule and the counter-inductive rule mentioned above are demonstrably unsatisfactory, and hence, they demonstrably fail to provide a suitable concept of inductive evidence. The important point is that something concerning the selection from among possible rules needs demonstration and is amenable to demonstration [1].

---

[1] For such demonstrations, see Wesley C. Salmon, 'Regular Rules of Induction', *Philosophical Review*, **65**, 3, 1956, and 'Inductive Inference', Bernard H. Baumrin, ed., *Philosophy of Science, The Delaware Seminar*, New York, John Wiley & Sons, vol. 2, 1963.

There is danger of being taken in by an equivocation. One meaning we may assign to the concept of inductive evidence is, roughly, the basis on which we ought to fashion our beliefs. Another meaning results from the relation of evidential support determined by whatever rule of inductive inference we adopt. It is only by supposing that these two concepts are the same that we suppose the problem of induction to have vanished. The problem of induction is still there; it is the problem of providing adequate grounds for the selection of inductive rules. We want the relation of evidential support determined by these rules to yield a concept of inductive evidence which is, in fact, the basis on which we ought to fashion our beliefs.

We began this initially promising approach to the problem of the justification of induction by introducing the notion of probability, but we end with a dilemma. If we take 'probability' in the frequency sense, we can find some reasons for accepting probable conclusions in preference to improbable ones. In so doing we shall be right more often. Unfortunately, we cannot show that inferences conducted according to any particular rule establish conclusions that are probable in this sense. If we take 'probability' in a non-frequency sense it may be easy to show that inferences which conform to our accepted inductive rules establish their conclusions as probable. Unfortunately, we can find no reason to prefer conclusions which are probable in this sense to those which are improbable. As Hume has shown, we have no reason to suppose that probable conclusions will often be true and improbable ones will seldom be true. This dilemma is Hume's problem of induction all over again. We have been led to an interesting reformulation, but it is only a reformulation and not a dissolution.

3.   *Vindication.* It is essential to make clear one fundamental area of agreement between those who look for a vindication of induction and those who support the views I have been discussing. All of us maintain that Hume demonstrated correctly and definitively the impossibility of proving that inductive inferences with true premises will ever again have true conclusions. We reject all attempts to justify induction by means of synthetic *a priori* principles or by

means of inductive justifications. I maintain, moreover, that a justification of induction is required for an understanding of the logic of science, but that it cannot take the form of proving that induction will sometimes yield true conclusions. This is, to say the least, an awkward position to maintain, but I do not think it is hopeless.

Many philosophers, often including those who seek a linguistic dissolution of the problem, have concluded that the main obstacle in the way of providing a successful justification of induction is the ultimacy of the very principles we seek to justify. How can we hope for a justification, the argument goes, if we are without more fundamental principles with reference to which a justification can be carried out? If we cast wholesale doubt upon all inductive canons at once, we have *ipso facto* deprived ourselves of all the equipment for any sort of justification.

It has long been recognized that the problem of induction calls for the justification of a rule of inference (which is neither true nor false), not for a proof that a statement is true. Professor Feigl has provided substantial elucidation of the problem through his fundamental distinction between two kinds of justification, *validation* and *vindication* [1]. In the first place, we sometimes justify rules by deriving them from more ultimate rules. In standard systems of deductive logic, for example, a rule of conditional proof is sometimes justified by proving the deduction theorem, a meta-theorem that states in effect that nothing can be proved by conditional proof that cannot be proved without it. This type of justification is validation. When we radically question induction we are depriving ourselves of any principles in terms of which to validate inductive rules. Ultimate rules or principles are patently incapable of being validated, but this does not mean that they are beyond all possibility of justification, for there is another kind of justification.

Vindication of a rule or principle consists in showing that its adoption is well-suited as a means to some desired end. Given

---

[1]   Herbert Feigl, 'De Principiis Non Disputandum . . . ?' Max Black, ed., *Philosophical Analysis*, Ithaca, N.Y., Cornell University Press, 1950.

that the aim of science is to establish far-reaching knowledge of
the world, a vindication of induction would consist of an argument
showing that induction is a good method for determining what
statements purporting to describe reality are true. A method that
does its job successfully is a good one. Hume's argument proves,
unfortunately, the impossibility of showing that induction will be
successful. Thus, it is tempting to suppose that vindication, like
validation, is impossible in principle.

The attempt to provide a vindication of induction is not, however, as futile as it looks at first glance; it is precisely the sort of
justification Reichenbach attempted to provide [1]. He argued that
inductive methods will yield predictive success if any method will.
If there are two methods for establishing general knowledge, one
of which must yield knowledge of uniformities if any exist while
the other may or may not, then we would seem to have a strong
reason for preferring the former to the latter as a rule for inferring
general hypotheses. This is the crux of Reichenbach's 'pragmatic
justification'. The fundamental difficulty is, as Reichenbach himself
realized, that the same argument justifies equally well all of the
so-called 'asymptotic rules'. Even so, it seems to me that the
argument provides powerful reasons for rejecting nonasymptotic
rules, and I suspect that such considerations are widely acknowledged, for the asymptotic property is often cited in support of
various statistical methods. It is apparent, nevertheless, that the
class of asymptotic rules is far too broad, and we cannot claim
a vindication of induction unless we can find suitable grounds for
drastically narrowing the choice.

The fundamental question giving rise to the problem of justification of induction concerns our warrant for inference from the
observed to the unobserved. The problem is not restricted to induction by enumeration or any other preselected mode of inductive
inference, but it applies quite generally to any form of ampliative
inference. As a staunch proponent of the frequency interpretation
of probability, Reichenbach was interested in inferring limits of

----

[1] Hans Reichenbach, *The Theory of Probability*, Berkeley and Los
Angeles, University of California Press, 1949, ch. 11.

relative frequencies. Such inference is obviously nondemonstrative, for any observed frequency is deductively compatible with any value for the limit. It is obviously ampliative, for the conclusion is a statement about a whole sequence, while the premises refer to only a part of it. However, one need not be a frequentist to be interested in this sort of inference, for frequencies play a fundamental role in any theory of probability. The aim of knowing something about 'long run' frequencies cannot be considered irrelevant to science.

Among the rules designed to serve this purpose, induction by enumeration is distinguished by its simplicity; it takes the observed relative frequency as the inferred value of the limit. Asymptotic rules are those in which the difference between the observed frequency and the inferred value of the limit converges to zero for increasing sample size. The asymptotic rules, including induction by enumeration as a special case, all satisfy a *convergence condition*. For any member of this class, if the sequence has a limit, the inferred values given by this rule become and remain accurate within any desired degree of approximation – that is, if the sequence has a limit, use of this rule will inevitably provide accurate inferences regarding its value.

I have suggested elsewhere that two other conditions be imposed upon rules of this type [1]. The first is a *normalizing condition*. Since limits of relative frequencies cannot be negative, and since the sum of the limits for a set of mutually exclusive and exhaustive attributes must be one, we impose these conditions upon our inferences. For instance, I have argued that the counter-inductive method (rule 3 above) is inadmissible because it requires us to infer that the limit of the relative frequency of one-or-two-or-three-or-four-or-five-or-six on tosses of standard dice has the absurd value five. This counterinductive rule also, incidentally, violates

---

[1] Wesley C. Salmon, 'Vindication of Induction', Herbert Feigl and Grover Maxwell, eds., *Current Issues in the Philosophy of Science*, New York, Holt, Rinehart and Winston, 1961; 'On Vindicating Induction', Henry E. Kyburg Jr. and Ernest Nagel, eds., *Induction: Some Current Issues*, Middletown, Conn., Wesleyan University Press, 1963 (also in *Philosophy of Science*, **30**, 3, 1963).

the convergence condition; it is obviously not asymptotic. These are two fundamental reasons for rejecting this rule as perverse.

The second requirement is the *criterion of linguistic invariance*. The basic idea behind this requirement is that the inferences we make concerning the limit of the relative frequency should not be a function of the language we use to formulate our evidence statements. Two logically equivalent descriptions of a sample should not enable us to infer two different values for the limit of the relative frequency. Thus, for instance, the *a priori* rule (rule 2 above) fails to meet this criterion. Suppose we have an urn containing balls we know by hypothesis to be red, yellow, or blue. We ask for the limit of the relative frequency of red, and the answer is $\frac{1}{3}$ because there are three color predicates involved. If, however, we define a new pair of predicates, 'light blue' and 'dark blue', which are mutually exclusive and together logically equivalent to 'blue', we would be forced to conclude that the limit of the relative frequency of red is $\frac{1}{4}$. It is for this kind of reason that we must reject any rule that makes the inferred value of the limit a function of k, the number of mutually exclusive and exhaustive predicates involved. This number can be changed by a purely verbal manipulation.

Taken together, the convergence condition, the normalizing condition, and the linguistic invariance condition are quite powerful. At one time I thought they provided a full vindication of induction by enumeration, but now I realize that this view is incorrect. Additional conditions are needed, but I have no idea what they might look like, or even whether there are any acceptable ones. Although I am not completely pessimistic about the prospects for a vindication, I should like to keep focused upon present problems instead of speculating about future developments.

The normalizing condition and the criterion of linguistic invariance can be regarded as consistency requirements; violation would allow our inductive logic to introduce a logical contradiction. This has seemed to me a sufficient reason for adopting these requirements [1]. It has been pointed out, however, that explicit contra-

---

[1] Wesley C. Salmon, 'Consistency, Transitivity and Inductive Support, *Ratio*, **7**, 2, 1965.

diction will result only if our inductive logic contains acceptance rules. If our inductive logic is framed (like Carnap's) entirely in terms of confirmation functions without rules of detachment, contradiction seems to be avoided. The point can be made clearest, perhaps, by considering estimates. In all cases in which we do not have exact knowledge of physical magnitudes we have to use estimates of one sort or another. Should we insist that estimated values be logically possible values of the magnitude? For instance, we might agree by definition that a family can have only an integral number of children, yet we might say that the estimate of the number of children in a certain family is $2\frac{5}{8}$. If we allow such estimates we must be careful how we treat them. Given that the foregoing is a correct estimate, we cannot simply assert that the Jones family has $2\frac{5}{8}$ children, for that would be a logical contradiction.

The same situation arises when we deal with limits of relative frequencies. Since we do not have direct knowledge of these limits, we must make estimates if we are to say anything about them. If we are to turn around and assert values for limits of relative frequencies on the basis of these estimates, we must, on pain of contradiction, insist that the limits asserted be logically possible values. If, however, we are never going to detach the estimates and assert them, it might be permissible to allow logically impossible values as estimates. If an inductive rule is a method for producing estimates, and if these estimates are never to be detached and asserted as actual values of the limits, then we might consider dispensing with consistency requirements like the normalizing conditions and the criterion of linguistic invariance. (If, however, estimates of relative frequencies are to be taken as betting quotients, we will want to adhere to the normalizing conditions and the criterion of linguistic invariance to preserve coherence of betting systems.)

The fundamental issue is whether inductive logic is to have rules for the acceptance of hypotheses. Carnap's inductive logic does not embody such rules; it has only analytic confirmation statements that relate hypotheses to evidence. There is no means for detaching the hypothesis and asserting it; instead, we are given methodological rules for the use of confirmation statements [1].

Consider Strawson's example of nondeductive reasoning, 'He's been travelling for twenty-four hours, so he'll be very tired' [2]. If we think of this as an inductive inference with premise and conclusion, and if we accept the premise, we might be tempted to detach the conclusion and assert, 'He'll be very tired'. This procedure seems harmless enough if we are considering whether to have the cocktail party in his honor on the day of his arrival, but it might be rash indeed (as any devotee of James Bond knows) if the question is whether to engage him in mortal combat as he steps from the train. The point is quite simple. Handling hypotheses that are supported inductively is more complicated than just accepting them or not. Instead of detaching them, Carnap offers rules of application like the requirement of total evidence and the rule of maximizing estimated utility. We keep the probability value attached to the hypothesis, and we use the probability value in determining what kinds of action are rational.

The situation becomes clearer in terms of the famous lottery paradox. Consider a fair lottery with as many tickets as you wish – i.e., with an arbitrarily large probability that any particular ticket will not win. If we detach and assert hypotheses that are sufficiently probable, we can assert that this ticket will not win. The same can be done for each ticket, so we deduce that no ticket will win. This contradicts the hypothesis that the lottery is fair. If, however, we simply state that on total evidence the degree of confirmation of the hypothesis that this ticket will win is $1/n$, then we can determine an acceptable price to pay for a ticket, and we get into no trouble. Inductive logic does embody probability statements, of course, and it provides the means for asserting them. These statements are, for Carnap, analytic. There is no

---

[1] These points were fully discussed in Rudolf Carnap, *Logical Foundations of Probability*, Chicago, University of Chicago Press, 1950, and I do not believe Carnap has subsequently changed his views regarding them, even though he now seems to regard the difference between an inductive logic that permits acceptance of hypotheses and one that does not as less fundamental than he did in 1950.

[2] Strawson, *op. cit.*, p. 235.

more problem about asserting them than there is about asserting
the laws of deductive logic.

Like many other philosophers, I have long felt dissatisfied with
the view that probability statements are analytic, for I have been
unable to see, in spite of Carnap's patient efforts to explain, how
such statements could constitute 'a guide of life' [1]. Suppose, for
example, that I wish to place a bet on Hoosier Boy to win in
tomorrow's Fifth Race at Santa Anita, and I seek advice from my
turf consultant who is an expert in probability theory. He informs
me that the degree of confirmation of the hypothesis h, that Hoosier
Boy will win this race, on some evidence e, is some number p; i.e.,

$$c(h, e) = p.$$

As Carnap has emphasized, this analytic statement, by itself, is
useless for prediction or betting. When I learn in addition, however, that the evidence statement e is true and that it encompasses
all available relevant evidence, Carnap maintains that I have a
basis for intelligent wagers and predictions on the outcome of this
future race [2]. It is not the analytic degree of confirmation statement
alone that serves as a guide of life, but the analytic statement in
conjunction with a synthetic evidence statement e [3].

This account does not seem entirely adequate, however, for the
synthetic evidence statement is a statement about past and present
events alone, and the analytic degree of confirmation statement
adds no factual content. Thus, when I seek guidance with respect
to future occurrences, I am given information about past and
present ones only. I feel inclined to express bitter disappointment

---

[1] Carnap, *op. cit.*, § 49. I am inclined to think that this is a basic source
of disagreement between Nagel and Carnap; see Nagel's essay and Carnap's
reply in *The Philosophy of Rudolf Carnap*, Paul Arthur Schilpp, ed., La
Salle, Illinois, Open Court, 1963.

[2] A. J. Ayer, in his penetrating essay, 'The Conception of Probability
as a Logical Relation', S. Korner, ed., *Observation and Interpretation*, London,
Butterworths Scientific Publications, 1947, has raised serious, and to my
knowledge as yet unanswered, difficulties regarding the requirement of total
evidence and the applicability of degree of confirmation statements.

[3] For purposes of this discussion we may safely ignore the case of
tautological evidence. See Carnap's reply to Nagel in Schilpp, *op. cit.*

in my turf consultant, for when I asked him for advice about a future event, he told me nothing about the future but only about the past and present. If there is one thing I have learned from Hume it is this: *the future is logically independent of the past and present.* In what sense, then, does the analytic degree of confirmation statement function as a guide of life?

Carnap's answer goes in the following direction. From a logical standpoint it is admitted that analytic statements are devoid of factual content, but they can still be extremely illuminating from a psychological standpoint. Consider, for example, the great practical utility of arithmetic calculation to a merchant in determining the day's total receipts or in discovering the net outcome of a year's business. In a similar fashion, we may expect the computations that yield degrees of confirmation to have significant pragmatic import as a guide of life.

This answer still seems not quite satisfactory. The admitted pragmatic value of analytic statements and deductive transformations lies in their ability to help us make explicit the factual content already implicit in a set of premises, but no extension of content is achieved. Just as the merchant can expect systematization and clarification of the information already available to him, so too, when we supplement our evidence statements about past and present events with any kind of analytic statements, we may procure some further clarification of these statements about the past and present. Since, as Hume has taught us, the future is logically independent of the past and present, the content of our evidence statements does not pertain either implicitly or explicitly to the future. Thus, the most we can expect from inductive logic, conceived as containing only degree of confirmation statements, is a device for transforming and elucidating statements about the past and present; from evidence about the past and present we cannot hope to get statements with any kind of genuine future reference.

Suppose I ask my turf consultant whether Hoosier Boy will win tomorrow. He replies that he does not know which horse will win, and because it is an honest race no one else does either. The best I can reasonably demand is a probability. He tells me he can compute the degree of confirmation on the total available evidence. I may be initially pleased at his willingness to do so, for I regard a probability as providing a basis for rational prediction and betting. When I reflect upon the analytic character of the degree of confirmation statement, however, my disquiet returns. If degree of confirmation is used to explicate the concept of rational behavior or belief, then it appears that a statement about rational prediction or betting on future events is really a disguised statement about past and present events. If this is so, then I am seriously puzzled regarding the force of the notion of rationality. The perplexity increases when I reflect upon the multiplicity of confirmation functions in terms of which this concept might be defined.

I find it difficult to escape the conclusion that synthetic probability statements are required if probability is to serve as a genuine guide of life, and frequency statements seem to fill the bill. These frequency statements must be assertable – just as Carnap's degree of confirmation statements are – if they are to serve their purpose. The crucial difference is, of course, their synthetic character. They cannot be asserted as laws of logic; they must be asserted on the basis of inductive evidence – they must be detachable. It seems, therefore, that inductive logic must contain rules of acceptance, at least for inductive conclusions of this particular sort. It is important to note, however, that detaching statements about limits of relative frequencies cannot lead to the lottery paradox. The trouble is avoided precisely because a bet on a limit statement can never be settled. Asserting that the limit of the relative frequency of B in A is p is, for this reason, fundamentally different from asserting that the man will be tired or that this ticket will not win the lottery. Notice that I am not attempting to assign a probability to the statement about the limit; instead, it is, in Reichenbach's terms, posited [1].

When Reichenbach turned from limit statements to statements about single events he was not sufficiently cautious. Though he spoke of the 'fictitious meaning' of probability statements about

---

[1] There seems to me to be a striking similarity between Reichenbach's notion of a posit, as a statement tentatively accepted until further evidence requires its revision or withdrawal, and Popper's concept of a conjecture.

single events, he did say that we could transfer probabilities from sequences to single events. He held that statements about single events could be asserted given sufficiently high probabilities. This procedure does lead to the lottery paradox.

Let me suggest the following modification of Reichenbach's theory in the light of some important lessons we have learned from Carnap. Carnap has emphasized the distinction between inductive logic and the methodology of induction, a distinction Reichenbach did not clearly draw. Probability theory proper, we might say, embodies limit statements only, but it does not include any of these fictitious single case 'probabilities'. Proper probability statements are, of course, synthetic, and they are to be asserted on the basis of inductive inferences conducted according to some *inductive* rule. When we want to apply probability considerations to single cases for purposes of betting or other practical action, we must apply *methodological* rules to determine which probability value should be used. The whole discussion of the assignment of probabilities to single events can be construed as an attempt to formulate a methodological rule for the application of probability theory in practical affairs. The rule for selecting the appropriate reference class is the rule for applying probabilities to single events; as such, it is strongly analogous to the requirement of total evidence. In addition, something like the rule of maximizing expected utility seems reasonable.

If the foregoing approach is adopted, then at least some of our inductive rules will be rules of inference; they will allow for the detachment of synthetic conclusions. Unless they conform to requirements like the normalizing conditions and the criterion of linguistic invariance explicit contradictions will arise. It will not do to treat these rules as procedures yielding estimates that need not be logically possible values of the magnitude being estimated. For this reason, I have carefully avoided talking about *estimates* of limits of relative frequencies, and referred instead to *inferred values* of such limits.

DISCUSSION

I. HACKING: *One problem about induction.*

Professor Salmon is the foremost authority on Reichenbach's vindication of induction, and to make full use of his expertise, I shall examine only that part of his paper dealing with Reichenbach's suggestions. Reichenbach's original theory came in two parts. There was a theory on inferring long run frequencies from very meagre statistical data, and a theory for reducing all inductions to just such inferences. Like Salmon, I shall study only the former aspect of Reichenbach's work.

Salmon and Reichenbach think they know a good rule for inferring from meagre data. I shall observe: (1) the reasons they give for this rule are not good reasons; (2) the reasons, even if they were good, are not sufficient to vindicate the rule; (3) the rule stated by Salmon is inconsistent; (4) another theory, taken from de Finetti, is less dubious, more fruitful, and does all that Reichenbach hoped for. A formal appendix establishes the actual necessary and sufficient conditions for the correctness of Salmon's rule. There are no good reasons for thinking that these conditions must be fulfilled.

1. *Frequencies.* Salmon rightly conceives of long run frequencies as physical characteristics of parts of the world. That is, suppose we have a device on which we can make successive trials, each trial having one of several possible outcomes. Then if there is a definite long run frequency of outcome E on trials of this kind, that is a physical property of the device in its current surroundings. Often, for brevity, I shall call this long run frequency the *chance* of E.

Salmon favours von Mises' sort of analysis of long run frequency in terms of a limit in an infinite sequence of proportions. Some of us, including our chairman, prefer rival analyses, but that does not matter here. We do agree that, in certain situations, the long run frequency of an outcome is a property of a set-up. We no more need to agree on the analysis of this property in order to discuss it, than we need to analyse length in order to discuss the length of this room.

2. *Inference.* Salmon is concerned with a very special case. Imagine a man, confronted with a device, able to make trials of some kind on it, but knowing nothing about the device except the possible outcome of any trial, and the actual outcomes of trials he has already made. I cannot emphasize too much how unfamiliar this situation is, but we can, I think, conceive of Adam tossing the first coin, or, more historically, tossing the heel bone of the first male deer.

We are to imagine this man trying to discover the long run frequency of various outcomes on trials from his device. That is the man's top priority. Salmon wants him to have a *rule of inference*, of this form: 'From your data d stating only the possible outcomes on trials of this kind, plus the actual outcomes of some past trials, infer that the long run frequency of outcome E on trials of this kind on your device, is $\mathscr{F}(E, d)$ – some function of the data d.' Here d is to range overall and only data of the sort we have described, in particular, stating outcomes of a finite sequence of trials. Among rules of this form, Salmon prefers the 'inductive' or 'straight' rule, in which, if d implies that of the n observed tosses, m have outcome E, then $\mathscr{F}(E, d)$ is the function m/n.

Salmon argues at some length that it is all right to speak of *inference* here. He is a little afraid logicians will say: but no inference from data is any good unless what is inferred follows logically from the data. Surprisingly enough, logicians do say that sort of thing. Salmon rightly protests that what we normally call inference does not fit the logicians' strait-jacket. An inference from data, he insists, is a statement made in the light of data. To be a good inference it has to be well supported by the data, but need not be entailed by it – indeed if the conclusion is too obviously entailed by the data, we do not speak of inference at all, but only of restating the data. Any of you who doubt this account may be persuaded to it by reading D. G. Brown's article on inference in the *Philosophical Review* for 1955. Nor need you read philosophical papers.

The law report in yesterday's *Times* states that in the opinion of a higher court, a lower court judge 'inferred from the fact' that the plaintiff had not immediately reported his injuries 'that he was on a frolic of his own' and accordingly dismissed the claim. The judge in question seems to have had a curious rule of inference in mind, and you will be glad to learn that a higher court has rejected the implied rule. But it was plainly a rule of *inference*: that is what we call inference.

Unfortunately the rule Salmon commends is as extraordinary as the inference made by the low court judge. Take an instance. Adam has made 20 tosses, say HHHTH . . ., giving him 17 H, 3 T. Now from this data Adam, you, and I would cheerfully infer – state categorically in the light of the data (though we may be wrong) – that the chance of heads exceeds $\frac{1}{10}$. Bolder spirits will infer that it exceeds $\frac{1}{2}$. But who dares infer that the long run frequency is exactly $\frac{17}{20}$, not say 0.8531 or 0.8351? No one. We are happy to estimate the long run frequency as $\frac{17}{20}$. But infer it? Not on your life. I infer, in the normal manner of speaking, that the chance of heads is greater than $\frac{1}{2}$, and estimate that it is 0.85. Any rule that permits me to infer the number 0.85 is, in the normal manner of speaking, an absurd rule, no matter how fine it is when transformed into a rule of estimation.

Some of you may feel that whether or not I want to infer 0.85, I may have to. Some future course of action, say betting at a roulette wheel, ordering some lumber, or designing a new experiment, may demand that I infer a long run frequency before acting. But as we normally speak, I can perfectly well act on an estimate. I estimate I shall use 63 board feet for my new fence, and order accordingly. I never need to infer – to state categorically on the data – that I shall use exactly 63 feet. I do not want to say that inference is never a necessary prelude to sound action, but in the cases we are considering, at most estimation is necessary.

By now I hear a muttered protest: 'Normal manner of speaking' – what does that matter to us? Who cares? Why cannot I just use the word 'estimate' if it pleases me? Because one of Salmon's defences for the straight rule depends on his using 'infer' to mean infer: if 'infer' means estimate, then he has given us a bad argument. We shall come to the matter shortly. For the moment I insist only on the oddity of even imagining that Salmon's rule is any good as a rule of *inference*. In real life we should never think of inferring that way.

Some of you will say that Salmon should have told us to infer not m/n but an interval around m/n. Indeed Reichenbach expressed his rule in the form, infer $(m/n) \pm \varepsilon$. But what is ε? It ought to be a function of the quality of the data, getting smaller as the data get greater. Neither Salmon nor Reichenbach tell us what sort of function is needed, nor does Salmon present his rule in this form. So I leave ε until we get to de Finetti, who will tell us what sort of function to use.

Before passing to the next point, let us be entirely clear about where I disagree with Salmon. He has just told us that, 'the fundamental issue is whether inductive logic is to have rules for the acceptance of hypotheses'. That may be one fundamental issue, but it is not where I take issue with Salmon. Of course we tentatively accept hypotheses on evidence short of deductive proof; of course we do this in a systematic way; of course rules can be set forth according to which we accept hypotheses; of course these will be a part of inductive logic. I contend only that the Salmon rule, as a rule of inference, is neither sound nor ever used. It would be absurd either to instruct or to allow someone to use that rule.

3. *Asymptoticity.* Now we begin to study Salmon's defence of the straight rule. Why choose m/n rather than some other function of the data? Salmon first demands that any sensible rule should converge on the true frequency, if there is one. The rule must be asymptotic.

This restraint is familiar to statisticians who usually insist that their rules of estimation be asymptotic. Their terminology is unfortunate, for it comes from an old paper of Fisher's: Fisher calls an asymptotic estimator *consistent*, and his usage remains. Naturally I prefer Salmon's word instead. Fisher, in presenting the condition, calls asymptoticity 'the common sense' criterion for choosing among estimators. Kendall and Stuart, authors of the encyclopedic *Advanced Theory of Statistics*, reflect most current opinion when they defend asymptoticity as a symptom of the 'increasing accuracy' of an estimator. Salmon agrees: today he commended asymptoticity by noting how asymptotic rules 'will inevitably provide accurate inferences' regarding the true value of the long run frequency, if it exists.

Increasing accuracy is a good defence of any rule, but is asymptoticity increasing accuracy? Let's consider a modest man who wants to be within 5 % of the truth. Call the following fact A: If there is a limiting frequency, there is some trial N such that, if you use the straight rule after N, you will be within 5 % of the true value. On Salmon's analysis of long run frequency, A is a fact. It is this fact (or rather, the generalization of it) which he calls inevitable accuracy.

Beside A let me put B: If there is a long run frequency and you use the straight rule after 3 trillion trials, you will be within 5 % of the true value. Now B, we must all agree, is no justification for any present human course of action. It will be thousands of years before the number of individually recorded experimental trials of all sorts put together gets to be 3 trillion.

B is no reason at all for any present course of human action. Yet B entails A, and A does not entail B. B is a stronger assertion than A. Since B is no reason for any course of human action, A cannot be either.

I do not imply that asymptoticity is altogether worthless. It is a property that does accompany the best of estimators, that is, estimators defended on most plausible grounds. The facts are very clearly explained in chapter 15 of Savage's *The Foundations of Statistics*.

4. *Additivity*. But let us suppose asymptoticity is good in itself. We still need more conditions to satisfy ourselves that the straight rule is uniquely best. Salmon correctly insists that his rule of inference be *consistent* (not Fisher's sense of this word). A rule is consistent if it cannot introduce inconsistency. That is, if given any consistent set of propositions and rules of inference, the closure of this set under the rule is also consistent. The closure under the rule is the new set of propositions that can be validly derived from the old set plus the old rules of inference, plus the new rule of inference.

We at once see that any rule for inferring frequencies must give frequencies between 0 and 1. It also ensures that the rule be additive: for any two mutually exclusive outcomes E and F, if the rule says, infer the chance of E is $P(E)$, and the chance of F is $P(F)$, it must also say that the chance of $E \cup F$ is $P(E) + P(F)$. So we rule out nasty rules like, 'For any E, infer $P(E)$ is $(m+k)/(n+k)$', where k is some positive constant.

Here is where the difference between inference and estimation matters. The requirement of consistency guarantees additivity if you have a rule of *inference*. It gets rid of many rivals to the straight rule. But if we are concerned with rules of *estimation*, I know of no conclusive argument that estimates have to be additive. Some well-known estimators – minimax ones – are not additive. Carnap is, I think, the only student who has ever tried to show additivity is in principle a necessary condition for estimators, and I do not think the arguments advanced in *Continuum of Inductive Methods* are, at this juncture, conclusive. Failing those arguments we do not get additivity for estimates and do not rule out a whole infinity of incompatible estimators. So Salmon was wise to insist that he wanted rules of inference. The only trouble is that no one would ever make the inferences his rules advise. Just the estimates that correspond to them. Here is Salmon's dilemma. He can prove additivity is necessary for a rule of inference – but the straight rule, as rule of inference, is, on other grounds, entirely silly. As a rule of estimation it sounds good – but he cannot prove that rules of estimation have to be additive, and so he cannot yet exclude a host of crooked rules.

5. *Invariance.* But suppose we accept the requirement of additivity. We are still not safe yet. For we have not excluded the following pair of rules:

From m/n heads observed,
    infer the chance of heads is $(m+K)/(n+K)$,
From m'/n tails observed,
    infer the chance of tails is $(m'-K)/(n-K)$,

where $K = 0$ or k according as $k \geqslant m'$ or $k < m'$, and k is an arbitrary constant. To exclude this sort of rule, Salmon invokes 'linguistic invariance' – inference should not change under translation into different languages – a principle we must all accept. But I do not know whether or not it does the job. The trouble is that Salmon has not yet published a rigorous statement of the principle, and explained how it applies to the problem of the straight rule. By rigorous I do not mean having the rigour of one of Carnap's systems, but just rigorous in the sense that an intelligent working statistician can use it without equivocation. Personally, whenever I have tried to cast Salmon's principle into a rigorous form, I have always got something too weak. The only principles which I have been able to devise, and which do what Salmon wants, involve the stronger sort of invariance studied by statisticians, and explained, say, in ch. 6 of Lehmann's *Testing Statistical Hypotheses*. (In the appendix I state an invariance principle of this sort.) My hunch is that nothing weaker will do. I hope I am wrong, and that Salmon will be able to give us a rigorous statement of the principle of linguistic invariance, and then prove it can do the work he intends. That will be a signal contribution to the foundation of inference about frequencies.

6. *Symmetry.* But suppose we agree on some sufficiently strong principle of invariance. Even then we are not home free. One well-known problem for Salmon's rule arises from Goodman's riddles about *grue* and *bleen*. Indeed the rule is hopelessly inconsistent unless restricted to apply only to 'natural' predicates like blue and green, and how can we either define the concept of a 'natural' predicate, or vindicate use of those predicates rather than of Goodmanic ones? I abjure discussion of the problem because I think it is too difficult. But suppose, what is manifestly contrary to fact, that we had a pleasing solution to Goodman's riddles. Even then the vindication of the straight rule is defective. Take this rival to it: From your data d infer that

$$P(E) = (m + kJ)/(n + k),$$

where d implies that n observations are made, m with outcome E, and also states the outcome of the first trial. J is 0 or 1 according as the first trial has outcome E, and k is an arbitrary positive constant. The rule is additive and so forth. I have explained in the *Journal of Philosophy*, **10**, 1965, why we cannot silently discard data about the order in which the different outcomes are observed. To exclude the above rule we need a principle that says the order of the outcomes does not matter, and that proportion is a sufficient statistic for the whole data.

Hence a necessary condition for singling out the straight rule has not been mentioned by Salmon. Cribbing from de Finetti's translators we can call this condition symmetry or exchangeability. Let us say a rule is symmetric if the inferences it advises are independent of the actual order of outcomes, and depend solely on proportions. Symmetry is a pleasing property, but I cannot think why a rule of inference has to be symmetric in this sense. (In the appendix it is proved that the condition of symmetry is sufficient as well as necessary: the straight rule is the only symmetric, invariant and additive rule.)

7. *Trivial inconsistency of the straight rule.* We have collected some requirements each of which is so far unjustified: asymptoticity, additivity, a solution to Goodman's riddles, and symmetry; these, together with the condition of invariance about whose justification we must be agnostic until it is fully stated, do conspire to single out the straight rule. If we were satisfied with the rule, we might start trying to justify the requirements. But the rule will not do either, in its present form.

Suppose Adam tosses the world's first coin for its first five times and observes HTTHT. He starts to infer according to the straight rule. He tells one son to infer the chance of getting a T preceded by H, the other to infer the chance of T preceded by T. Adam himself will infer the chance of T. Abel sees four pairs: HT, TT, TH, HT, so he infers the chance of HT is $\frac{1}{2}$. Cain infers the chance of TT is $\frac{1}{4}$. Adam naturally infers the chance of T is $\frac{3}{5}$.

The serpent observes to Eve that since either H or T must turn up at any valid throw, the long run frequency of T preceded by H, plus the long run frequency of T preceded by T, must, together, add up to the chance of T itself. So she infers the logician's original sin: $\frac{3}{4}=\frac{3}{5}$.

8. *Summary of results so far.* We have seen four unjustified requirements, one requirement about which we have to be agnostic, and a rule which, as currently stated, is formally inconsistent.

I do not say you cannot start patching up the rule. Nor do I deny that in the course of time you may get better and better defences of Salmon's requirements on rules. Indeed, being a Popperian, I think it is much better to be bold and wrong than silently right. But being wrong is worth while only if you can learn by mistakes. Frankly, I think that, in the past half century when Reichenbachian vindications have been in the air, the learned world has learnt nothing significant from the mistakes: for example the silly inconsistency which I have just presented to you is, I think, entirely uninstructive, though it can be adapted to teach us something valuable about additivity in estimation. So I invite you to examine another theory, which, so far as I can see, does everything that someone with Salmon's preconceptions could hope for, is entirely free from my objections, and, most important, is one of the most stimulating probability theories of our time.

9. *How Reichenbach can use de Finetti's work.* If, like Salmon and Reichenbach, you have to insist that a rule be symmetric in the sense defined above, then, presumably, you have no expectation (given only data within the domain of the straight rule) that any one order of outcomes is more likely than any other order in which there is the same number and proportion of outcomes that interest you. You are presumably no more or less confident that you will see 17 H followed by 3 T, than that you will get the same proportion of T jumbled up in any other way among the 20 outcomes. If you were more confident of one order than of another, you would be silly to use a symmetric rule. When your personal degrees of confidence are like this, de Finetti says that the outcome T is symmetric, or exchangeable, with respect to your personal degrees of confidence. I shall use the latter word, to avoid punning with my use of 'symmetric' in connexion with rules of inference. If anyone like Reichenbach or Salmon insists on symmetric rules for certain data then, on that data, the relevant outcomes must be exchangeable with respect to his personal degrees of confidence. The 'must' here has the following force: on pain of being called stupid or irrational such a man's personal degrees of confidence must satisfy the stated condition.

The above paragraph assumes only that one can compare confidence in hypothesis h, given d, with confidence in i, given e. I do not assume that confidence is numerically measurable. But suppose confidence can be measured, say by a sophisticated use of betting quotients. Then there are overwhelming reasons for making your numerical degrees of confidence satisfy the probability calculus. I refer to the six following arguments. The reference attached to each does not necessarily cite the original author, but only a good authority.

1. Bayes' arguments. (*Phil. Trans. Roy. Soc.*, 1763).
2. Metrization argument: if a metric is induced on comparisons of confidence, it must, subject to very feeble conditions, satisfy the probability axioms. (Savage, *Foundations of Statistics*, 3.3).
3. Joint development of utility and degrees of confidence. (Ramsey).
4. Dutch book or coherence argument. (Kemeny, *Journal of Symbolic Logic*, 1955).
5. Subjective version of arguments in Jeffrey's *Theory of Probability*.
6. Differentiation argument: if you want degrees of confidence to be mathematically tractable, and to admit of some sort of learning from experience, they have to satisfy the axioms. (Cox, *A Theory of Probable Inference*, part I.)

If you admit numerical degrees of confidence at all, I do not think you can consistently and simultaneously argue against all these arguments. For example, the popular Dutch book argument seems to me the weakest of the five modern arguments – I think Ramsey was right to take avoidance of a bad book as a pleasant corrollary of the axioms got by method 3, and not as the justification of the axioms. But in arguing against the Dutch book argument one produces facts that support the other arguments. To attack one argument is almost to defend the others. So if Reichenbach admits of numerical degrees of confidence, he must admit that they satisfy the probability axioms.

The probability axioms, plus exchangeability of some exhaustive class of outcomes relative to a person's degrees of confidence, have four nice consequences.

(a) Virtually regardless of your initial confidence in the occurrence of any possible outcome E at trial T after observing a reasonable number of trials, say 20 or 30, but not including T, your confidence in getting E at T will be about equal to the proportion of E among the observed trials.

(b) If we draw a curve of your confidence in different hypotheses about the chance of E, it will peak near the observed proportion of E, and curve smoothly down on either side.

(c) If you, like Salmon and I, want to make inferences when you are say 95 % sure of the proposition inferred, you will infer that the true frequency of E is in an interval around the observed proportion, and the size of this interval, which is wide after only 2 or 3 trials, becomes narrower as the observed trials increase; after 3 or 4 hundred trials it will be a very narrow interval around the observed proportion.

(d) If you want to estimate the chance of E as the chance of which you are most confident, namely the chance at the peak of your confidence curve, you will very nearly follow the straight rule for estimation, and, after a fairly small number of trials, will follow it exactly to within 2 or 3 places of decimals.

Here then is a theory with no confusion between inference and estimation, which prescribes inferences where wanted, provides for estimates in their place, and seems pretty well to answer to the hunches that underlie Reichenbach's approach to the straight rule. Moreover, if you are doubtful whether a rule ought to be symmetric, and exchangeability does not hold, the theory still has a lot to say. So I advance it as a better tool for Reichenbach's kind of work than the tools Salmon has been using.

10. *Goodman's riddles.* To enforce the virtues of the de Finetti theory, let me return to Goodman's plaguey riddles. To get results (a)–(d) in their simplest form, you must have exchangeability of a class of possible outcomes with respect to your degree of confidence. But exchangeability of the class of outcomes (blue, green) is not exchangeability of the class (grue, bleen). Those who think they can characterize 'natural' predicates, and justify use of 'natural' predicates rather than Goodmanic ones, can plug their characterization and justification into de Finetti's theory, saying that one *ought* to have exchangeability of any class of 'natural' outcomes with respect to one's betting odds. But those of us who, though betting that emeralds are green, can see no conclusive reason for preferring that bet to the bet that emeralds are grue, will say it is only a mere matter of Humean human nature and custom, that our degrees of confidence are exchangeable for what we like to call 'natural' predicates and not for grue and bleen. But from then on the de Finetti theory works just as it works for those who 'solve' Goodman's riddles. The theory works independently of other philosophical difficulties, and this I take to be a great virtue of it for Reichenbachian enquiries. We humans have to do things by bits and pieces. Salmon found himself doing everything at once, even solving Goodman's riddles. Now we can attack Goodman's problem on the one hand, and 'learning by experience' on the other. We use de Finetti's analysis of 'learning by experience' to justify our estimates and our inferences given our predilection for 'natural' properties. Then we can try, separately, to justify that predilection.

11. *Practice.* If you want a global, encyclopedic, and in a way mechanical theory of learning by experience then, I contend, de Finetti's ideas are more promising than those of Reichenbach. But however elegant a global theory may become, what about practical experiments? What would you really do if you had a chance device and could make some trials on it, and had to find out the chance properties of the device? You would take it apart to see how it works. But if it is an atom or a coin or a man or a star you may be limited to Salmon's meagre data – especially if you have never before heard of anything much like your device. Would you then use the straight rule as defended by Salmon or de Finetti? I doubt it. You would make a lot of trials, say 20 or 30 or even 1000 if trials are cheap and brief. Floundering, you would hope that the trials are independent, but would also fear you had a decay process on your hands, or worse, some generalized stochastic process. You would speculate on the nature of your device to see what kind of process might be expected, and whether the chances of some sort of outcome might be constantly changing according to some law. You would test your hypothesis of independence against the plausible rivals that occurred to you. At some point, baffled by the data, you might notice how the sequence of outcomes suggests that some kinds of outcome as it were queue up behind others, and since the structure of queuing has quite tractable mathematics, you would test a queuing hypothesis against some other idea.

After contemplating the straight rule, such behaviour seems indecently messy, but it is just the Popperian dialectic of conjecture and rejection. It is a difficult philosophical problem to determine the rationale of the statistical tests being used, but interesting rationales can be given. Perhaps they will have to be given piecemeal for some time, and not in the global way typical of de Finetti's theory. This is as it should be, for the world of inference is too complex to be embraced in its entirety, yet.

However, de Finetti's theory is so potent that it can explain its own inabilities. For we may show, within the theory, that the theory gives no account of how we learn from experience when we conceive of a new hypothesis, which never occurred to us before, and which, in the light of the data, suddenly strikes us as attractive. Careful examination shows how the theory is appropriate only to situations in which there is a fairly stable family of pertinent hypotheses among which we have to choose. As soon as there is a breakthrough we have a discontinuity not acknowledged by the present theory. The theory is good at studying many common situations where breakthroughs are the exception, not the rule. But in Salmon's situation where we begin with total ignorance and literally do not know what to expect, the success of the unexpected hypothesis will be customary, not exceptional. When we are ignorant, we humans are not prescient enough to know what to look for. When we really are ignorant, no mechanical rule, straight or crooked, has any validity. We have no alternative to piecemeal guessing and testing, weighing and rejecting, dreaming and correcting.

Appendix

We establish that a certain form of the straight rule is the only rule of inference that satisfies the conditions of *consistency*, *symmetry*, and *invariance*, and thus we solve the problem set by Salmon on page 37–8 of his paper.

Let $\mathscr{A}$ be a sample space of mutually exclusive possible results of trials of kind K on a chance set-up. Let $\mathscr{X}$ be a field or sigma-field based on $\mathscr{A}$ that is, the closure of $\mathscr{A}$ under intersection, (countable) union, and complementation. Let Ω be the union of elements of $\mathscr{X}$. Elements of $\mathscr{X}$ are to be called *outcomes*; Salmon is concerned with rules for inferring chances of outcomes. We postulate that chances of outcomes satisfy the probability axioms. The following symbolism will be used:

A sequence of non-empty outcomes of n successive trials of kind K will be represented by S_n.

$\pi(S_n)$ stands for a permutation of members of the sequence S_n.

Where E is disjoint with every outcome in S_n except itself and possibly F, $_E^F S_n$ stands for the sequence which results from interchanging E and F, or, when E does not occur in S_n, from replacing F by E.

$\mathscr{F}(E, S_n)$ is a function of E and S_n, and is to be interpreted as the inference about the chance of E that is to be drawn from S_n. It is defined only for arguments E and S_n such that for each F in S_n, $EF = 0$ or $F \subseteq E$. The following conditions are to be imposed upon $\mathscr{F}$:

(1) *Consistency*: for any S_n, $\mathscr{F}$ is an additive non-negative set function of elements of $\mathscr{X}$, and $\mathscr{F}(\Omega, S_n) = 1$.

(2) *Symmetry*: For any outcome E and any permutation $\pi(S_n)$,

$$\mathscr{F}(E, S_n) = \mathscr{F}(E, \pi(S_n)).$$

(3) *Invariance*: For any two outcomes E and F that are disjoint with every other outcome in the sequence S_n,

$$\mathscr{F}(E, {}_E^F S_n) = \mathscr{F}(F, S_n).$$

Theorem. For any space of three or more possible results, the only function satisfying our three conditions is

$$\mathscr{F}(E, S_n) = m/n,$$

where m is the number of outcomes F in S_n such that $F \subseteq E$.   (1)

Proof. Consistency determines that $\mathscr{F}$ is a probability function for given S_n. Hence symmetry determines that $\mathscr{F}(E, S_n)$ is a function of the proportion of E among the members of the sequence S_n, that is, the number of elements F of S_n such that $F \subseteq E$. (See, for example, chapter 3 of de Finetti's *La Prévision* in Kyburg and Smokler's collection, *Studies in Subjective Probability*.) Let us represent this proportion by ES_n; then there is a function $\mathscr{G}$ such that:

$$\mathscr{F}(E, S_n) = \mathscr{G}(E, ES_n). \tag{2}$$

Lemma. For any outcome $E \subset \Omega$ and rational fractions a and b such that $a \geqslant 0$, $b \geqslant 0$, $a + b \leqslant 1$,

$$\mathscr{G}(E, a) + \mathscr{G}(E, b) = \mathscr{G}(E, a + b). \tag{3}$$

Proof of lemma. Consider any two outcomes F and G such that $F \neq 0$, $G \neq 0$, $FG = 0$, and $F \cup G \neq \Omega$ and $E \subseteq (F \cup G)$. Such F and G exist so long as the space has three or more possible results. Let $H = \Omega - (F \cup G)$. Let S_n be a sequence in which the proportion of F is a, and of G is b, and in which the only outcomes are F, G, and H. $S_n{}'$, $S_n{}''$ shall be like S_n but with H replacing respectively G and F. By consistency, we have the additivity axiom,

$$\mathscr{F}(F, S_n) + \mathscr{F}(G, S_n) = \mathscr{F}(F \cup G, S_n). \tag{4}$$

By symmetry, which gave us (2), (4) implies

$$\mathscr{F}(F, S_n{}') + \mathscr{F}(G, S_n{}'') = \mathscr{F}(F \cup G, S_n). \tag{5}$$

For any outcome E, invariance and (5) imply,

$$\mathscr{F}(E, {}_E^F S_n{}') + \mathscr{F}(E, {}_E^G S_n{}'') = \mathscr{F}(E, {}_E^F [{}_F^G S_n]). \tag{6}$$

(6) and (2) together imply (3).

This essentially completes the proof of our theorem, for the only function satisfying (2), (3), and $\mathscr{F}(\Omega, S_n) = 1$ is a function such that

$$\mathscr{F}(E, S_n) = ES_n.$$

Consistency implies that this function must be that labelled (1) above.

Remarks

(1) *Linguistic invariance.* Evidently the theorem does not hold for sample spaces with exactly two possible results, for the rule, 'infer that the chance of either non-certain outcome is $\frac{1}{2}$' is consistent, symmetric, and invariant. It can be erased by Salmon's linguistic invariance on page 37 of his paper. This is the only point at which linguistic invariance is needed. Until the idea of linguistic invariance is stated more clearly, we remain agnostic about the dubious proposition that linguistic invariance might entail the kind of invariance used in the proof. Note that conditions (1)–(3) are all necessary, as well as being sufficient.

(2) *Asymptoticity* is not required for the proof. It is not, as Reichenbach thought, the lynch pin of the vindication of the straight rule but, as is usual in statistics, an accidental by-product. This is good, for it is plainly worthless as vindication.

(3) *Application: Goodman's riddles* must be solved in order to determine what sample spaces are 'correct': symmetry in a sample space including 'blue' and 'green' is asymmetry in the corresponding Goodmanic sample space.

(4) *Application: Choice of basic sample space.* For any given large sample space there is a unique invariant, symmetric, and consistent rule, namely the straight rule, for inferring chances on the basis of a sequence of results from the space. But in practice any given set of results of trials defines a lot of related sample spaces, for example, the space whose elements are successive pairs of results from another space. Thus experimentally we are confronted by a family of related spaces. The inconsistency explained on page 51 of this volume shows there is *no* consistent, symmetric, and invariant rule that is applicable to a family of related spaces. Hence in applying the rule we must arbitrarily choose one member of the family, and incidentally violate the most plausible of all invariance conditions (it might be expressed in terms of linguistic invariance): rules of inference should be invariant under transformation of sample space.

W. C. KNEALE: *Confirmation and rationality.*

I want to comment on what Professor Salmon has said about the use of confirmation statements which are supposed to be analytic. What I am going to say seems to me to support his general conclusion, but I shall put the problem in a slightly different way.

Let us suppose, as he said in his lecture, that e is the total available evidence for and against some hypothesis h about the future and that the degree of confirmation of h on e is p according to a theory in which statements of that form are always analytic. We feel inclined to argue

The total available evidence for and against h is e.
$c(h, e) = p$.
∴ The probability (in an absolute sense) of h is p.

And if p is sufficiently large, we may go on to say that in planning for the future we had better assume the truth of h. But there seems to be something queer in saying that our two premises can give any indication of the attitude we should adopt towards the future. For the first premise is a synthetic statement wholly about the past, and the second, being an analytic formula, is, strictly speaking, superfluous according to the principles commonly accepted by logicians. That is to say, any conclusion we can draw from the two premises taken together we should be able to obtain from the first alone, and yet the first premise gives us no information about the future. This, I think, is Salmon's point, and I expect it worries other people just as it has worried me. But I think that it is possible to put the matter in another way which is equally disturbing.

Let us consider an analogy. Suppose we have as data the two premises

Brown's age is 64.
$\sqrt{64} = 8$.

Since the second is analytic, it may be argued that any conclusion which follows from the two premises taken together must follow from the first alone. But we can if we like think of the first premise as a licence to make a substitution in the second and so go on to assert

The square root of Brown's age is 8.

No doubt the proposition which we reach in this way is a logical consequence of the first premise alone, but there is some interest in establishing it as I have done, because this procedure shows that a synthetic proposition may be derived from one that is analytic by means of a substitution which is itself licensed by a synthetic statement of identity. In precisely similar fashion we may argue

The total available evidence for and against h is e.
$c(h, e) = p$.
$\therefore$ The degree of confirmation of h in relation to all the available evidence is p,

where the conclusion is synthetic.

But now let us come to the real crux of the matter. Can the new synthetic statement be of any use to us when we try to decide what attitude to adopt to the future? It seems that the answer must be 'No' unless the concept of confirmation which we use has built into it the notion of relevance to decisions about the future. In other words, if confirmation theory is to be the guide of life, confirmation itself must be defined by reference to the rationality of action in the future. But I do not see how in that case statements of the form $c(h, e) = p$ can ever be analytic. I wonder whether Salmon agrees with this presentation of his case.

J. W. N. WATKINS: *Non-inductive corroboration.*

According to Popper:

(1.1)   science is not inductive;
(1.2)   hence there is no need to try to justify inductive inferences.

According to Ayer and Strawson:

(2.1)   science *is* inductive;
(2.2)   *nevertheless* there is no need to try to justify inductive inferences.

But, says Salmon, Popper has not established (1.1), and Ayer and Strawson have not established (2.2). According to Salmon:

(3.1)   science is inductive (*some* sort of ampliative, non-demonstrative inference is needed in science);
(3.2)   hence there *is* a need to justify (or at least to vindicate) inductive inferences.

I shall make an approving comment on Salmon's criticism of Ayer and Strawson, and a disapproving comment on his criticism of Popper.

1.   A funny statement may be serious and true. 'They seem to argue', writes Salmon of Ayer and Strawson, 'by a kind of logic that frankly escapes me, that induction needs no defense because

it is indefensible'. (p. 24). Quite so; and because they regard it
as needing no defence or justification they feel no need to tell us
what *it* is. Unlike philosophers who try to justify some sort of
inductive inference and who are thereby obliged to say *what* sort
of inference it is that they intend to justify, Ayer and Strawson
prudently refrain from spelling out the nature of inductive inference. All we learn is that such inferences are not deductive and
do permit us to take in our stride the logical gaps in inductive
thinking [1].

Now when an inductivist reflects how fragmentary and local
are the scraps of evidence from which (according to him) the soaring,
sweeping theories of modern science are inductively inferred, he
should admit that the logical gaps, here, are very large indeed.
From the point of view of deductive logic, these (alleged) inferences
must seem wildly illogical. But if wildly illogical inferences are
in order within science, are they not equally in order outside
science – in courts of law, for instance? And can any objection any
longer be sustained against the so-called 'naturalistic fallacy'? Ayer
has elsewhere appealed to the 'sound and respectable point of
logic . . . that normative statements are not derivable from descriptive statements' [2]; but if we may stride across logical gaps
within the factual domain, why should we not take the *is-ought*
gap in our stride? [3] Systematic adherence to the (2.1)–(2.2) combination should, it seems to me, lead to a general breakdown of
rational standards.

2.   Now I shall comment on Salmon's claim that Popper 'has not
succeeded in purging the logic of science of all inductive elements'
(p. 28). Salmon argues as follows: given a multiplicity of competing and unfalsified hypotheses, and a set of accepted basic
statements, Popper's notion of corroboration may justify us in

---

[1] P. F. Strawson, *Introduction to Logical Theory*, 1952, pp. 233–234,
246–248; A. J. Ayer, *The Problem of Knowledge*, 1956, p. 80 and *passim*.

[2] A. J. Ayer, ed., *Logical Positivism*, 1959, p. 22.

[3] More consistently, perhaps, A. C. MacIntyre has commended *is-ought*
inferences as well as non-deductive *is-is* inferences, *Phil. Rev.*, **68**, pp. 451–
468.

preferring one hypothesis as the best corroborated so far; but such a preference could not be justified merely by making deductions from the basic statements; *ergo,* Popper's notion of corroboration is not purely deductive.

I agree, first, that corroboration involves something more than deductions from basic statements; and second, that this extra something *would* need to be of an inductive character *if* to appraise a hypothesis as well corroborated by past evidence were to involve some sort of prediction about its continued success in the future. But (to take the second point first) such an appraisal involves no such prediction. Later in his paper Salmon has stated very sharply (with some acknowledgement to Ernest Nagel) his reasons for doubting Carnap's claim that inductive logic could be a guide to future conduct: for if *e* consists of evidence about the *past,* and if $C(h, e) = p$ is *analytic,* how can the conjunction of the two tell us anything about the *future?* (Kneale also discusses this point and concludes in favour of Salmon.) However, when we turn from Carnap's 'degree of confirmation' to Popper's 'degree of corroboration', we no longer meet this difficulty: a Popperian corroboration-appraisal *is* analytic and does *not* have predictive implications [1]. Consider a corroboration-appraisal of the following form:

$$C(h_2, e) > C(h_1, e) \geqslant 0.$$

Assume that h_2 is some predictively powerful hypothesis and that *e* incorporates the results of all the tests so far made on h_1 and h_2. Then the formula states that h_2 is positively corroborated, and also that it is better corroborated than h_1. But this appraisal by no means implies that h_2 is likely to go on surviving tests upon it; nor does it imply that h_2 is more likely to do so than is h_1. Rather to the contrary: if h_1 is a less general or a vaguer or more *ad hoc* or more metaphysical (or otherwise watered-down) version of h_2, then h_2 may very well be both *better* corroborated by past tests and *less* likely to survive future tests.

---

[1] See *Logic of Scientific Discovery,* § 82. J. Agassi has also emphasized this: 'Corroboration of a theory is merely an appraisal of the way it stood up *so far* to severe criticism', *The British Journal for the Philosophy of Science,* **9**, 1959, p. 317.

What (to revert to the first of the two points mentioned above) is the extra something – something besides deductions from basic statements – which Popper's notion of corroboration involves and which allows us, in favourable cases at any rate, to prefer one hypothesis as better corroborated, so far, than its known rivals? A full answer is in *The Logic of Scientific Discovery*, Appendix ✶ix. I will only indicate enough of it to suggest that this extra something does not covertly contain any darkly inductivist ingredients.

Salmon rightly says that the methods of science should be well-suited to the aim of science. But the aim he imputes to science – the verificationist aim of *establishing* 'far-reaching knowledge of the world' (p. 35) – is very different from Popper's. Popper's methodology derives from the assumption, first that science aims at (conjectural) *explanations*, and second that an explanation is better (other things being equal) the less *ad hoc* it is relative to what it explains. From the second part of this it follows that one explanatory theory is better than a rival one if it is both more testable and has actually withstood more severe tests. Now comparative testability is an idea which can be explained with the help of deductive notions and without the help of inductive ones. No ampliative, non-demonstrative inferences are called for. True, Popper has used logical probability to help to explain it; but he uses it as a generalization of classical logic which makes possible new kinds of *deductive* derivation. Thus his partial formalization of the idea of the severity of a test on a hypothesis h involves comparing the probability of a test-statement e relative to the conjunction of h and background knowledge k, with the probability of e relative to k alone. In the case of a very severe test, the value of $p(e, hk)$ will be one (or almost one), and the value of $p(e, k)$ will be almost zero. (Example: Poisson, who was a very keen adherent of a corpuscular theory of light, triumphantly extracted from Fresnel's wave-theory of light the seemingly preposterous implication, and one unnoticed by Fresnel, that in a suitable set-up a bright spot should appear at the centre of the shadow cast by a circular screen! However, when this implication of Fresnel's theory was tested, it survived the test, and the theory was highly corroborated thereby.) Notice that no use is made here of probabilistic inferences in an inductive direction: corroboration of h by e does *not* mean that the probability of h relative to e and k is higher than the probability of h relative to k alone.

To sum up: corroboration does indeed involve something more than deductions from basic statements; but this something more has been defined with the help of deductive concepts without the help of inductive concepts [1].

One last point: it will be said that relative appraisals of the degrees to which different hypotheses have been confirmed, or corroborated, are needed in the planning of future action; hence there is something fishy and hypocritical about the Popperian disclaimer that corroboration appraisals have no predictive implications.

Now our methods of hypothesis-selection in practical life should be well-suited to our practical aims, just as our methods of hypothesis-selection in theoretical science should be well suited to our theoretical aims; and the two kinds of method may very well yield different answers in a particular case. Suppose that in some practical problem-situation we have to rely on one or other of two incompatible hypotheses, h_1 and h_2; and suppose that we should, from a theoretical point of view, prefer h_2 as the better corroborated hypothesis. From a practical point of view, however, it may be wiser to prefer h_1; for it may be that to act on the assumption that h_1 is true will be highly profitable if h_1 is in fact true and not very unprofitable if h_2 is true, whereas to act on the assumption that h_2 is true will be not very profitable if h_2 is in fact true and highly unprofitable if h_1 is true. Indeed, in practical life it is often wise to act on a hypothesis which one actually believes to be false. The navigator of a ship in foggy weather, for example, may prudently assume that she is nearer a rocky shore than he believes her to be and set course accordingly.

Now suppose that, for a particular agent, the mutually incompatible hypotheses h_1 and h_2 are on a par utility-wise, and that in the situation in which he finds himself, he has *got* to act since

---

[1] I make a similar point apropos Popper's theory of verisimilitude in section 3 of my note, 'Hume, Carnap and Popper', *this volume*, pp. 276 ff.

'inaction' would itself be one mode of action. Then if h_1 is the only alternative to h_2 before him, he *has* to choose one of them. Then it would be rational for him to choose the better corroborated one, the one which has withstood the more severe criticism, since he has nothing else to go on. But a rational choice, here, may of course turn out to have been an unlucky choice.

Y. BAR–HILLEL: *Inductive logic as 'the' guide of life.*

1. Professor Salmon – like Professor Kyburg in his paper 'The Rule of Detachment in Inductive Logic' – takes time off to insist that 'If science consisted literally of observation statements supplemented only by deductive inferences from them, the talk about theories, their falsifiability, and their tests would be empty' [1]. One wonders against whom these remarks are directed. Though there might still exist people who adhere to such views, I am sure that none of them attended the London Colloquium.

2. Some people have learned too much from Hume. Salmon claims [2] to have learned from Hume that, *'the future is logically independent of the past and present'* and therefore finds it difficult to understand, in spite of Carnap's patient explanations, how analytic degree of confirmation statements can function as a guide in life. But what Hume had insisted upon – and what later impressed Wittgenstein so much – was, of course, only that observation statements of the future were *deductively* independent of observation statements of the past and present. (Neither Hume nor Wittgenstein used, of course, this terminology.) Hume's point has inherently nothing to do with future, past, and present (as Wittgenstein fully realized); it works equally well for any observation statements referring to different time points. In Salmon's illustration: had he, for whatever reason, been interested in Hoosier Boy's performance in some *past* race and had his turf consultant been able to tell him only that Hoosier Boy won six out of the

---

[1] *This volume*, p. 26.

[2] *This volume*, p. 41.

seven races in which he participated, there would still exist no deductive relationship between this information and his performance in the race in question. But it is wrong (or question-begging) of Salmon to formulate this triviality as having thereby been told 'nothing about the future but only about the past and present'. On the contrary, I am sure that this information would have influenced his betting behavior (as it would have influenced his estimate of Hoosier Boy's *having won* the other race).

3.   Professor Kneale has the same qualms as Salmon but he chooses to reinforce them by two strange formulations. First, he uses the phrase '*the* guide of life [my italics]' with regard to confirmation theory. But I don't think anybody has made a claim to this effect. I think it was always (and I am sure it was so since Carnap) '*a* guide'. And I don't think that if you replace 'the' by 'a', the argument 'if confirmation theory is to be the guide of life, confirmation itself must be defined by reference to the rationality of action in the future' retains any of its attraction.

Second, he finds it of 'some interest' to establish that a synthetic proposition can be derived from an analytic one by means of a substitution based upon a synthetic identity statement. Since Kneale's own illustration is both over-simplified in its formulation (he has 'The square root of Brown's age is 8' instead of 'The positive square root of Brown's age-in-years is 8') and involves arithmetic (and there are people for whom arithmetic is not analytic), let me give a simpler illustration of his point. If one insists on putting it this way, he certainly may say that one can.

The number of Brown's eyes equals the number of Brown's ears follows from the analytic proposition

$$2 = 2$$

by means of two substitutions of identicals based on the two synthetic identity statements

The number of Brown's eyes equals 2
and
The number of Brown's ears equals 2.

That this is a *strange* way of putting things, I would agree, but
I fail to see why Kneale finds it *interesting*, unless he means that
it is interesting that by fooling around a little bit, and seemingly
innocuously, with such expressions as 'from' and 'by means of'
one can arrive at strange-looking formulations. But Kneale obviously thought that the illustration taught him some important
lesson which reinforced Salmon's point. And this I completely
failed to see.

4. Professor Watkins takes up Salmon's (and Kneale's) point
again, and approvingly. (Incidentally, while Kneale switches from
Carnap's '*a* guide *in* life' to '*the* guide *of* life', Watkins saddles
Carnap with the claim that inductive logic is 'a guide to future
conduct'. Carnap, of course, never used the adjective 'future' in
this context – it is clearly either pointlessly redundant or straightforwardly wrong.) But his particular formulation of this common
'puzzle' is interesting and perhaps revealing: '. . . if *e* consists of
evidence about the *past*, and if $c(h, e)$ is *analytic*, how can the conjunction of the two tell us anything about the *future*?' Assume, in
order to give Watkins' point some initial appeal, that *h* refers 'to
the future' (which it may, of course, though it need not). Then
from the conjunction of '*e* is all the available evidence relevant to
h' and '$c(h, e) = p$' follows – by simple rules of English – 'the degree
of confirmation of *h* on all the available relevant evidence is *p*'.
Now, does this tell us something about the future? The obvious
answer is: in one sense, yes, in another, no; both these assertions
are trivial, even if the senses are specified, which everyone should
be able to do at a moment's notice. That Watkins should fall into
the trap of fusing these senses and think that Carnap could for
a minute have interpreted the conclusion of the above argument
– if it deserves that name – as making a prediction about the future,
is hard to believe but unfortunately exactly what happened. The
whole confrontation of Carnap's 'degree of confirmation' with
Popper's 'degree of corroboration' is therefore completely perverse.
A Popperian corroboration appraisal is indeed analytic and indeed
does not have any predictive implication, but exactly the same
holds, of course, for a Carnapian 'confirmation appraisal' – degree

of corroboration being a mathematical function of the various degrees of prior and posterior confirmation involved. This, of course, does not make Popper an inductivist. An inductivist is presumably a person who uses inductive logic and 'inductive concepts' [where has this new red herring been caught?] in evaluating and comparing theories whereas Popper uses only probability logic and exclusively deductive concepts. The fact that inductive logic, is, in Carnap's view, exactly the same (*qua* explicanda – there may be any number of differences in the explication) as Popper's probability logic (Carnap's book, amazingly enough, was even called *Logical Foundations of Probability*) is just disregarded. Popper's insistence that his own criteria for comparing theories are not only different from, but almost diametrically opposed to those of Carnap's, is strange. (As I have stressed many times, they are unfortunately too much alike and therefore both of them far from exhaustive.) That this insistence should take the form of an attack on inductive logic and a denial that there is such an animal, cannot be explained, I am afraid, on purely rational grounds (though I don't think that 'fishy' and 'hypocritical' are the right adjectives to describe the situation).

I have, of course, no quarrel with Watkins' last three paragraphs. They look like a somewhat watered-down version of what Carnap and many other decision-theoretic methodologists have said many times before. This being so, isn't it time to stop bickering and start working towards improving the common basic conception (which, unfortunately, is very much in need of improvement) while also continuing with a division of labour, the Carnapians concentrating mostly on a rational synchronic reconstruction of science and the Popperians remaining mostly interested in the diachronic growth of science?

D. W. MILLER: *On the subjective interpretation of probability.*

The main purpose of this note is to criticize Professor Hacking's use of the subjective interpretation of probability in order to solve Reichenbach's and Salmon's problem – the problem of how to infer values of chances from frequency 'data'. With the first half of Hacking's paper, where he explodes the view that the straight rule of induction can be vindicated, I am in almost complete agreement [1].

1. Reichenbach, unlike Salmon, presented the straight rule as an 'approximate' rule of inference: that is, as a rule that would instruct us to infer not that $p(H)=r$, say, but only that $p(H)=r \pm \varepsilon$, where ε is some function of the quality of the data, decreasing when we have more evidence at our disposal. But, says Hacking, Reichenbach gives no indication of what sort of function ε might be, and it is not easy to see what it could be. 'So I leave ε', Hacking says, 'until we get to de Finetti, who will tell us what sort of function to use'.

By 'de Finetti' Hacking means de Finetti's subjectivist theory of so-called personal probabilities, or personal degrees of confidence, *combined with an objectivist theory of chance*, such as the one he himself holds [2]. And one supposed advantage of de Finetti's theory is the following: 'The probability axioms [for degrees of confidence], plus exchangeability of some exhaustive class of outcomes relative to a person's degrees of confidence' have the 'nice' consequence that if you 'want to make inferences when you are say 95 % sure of the proposition inferred, you will infer that the true frequency of E is in an interval around the observed proportion . . .; after 3 or 4 hundred trials . . . a very narrow interval around the observed proportion.'

Thus Hacking recommends de Finetti's theory at least partly because it gives us some way of fixing ε – by reference to our own beliefs.

Now the subjectivist theory has many defects – some of which have been pointed out by Hacking himself. Among them is the fact that it is absurdly comprehensive – it would instruct us to

---

[1] I say 'almost' because, first, I cannot work up any interest in the problem of what the word 'inference' means: and secondly, I disagree that the straight rule, as formulated by Salmon, is a good rule of estimation. See my paper in *The British Journal for the Philosophy of Science*, **17**, 1966, pp. 59–61.

[2] See Ian Hacking, *Logic of Statistical Inference*, 1965, especially the first two chapters.

measure boiling points by reference to our beliefs, even though we can satisfactorily give degrees of accuracy for thermometers. Another is that it is impossible to understand, from the point of view of a *consistent* subjectivist theory, how experience can ever force us to correct our most firmly held beliefs [1].

So if we are to adopt de Finetti's theory it must be with good reason, for we do so at our peril. But it seems to me that Hacking has given no good reason, and, indeed, that there *is* no good reason. In particular, if the subjectivist theory can give us a satisfactory rule for inferring '$p(H) = \dot{r} \pm \varepsilon(n)$' from the experimental report 'in n throws the relative frequency of heads was r', *then so can an objectivist theory* (for instance, the logical theory of probability).

The reason for this is pretty plain. According to the subjectivist theory your degree of confidence in the hypothesis

(*) $$p(H) = r \pm \varepsilon$$

is virtually independent of your initial degree of confidence in the same hypothesis, if you observe a reasonably large number of trials. In particular, your degree of confidence in (*) will be very close to, or equal to, the logical probability of (*) on the same evidence. Thus there is absolutely no need to phrase the straight rule in terms of subjective probabilities. If the rule instructs us to infer (*) when we are 95 % certain of it, then it could equally instruct us to infer (*) when it has a logical probability of 0.95.

It may be argued that we will still need the subjectivist theory as a means of calculating the logical probabilities. For, it may be said, it is in general impossible to calculate logical probabilities directly, and it can only be done by calculating subjective probabilities first, and then using the equivalence mentioned above. Quite apart from the fact that the calculation of subjective probabilities is a task that requires considerable, if not unattainable, inductive sophistication, this objection fails when we remember that we are here supposed to be giving a *rational reconstruction* of

---

[1] For a sustained attack on the subjective interpretation of probability see K. R. Popper, 'Probability Magic, or Knowledge out of Ignorance', *Dialectica* 11, 1957, no. 3/4, pp. 354–374.

scientific practice not a factual account. And in this context the actual calculation of probabilities is a technical detail [1].

2. But the strongest argument for still employing the subjectivist theory of probability is no doubt that with it we can in some sense 'justify' or 'vindicate' our rule of inference, and in particular our choice of ε. Whereas the choice of ε must be almost completely arbitrary from an objective point of view.

I agree that it is a problem to give objective reasons for the choice of ε. But I disagree that there could be any good subjectivist reasons.

Hacking has, I think, virtually conceded this in his admirable last section on '*Practice*'. For here he admits that 'the theory [the de Finetti theory] is appropriate only to situations in which there is a fairly stable family of pertinent hypotheses among which we have to choose'. But for this very reason our knowledge of the stability of the family can only be *conjectural* (presumably it will be well tested). Thus no inference based on it can possibly hope to be itself anything better than conjectural. In which case why not admit the conjectural character of all our theories and give up any attempt, subjectivist or otherwise, to justify them? A statement validly derived from unproved assumptions is itself unproved. How much more then is a statement partially justified (rendered probable) on the basis of complete conjectures itself totally conjectural?

H. E. KYBURG, JR.: *Detaching estimates.*

Professor Hacking argues, against Salmon, that what is inferred or accepted in what we might call relative frequency induction, is not a straight point estimate, but an interval estimate. This sounds very plausible: it is hard to imagine how we can have grounds for claiming that the relative frequency of A's among B's is exactly p, and not a wee bit less or a shade more; but quite easy and natural

---

[1] Nothing in this note should be taken to suggest that I think that any rule of inference whatever is satisfactory. I do not.

to suppose that we can justifiably claim (after enough evidence) that the frequency is in the range $p \pm \varepsilon$. Salmon himself sometimes talks as though this would be a perfectly good approach to the reconstruction of relative frequency inference. Indeed, it was the approach of Reichenbach. It raises the difficulty of how to determine ε, to be sure, but this does not seem insuperable. Hacking offers one approach to the selection of ε. No doubt others could be found. I myself am perfectly sure that statistical hypotheses can be accepted, that there are rules for inferring them from relative frequency evidence, and that the hypotheses that can be accepted generally have this interval character: they assert that a certain limiting frequency, or a certain chance, lies in a given interval, and not that it has a particular value. I think, but I am not sure, that Salmon would accept this; I think, but I am not sure, that he deals with point estimation rather than interval estimation because it is in some respects simpler and because he regards it as a close enough approximation to real life, for the purposes of his rational reconstruction.

Now Salmon claims that 'detaching statements of limits of relative frequencies cannot lead to the lottery paradox. The trouble is avoided precisely because a bet on a limit statement can never be settled.' But if the statements we 'accept' or 'infer' are interval statements, as persuasively argued by Hacking, then we can easily generate the lottery paradox after all. Suppose we have examined a lot of B's, and found that of n, m are also A's. Let n, ε_1, ε_2, ε_3, ε_4 be such that we will be able to:

(1) Accept the hypothesis that the limiting frequency is *not* between

$$(m/n) - \varepsilon_2 \text{ and } (m/n) + \varepsilon_3 \text{ (including endpoints)}.$$

(2) Accept the hypothesis that the limiting frequency *is* between

$$(m/n) - \varepsilon_1 \text{ and } (m/n) + \varepsilon_3$$

(3) Accept the hypothesis that the limiting frequency is between

$$(m/n) - \varepsilon_2 \text{ and } (m/n) + \varepsilon_4$$

| 0 | $(m/n) - \varepsilon_1$ | $(m/n) - \varepsilon_2$ | m/n | $(m/n) + \varepsilon_3$ | $(m/n) + \varepsilon_4$ | 1 |

If we accept a principle of conjunction (if we accept both A and B, we can also accept the conjunction of A and B) as Salmon, Bar–Hillel, and almost everybody else seems to want to do, then we have an explicit contradiction. Despite the fact that bets about limiting frequencies can't be settled, I will bet Salmon anything he likes that the statements mentioned in (1) and (2) and (3) are not all true.

One could only escape by arguing that in this case there might not *be* a limiting frequency. We could take the statement mentioned in (1) to be: '*If* there is a limit, it does not lie between $(m/n) - \varepsilon_2$ and $(m/n) + \varepsilon_3$', etc. But if this is how we are to construe the statements mentioned in (1) and (2) and (3), then the conjunction of those statements will *entail* 'there is *no* limiting frequency'. Surely it is odd to be able to infer, on the basis of the observation of n B's, m of which are A's, that the relative frequency of A's among B's has no limit!

W. C. SALMON: *Reply.*

In my initial paper I attempted to provide something – i.e., a point of dispute – for almost everyone who deals with inductive logic. There are those, like Mr. Strawson and Professor Ayer, who have no serious qualms about inductive rules of inference, but who reject entirely the notion that any sort of *justification* is required. I regret that no one saw fit to take up the cudgels on this issue [1], but I am extremely grateful for Professor Watkins' incisive agreement on this point. Others, like Professor Popper, who have nothing against justification of rules of inference, reject the notion of an *inductive* rule. I shall discuss Watkins' argument on this point below; it is odd that Professor Bar–Hillel wonders who holds this view. Finally, there are some, following Professor Carnap mainly, who endorse some sort of justification (e.g., the need for a rationale for selecting a particular type of confirmation

---

[1] In 'Symposium on Inductive Evidence', *American Philosophical Quarterly*, **2**, 4, (1965), Stephen Barker comes to the defense of this view; see his contribution and my reply.

function), but who reject the notion of a *rule of inference* of a straightforwardly inductive sort. Carnap has not unqualifiedly denied that there are inductive inferences, but he has urged that there are no rules of acceptance (or 'detachment') for synthetic hypotheses. This is the basic issue on which the last, and main, section of my paper was focused. In that section I had two major concerns: (1) to show that we need rules of acceptance for synthetic hypotheses – in particular, hypotheses that are synthetic probability statements – and (2) to defend certain *types* of conditions as contributing to a justification (in the sense of *vindication*) of some sort of inductive rule of acceptance, in virtue of which observed statistical data can legitimately be said to support hypotheses concerning limiting frequencies.

Since the first of these two issues is *the* topic of the symposium on 'The Rule of Detachment in Inductive Logic', the two symposia are intimately interrelated. While I am in complete agreement with Professor Kyburg on the need for a rule of acceptance (detachment) in inductive logic, we are in rather deep disagreement about the nature of the rule. Moreover, because of a basic difference in our conceptions of probability, he cannot accept what I take to be the most profound reason for demanding rules of acceptance, namely, my contention that analytic probability statements cannot fulfill their needed function as a 'guide of life'. In spite of other important disagreements, Kyburg and Carnap both subscribe to some form of a logical interpretation of probability, and both are committed to the view that such probabilities can be a 'guide of life'. In my brief comment in the discussion that followed Kyburg's paper I offered this as one reason – one which could not be acceptable to Kyburg, as I fully realized – for the view that inductive logic must embody rules of acceptance. In those remarks I did not spell out the reasons, which had been given in some detail in my initial paper in this symposium, but made only passing reference to them. These reasons were clearly understood by Professor Kneale, whose insightful contribution presents precisely the same point in a different and forceful way. Carnap, unfortunately, responded only to my brief presentation in the discussion of Kyburg's paper, so he answered only an old argument I explicitly disavowed in my lead paper [1]. I am indeed sorry that he did not attempt to resolve the difficulty which Kneale and I, at least, feel rather keenly.

Bar–Hillel's remarks on this problem also miss the point, I fear. We all recognize that the temporal relations among events are essentially irrelevant to the problems of inductive inference. The crucial problem involves inference from the observed to the unobserved, or more generally, from statements about a certain set of events to statements about events which are not identical with them. It is convenient to talk about inference from past to future because future events are obviously distinct from past events, and this manner of speaking should cause no confusion.

Now, the problem is this. Given two distinct events, a and b, and given a statement e which says something about a but nothing about b, how can e in conjunction with an analytic statement (in particular, a degree of confirmation statement) provide any information about b? Clearly it cannot. How, then, can the statement e in conjunction with an analytic statement provide a basis for rational action with respect to the event b? The fact that a and b are logically independent – i.e., deductively independent – does give rise to a problem. One way to deal with this sort of problem is to introduce an inductive rule of inference, e.g., induction by enumeration, and attempt to justify it. That is one way of making a transition from information about some events to conclusions about logically distinct events. But it is by no means apparent how analytic degree of confirmation statements can fulfil the same function. Bar–Hillel's observation that information about past horse races would, in fact, influence betting behaviour on future races is not a solution. It merely restates the problem.

In rejecting the notion that logical probabilities have the predictive import required in everyday life and in science, I was arguing that some alternative conception is needed. With either a limiting frequency concept, a finite frequency view, or Popper's propensity interpretation we have probability statements which embody the factual content I maintain we must have. Carnap

---

[1] pp. 24–43.

and Kyburg claim, however, that finite frequency or limiting frequency statements are intimately related to logical probabilities. Indeed, Carnap has held that degree of confirmation statements may sometimes function as *estimates* of statistical probabilities. On this view, one can assert that, although limiting frequencies are highly relevant to decision and prediction, it is not necessary to have an inductive acceptance rule for *inferring* limiting frequencies. All we need is a method of *estimating* these frequencies, and logical probabilities provide just that. In my initial paper I argued that we need something more than estimates, for estimates share all of the shortcomings of logical probabilities – at least they do if estimates are identified with a subset of logical probabilities.

There is a *prima facie* case for supposing that the kinds of requirements it is appropriate to impose upon rules of inference are not at all the same as the kinds of requirements methods of estimation must satisfy. Thus, to deal with the second basic issue of the final section of my paper, it is necessary to become quite clear whether we are talking about inferences or estimates. In particular, there are consistency requirements that must be imposed upon rules of inference, but from which methods of estimation *may be* exempt. *It depends entirely upon the circumstances under which estimates can, if ever, be detached and treated 'as if' they were actual values of the magnitudes of which they are estimates.* This issue is, it seems to me, absolutely fundamental. Hacking and Kyburg take me to task for insisting upon inferences instead of estimates, yet in their remarks the basic issue seems to be submerged. In my detailed discussion of this issue, I shall attempt to bring it to the surface once again.

Although I have argued elsewhere that induction by enumeration is the correct basic inductive rule, I did not endeavor to defend it in this symposium. I attempted, rather, to defend certain very general requirements which I believe inductive rules must satisfy. When I mentioned three possible candidates – induction by enumeration, the *a priori* rule, and the counter-inductive method – it was only to underscore the philosophical import of the fact that there are widely diverse possibilities to be considered. When I subsequently used the latter two rules to illustrate the application of the *convergence condition*, the *normalizing conditions*, and the *criterion of linguistic invariance*, it was only to show how these criteria enable us to make negative judgments and eliminate candidates. There was a time when I believed that these requirements were sufficient to select and vindicate a unique rule for inference to limiting frequencies. I have since become convinced, partly because of Hacking's efforts, that my former arguments were inadequate. In this symposium, therefore, I did not mean to suggest, openly or covertly, that I was presenting an actual vindication of induction by enumeration. I do maintain, however, that these requirements do constitute a sound basis for rejecting the counter-inductive rule, the *a priori* rule, and a host of others like them. Although these requirements seem to me necessary conditions a rule must satisfy to be acceptable, I no longer believe they are jointly sufficient to select induction by enumeration or any other unique rule. In the absence of sufficient criteria to vindicate a particular rule, I do not wish to claim that any one is justified, nor that it is justifiable. The straight rule may be the wrong rule; I do not think it is, but it may be.

Hacking's attack on induction by enumeration is, therefore, really irrelevant to the present discussion, but I shall defend it against his charge of inconsistency, partly because I think the attack is ill-founded and partly because I think the straight rule, though not vindicated, is still in the running. Hacking mentions the Goodman grue-bleen paradox, but does not dwell upon it here. I shall do likewise, only mentioning that I have attempted elsewhere to resolve it. I still believe the attempt was successful [1]. Beyond that, Hacking has constructed his own paradox, and one cannot ignore such ingenious arguments. Close analysis cannot fail to be instructive.

Both Hacking and Kyburg remark pointedly upon the fact that I deal with rules for inferring exact values of limits instead of intervals within which to locate the limit. The issue here is *not* one of deciding between inferences and estimates. There are point estimates and there are interval estimates. Likewise, one can infer

---

[1] 'On Vindicating Induction', *Philosophy of Science*, **30**, 3 (1963) and in *Induction: Some Current Issues*, eds., H. Kyburg and E. Nagel, Wesleyan University Press, 1963.

(or try to do so) the exact value of the limit, or one can infer that it lies between two given values. The question is one of exactitude. Now I must confess explicitly that Kyburg is right in suggesting that my reason for eschewing interval inferences is that intervals do not behave as nicely as points with regard to the kinds of criteria I am concerned to defend. (Kyburg built intervals into his definition of probability, and the price he paid was forfeiture of the probability calculus [1]!) I would, however, be most amenable to efforts to vindicate methods of interval inference. In fact, I am inclined to think that our inferences ought to take the form $p \pm \varepsilon$, as Reichenbach suggested, but where rules for the determination of ε are provided – a gap Reichenbach left in his presentation. It may be necessary, however, to treat the midpoints p of such intervals, in some ways at least, as if they were point inferences, and hence, exact values. For example, it seems to me that the whole set of values p_i – midpoints of intervals associated with a mutually exclusive and exhaustive set of attributes B_i – should constitute a logically possible set of values. Unfortunately, I do not have any compelling argument to offer at present beyond the observation that it would be neat. Thus, I must acknowledge the desirability of serious concern for rules for inferring intervals, and it seems entirely possible that the suggestions Hacking offers, following de Finetti, are useful ones (though, with Miller, I would reject the subjectivism in de Finetti's approach).

While the work of de Finetti, Savage, and other personalists (Bayesians) provides important insights for inductive logic and the foundations of statistics, it does not, in my opinion, provide an adequate answer to the philosophical problem of justification of induction. This is the fundamental problem to which my initial paper was addressed. The paper was devoted, in large part, to showing that this problem cannot properly be evaded or dismissed, but must be faced squarely if we hope to achieve philosophical understanding of the logic of science. Space does not permit a detailed critique of Hacking's positive suggestions, but I have

---

[1]   *Probability and the Logic of Rational Belief*, Wesleyan University Press, 1961.

tried elsewhere to show the insufficiency of that sort of approach [1]. There is, however, one point that deserves explicit mention. When Hacking takes issue with my search for a 'global' theory, I believe he is objecting to the whole enterprise of attempting a justification (vindication) of induction. Statisticians (rightly, I believe) are not usually concerned with this problem; they seem, rather, to assume some general solution and to pursue their interests in statistical inference (or estimation) in that context. Philosophers, on the other hand, find Hume's problem as part of their heritage, and they must somehow come to terms with it. I am not suggesting for one moment that statisticians and philosophers should try to insulate themselves from each other's concerns – quite the contrary. I am maintaining, however, that there is a peculiarly philosophical problem to which no complete answer is likely to be forthcoming from the literature of statistics alone.

The foregoing remarks have been designed to bring the major issues back into focus, and to set the stage for more detailed discussion of certain specific issues. There are five points that demand scrutiny.

1. *Hacking's pair paradox.* Hacking has propounded an ingenious paradox designed to convict the rule of induction by enumeration (the straight rule) of 'trivial inconsistency'. While he does succeed in eliciting an explicit contradiction by applying this rule, I shall attempt to show that the fault lies not with the rule itself, but rather with the way it was applied.

Suppose a coin has been tossed five times, and all we know is that the results have been

H T T H T.

In order to resolve the paradox in the form stated in Hacking's paper, I shall begin with a version he communicated privately. We examine the four pairs

HT, TT, TH, HT.

---

[1] 'The Foundations of Scientific Inference' in *Mind and Cosmos*, ed. R. Colodny, University of Pittsburgh Press, 1966, pp. 213–217, 255–257.

Counting relative frequencies in the sample and using induction by enumeration, we infer that the limit of the relative frequency of pairs beginning with H is $\frac{1}{2}$, the limit of the relative frequency of pairs ending with H is $\frac{1}{4}$, and the limit of the relative frequency of H is $\frac{2}{5}$. Manifestly, however, the limit of the relative frequency of pairs beginning with H must equal the limit of the relative frequency of pairs ending with H, and both of these are equal to the limit of the relative frequency of H. Hence, a contradiction.

The first thing to note is that, although we have observed only four complete pairs, we have seen part of the fifth pair whose first member is T and whose second member is yet to come. This is sufficient to show that it does not begin with H. Thus, if we are to use all of the available evidence, we must consider the five pairs

$$HT, \ TT, \ TH, \ HT, \ T-.$$

We conclude, therefore, that the limit of the relative frequency of pairs beginning with H is $\frac{2}{5}$, which agrees with our inference concerning the limit of the relative frequency of H.

It is a well-established fact that the application of inductive logic must conform to some sort of *requirement of total evidence* [1]. As a consequence of this requirement, an inference by the straight rule from a given sample to the limit of the relative frequency is superseded by another inference from a larger sample whenever the larger sample becomes available. To have inferred on the basis of the given evidence that the limit of the relative frequency of pairs beginning with H is $\frac{1}{2}$ would have been an obvious violation of that requirement, for it would have been an inference from a sample of four members when a sample of five members was available. One part of the paradox is thus resolved, and the resolution shows, as I said, that the fault lies not with the rule of inference but with the way it was used.

The other part of the paradox can be resolved on the same basis, but not quite so simply. Since there are only four pairs

---

[1] Although there are serious difficulties surrounding any particular formulation of this requirement, it seems to me there can be no doubt whatever that some such requirement must be imposed.

with second members available for inspection, it seems at first glance that we have only a sample of four pairs from which to infer the limit of the relative frequency of pairs ending with H. More careful reflection shows, however, that this is a mistake. We do have a sample of five, not because we have seen the second member of a fifth pair, but because the limit of the relative frequency of pairs ending with H is necessarily equal to the limit of the relative frequency of pairs beginning with H (as well as to the limit of the relative frequency of H). Since the limit of the relative frequency of pairs beginning with H (as well as the limit of the relative frequency of H) can be inferred from a sample of five, this guarantees that the limit of the relative frequency of pairs ending with H can also be inferred from a sample of five. It would therefore be a methodological error to use the sample consisting of only four pairs as a basis for this inference, for the larger sample can be employed [1].

The version of the paradox set forth in Hacking's paper can be resolved in the same way. It is a mistake to infer the limit of the relative frequency of pairs ending with T on the basis of a sample of only four members, for this limit is equal to one minus the limit of the relative frequency of pairs ending with H – a limit we have already inferred from a sample containing five members. It may not be obvious at first glance that the inference can be made on the basis of a sample of five, but a little thought shows that it can after all. We find, then, that the original sin was not the deductive logician's sin of asserting a contradiction, but the inductive logician's sin of violating the requirement of total evidence. The paradox is fully resolved; the straight rule has not been convicted of inconsistency.

I should like to make one further observation regarding Hacking's

---

[1] The fact that four pairs comprise five tosses does not mean that the sample is a sample of five. The reference class determines how to count the number of elements in the sample. The fact that we seek the relative frequency of pairs ending with H determines that *pairs*, not individual tosses are members of the sample. Thus, the same set of five tosses gives us a sample of five when we deal with the frequency of H among single tosses, but a sample of only four when we deal with pairs ending in H.

paradox. The paradox arises because the first member of the entire sequence enjoys the unique distinction of not being the second member of any pair. But should we attach any inductive significance to the fact that a particular element is the first element of the sequence – especially in view of the fact that it may not be the first element produced by the mechanism in question, but only the first we noticed? If we take this point seriously, we might be tempted to say that the first member of the sequence is, in fact, to be regarded as the second member of a pair – a virtual pair if you like – a pair whose first member is not available for inspection. In that case, the second part of the paradox would vanish immediately, for we should have second members of five pairs to examine:

– H, HT, TT, TH, HT.

This point has far-reaching implications, as we shall see [1].

2.   *Internal structure of sequences.* Even though Hacking has not convicted the straight rule of trivial inconsistency, it does not follow that the straight rule is not just silly. As a matter of fact, it *is* silly in most real circumstances, as even some of its staunchest defenders have insisted. Induction by enumeration is a rule for inferring from meagre data. Given a sample of size n, we attempt to infer the limit of the relative frequency from the observed relative frequency within that sample. When we say that the data are meagre, this does not imply that n is a small number. It may be very large. The point is that the observed frequency in the sample is the only kind of data used. If there is other relevant information available, it would be an error to use the rule of induction by enumeration, for to do so would be a violation of the requirement of total evidence.

Most cases in which we have knowledge of the relative frequency of an attribute in an observed sample are, as Hacking emphasizes, cases in which we also have a good deal more information – infor-

---

[1] Popper clearly recognized the significance of this consideration, see *The Logic of Scientific Discovery*, 1959, § 53–58, especially pp. 172 f.

mation concerning the order in which the instances occurred, and telling us which particular trial yielded which particular result. Induction by enumeration ignores this additional information, even though it is the sort of information that can be derived from a description of the observed sample alone. In order to vindicate induction by enumeration, Hacking suggests, it would be necessary to establish a symmetry condition which would render the order of the results irrelevant to the inference to the limit of the relative frequency.

Granting, then, that we usually have knowledge of the internal order of our sample as well as the overall relative frequency of the attribute in question, to what conclusions are these data relevant? Frequentists like von Mises and Reichenbach gave part of the answer at least: data concerning the internal structure of the sample are relevant to questions concerning the internal structure of the whole sequence. These men have shown that important structural properties of the whole sequence can be explicated in terms of limits of relative frequencies in certain kinds of subsequences. For instance, von Mises introduces the notion of a *place selection* in order to characterize one basic type of subsequence. The very definition of a probability sequence – a *collective* – is given in terms of *randomness*, and randomness is defined in terms of the limits of the relative frequencies in subsequences determined by place selections. Reichenbach gives a less restrictive definition of a probability sequence, but he distinguishes various types of internal order of probability sequences in terms of the limits of relative frequencies in various kinds of subsequences. For example, he defines the *normal sequence* as one that is random in a weaker sense than that of von Mises, and he defines sequences with various types of after-effect. For Reichenbach at least, induction by enumeration is the basic rule for inferring limits of relative frequencies in subsequences as well as in the main sequence. Consider the following initial section of a sequence of heads and tails (not necessarily produced by a fair coin tossed fairly):

H H H T T H H T H H H H H T T T T T T T.

The relative frequency of heads in this sample is one-half, but the relative frequency of a head following a head is seven-tenths. In the sample, there is an after-effect. Using induction by enumeration we infer that the whole sequence is not random. We infer that the limit of the relative frequency of heads in the entire sequences is $\frac{1}{2}$, while the limit of the relative frequency of heads among immediate successors of heads is $\frac{7}{10}$. These inferences are by no means incompatible with each other.

In the foregoing inferences, the order of the elements in the sample is taken to have no bearing upon the inference to the limit of the relative frequency of heads in the entire sequence, though it does determine the inference concerning the limit of the relative frequency of heads in certain subsequences. The only way in which an apparent conflict might arise is in connection with the question of the probability of heads on some individual toss. Here, it might be said, we have various probability values available. Is the probability of heads on the next toss $\frac{1}{2}$, $\frac{3}{10}$, or some other number? The apparent conflict is, however, unreal, for there are rules governing the selection of the sequence. These rules demand that the sequence be random (or the reference class homogeneous). We have already inferred that the main sequence is not random; this conclusion may be false, but it is the conclusion we have drawn. In the light of this conclusion, we must reject $\frac{1}{2}$ as the value, and assign a value more like $\frac{3}{10}$, taking account of the fact that the next toss will be one that follows a tail.

Unfortunately, things do not always work so smoothly for induction by enumeration. Consider the following initial section of the sequence:

H T T H T H T H H H T H T H H H T H T H.

This time the relative frequency of heads is $\frac{6}{10}$. However, in this sample each prime toss yields tails, while each non-prime toss is a head [1]. Using induction by enumeration, we infer that every prime toss yields a tail and every non-prime toss yields a head. Knowing that the limit of the relative frequency of primes is zero,

---

[1] I have adopted the usual convention of excluding the number one from the class of primes.

we infer that the limit of the relative frequency of heads is one. This is a contradiction.

The foregoing paradox (hereafter called 'the prime paradox') is, in my opinion, more difficult than Goodman's grue-bleen paradox or Hacking's pair paradox. I do not presently have an answer I consider satisfactory. It is worth noting, however, that this particular form of the paradox depends in a crucial way upon identifying the initial member of the sequence. If we assume we do not have any way of identifying the first member of the sequence – i.e., any way of telling whether the first observed member is the first (or some other ordinal) member of the sequence – then we cannot tell which tosses are the prime tosses and which are not. In the absence of this information, it is of course impossible to count the relative frequency of heads among prime tosses. On this basis we might conclude that there is something suspect about the inference that all prime tosses are tails; indeed, it has been suggested that this inference violates linguistic invariance [1]. In order to be able to name the subsequence we are dealing with it is necessary to assign ordinals to the members of the sequence. A different naming – e.g., assuming there are three unobserved members that precede the observed members – would result in an entirely different relative frequency of heads on prime tosses. Yet, the limit of the relative frequency is not changed by arbitrarily adding or removing a finite number of elements. This suggests that the issue of identification of the first member of the sequence has profound consequences. Nevertheless, we do not want to get carried away with that idea; it must be possible to determine inductively that there is a trend toward more or less frequent occurrence of an attribute. If not, what are we to make of such notions as the decrease in the rate of death due to tuberculosis?

3. *Additivity, invariance, and symmetry.* As I remarked above, I once believed that it was possible to provide a vindication of the straight rule on the basis of the *convergence requirement*, the *normal-*

---

[1] By my student, Mr. Clark Glymour.

izing conditions, and the *criterion of linguistic invariance*. Several considerations, advanced by several people, convinced me that I was wrong, and that my purported demonstration was actually fallacious. Professor I. Richard Savage [1] pointed out that my argument failed to exclude a rule of the following sort:

Given a mutually exclusive and exhaustive set of attributes B_i, and given an observed sample of n members in which m_i have the attribute B_i, choose that attribute, say B_j, for which the frequency in the sample is maximum (i.e., $m_j > m_i$ for each $i \neq j$). Infer that the limit of the relative frequency of B_j is one, and that the limit of the relative frequency of each other attribute is zero. In case r $(r > 1)$ attributes have the same maximal value in sample, let $1/r$ be the inferred value for the limit of the relative frequency of each.

As it stands, this rule does not violate the *normalizing conditions* or the *criterion of linguistic invariance*, though it is obviously neither additive nor convergent. Its failure to meet the *convergence requirement* can be overcome, however, by a fairly simple grafting of this rule on to some convergent rule, in such a way that this rule becomes less dominant as sample size increases. As a matter of fact, much the same effect is achieved by the rule Hacking introduces in his discussion of symmetry [2]. The fact that Savage's rule is non-additive, but satisfies the *normalizing conditions*, shows that the *condition of additivity* is stronger than the *normalizing conditions*. Additivity is, as Hacking suggests, a plausible condition to impose upon rules of inference, but I do not believe it can quite be construed as a consistency requirement. For this reason, I have tried to make do with the weaker *normalizing conditions* and resisted the temptation to insist upon additivity.

As I understand *linguistic invariance*, it is a consistency requirement, and it is *not* the stronger kind of invariance to which

---

[1] Professor Savage, who was in 1963 a member of the Department of Statistics at the University of Minnesota, presented this criticism at a meeting in the Minnesota Center for Philosophy of Science.

[2] p. 50.

Hacking refers. Hacking complains that I have never published a rigorous statement of my requirement, but I think the complaint is ill-founded. My latest formulation [1], which is entirely equivalent to earlier formulations, is:

> If S and S' are statements in the same or different languages such that (1) S asserts that a certain relative frequency $F^n(A, B)$ obtains in a sample of size n, (2) S' is equivalent to S by virtue of the semantical and syntactical rules of the languages in which they occur, and (3) rule R sanctions the inference from S that
>
> $$\lim_{n \to \infty} F^n(A, B) = p,$$
>
> then R must not sanction the inference from S' that
>
> $$\lim_{n \to \infty} F^n(A, B) = q$$
>
> where $p \neq q$.

The problem is that the requirement refers to the syntactic and semantic rules of the languages being used, and for natural languages it is often difficult to say precisely what these rules are. The vagueness of the languages gives rise to the difficulty, not the imprecision of the *criterion of linguistic invariance*.

In his section on invariance, Hacking offers a couple of 'rules' and asks whether linguistic invariance excludes them [2]. As they stand they are very odd, for they mention the attributes *heads* and *tails* explicitly. As stated, they introduce a bias for heads and against tails. Normally, a rule of inference would not make specific mention of particular attributes; rather, the formulation would be more like this:

> Given two mutually exclusive and exhaustive attributes B_1 and B_2, and given that the observed frequency of B_1 is m/n in a sample of size n, infer ...

---

[1] 'The Foundations of Scientific Inference', in *Mind and Cosmos*, ed. R. Colodny, University of Pittsburgh Press, 1966, p. 235.

[2] p. 49.

If the rule is stated generally, it seems to me that the identification of B_1 with heads and B_2 with tails is a linguistic convention, so the counterpart of Hacking's rule falls to the criterion of linguistic invariance. If, however, we take the rules literally as given by Hacking, linguistic invariance unfortunately does not apply. Linguistic invariance can exclude any rule that imposes a bias in virtue of a predicate – the *name* of an attribute – but not a rule that imposes the bias in terms of the attribute itself.

If an inductive rule is to impose a bias for or against an attribute, there must be some method for selecting the attribute and determining the amount and kind of bias. One way is simply to make the choice *a priori* and write it into the inductive rule; that is what Hacking did in the two rules just mentioned. How we could possibly have an *a priori* basis for this procedure is quite a different question. Another way of picking the attribute is to compare the observed frequencies, and to let them determine the bias as in the Savage rule. Still another way to choose the attribute is to let the first trial, or the kth trial, determine the bias. In his discussion of symmetry, Hacking introduces a rule of this type – a rule that has a positive bias for the attribute that occurs first [1]. Notice, incidentally, the crucial role played by the first (or some ordinally determined) element.

At this point, I can only express my gratitude to Hacking for showing, in the appendix to his paper, the necessary and sufficient conditions that would single out the straight rule as a uniquely justifiable rule. I do not, at present, know how to argue for these conditions; perhaps they are indefensible. *Additivity* seems acceptable, but it is somewhat more problematic than the *normalizing conditions*. An *invariance* principle, stronger than *linguistic invariance*, seems difficult to defend, but perhaps not hopeless. *Symmetry*, it would seem, is a particularly problematic condition. We cannot, as Hacking has forcefully shown, ignore the information we have about the internal structure of our samples. In many cases this information can be used to make inferences about the internal structure of the entire sequence, without affecting the inference

---

[1]   p. 50.

about the limit of the relative frequency in the main sequence. In these cases, symmetry is preserved without violating the requirement of total evidence. The prime paradox, however, seems to show that symmetry does not always obtain. It appears that the straight rule can be used to show that the symmetry condition fails, and hence, induction by enumeration on the whole sequence is not legitimate. The only way to escape this conclusion, I fear, is to conclude that the symmetry condition rules out the use of induction by enumeration on subsequences of the type involved in the paradox – a most unappetizing result.

4. *Inference vs. estimation.* In the philosophical literature, Carnap has pre-empted the term 'estimate' in an unfortunate way [1]. What he calls an 'estimate' might better be called an 'expectation' – or, to distinguish it from a statistical expectation – a 'c-expectation'. Carnap's estimates have several crucial characteristics not shared by what others recognize as estimates, but he has a claim of about two decades on the term, so I have sought to avoid using it in a sense radically different from his. The important thing, of course, is to become clear on the issues, not to battle over a word. Nevertheless, in view of the amount of confusion generated by the terminology, and in view of the fact that 'estimate' is short for 'c-mean estimate' in Carnap's terminology, I suggest we adopt the convention of referring to Carnap's estimates as 'c-estimates', reserving the term 'estimate' for its more common usages.

As a result of Carnap's definition, c-estimates are so closely associated with logical probabilities that they share many characteristics in common. Every c-function uniquely determines a c-mean estimate function; c-estimate statements are analytic once the c-estimate function is chosen, just as degree of confirmation statements are analytic once the confirmation function is chosen. By virtue of its analytic status, a c-estimate, just like a confirmation statement, lacks predictive force. A statement of the form, 'The

---

[1] R. Carnap, *Logical Foundations of Probability*, University of Chicago Press, 1950, ch. 9, and *The Continuum of Inductive Methods*, University of Chicago Press, 1952, § 6.

c-estimate of magnitude M on evidence e is x', has no factual content. The evidence statement e is, of course, synthetic in the interesting cases, but the combination of the c-estimate statement and the evidence statement, even if the latter embodies total relevant evidence, has no factual content beyond that of the evidence statement alone. We can say, roughly, that a c-estimate does not convey any more than a reformulation of the evidence; in particular, it is not a statement about the actual value of the magnitude being estimated, and it makes no prediction about future measurements or determinations of that magnitude.

Degree of confirmation statements and c-estimates have another fundamental feature in common. Just as a degree of confirmation statement does not, strictly speaking, even in conjunction with evidence, provide a basis for accepting a synthetic hypothesis, so does a c-estimate fail to provide a ground for accepting a synthetic statement about the actual value of the magnitude being estimated. In short, c-estimates, degree of confirmation statements, and observational evidence taken all together do not provide any factual information about the future. For the reasons explained at some length in my initial paper, I am skeptical that logical probabilities can function as a 'guide of life', and I am skeptical that c-estimates can provide any significant help in practical decision and action for precisely the same reasons.

The present symposium is concerned with inferring or estimating relative frequencies. It is a consequence of Carnap's definitions that the c-estimate of the relative frequency is the degree of confirmation of the singular predictive inference. Thus, a c-estimate of the relative frequency in the population provides neither a statement about the relative frequency (or limit thereof) in the total population nor a prediction of future observed frequencies when larger samples are examined. For reasons already mentioned, I do not think c-estimates of relative frequencies have the kind of predictive import needed.

Statisticians and ordinary people do not use the term 'estimate' to mean 'c-estimate'. Jerzy Neyman, for example, says, 'The general problem of statistical estimation consists in devising a *method of making assertions* regarding the value of one (or more) parameter[s] . . .' [1] Nowhere in the writings of statisticians have I found any indication that estimate statements are, for them, analytic or devoid of predictive import. Nor do I find any indication that estimated values cannot, upon occasion at least, be detached and asserted as actual values of magnitudes. In these fundamental respects, then, estimates are *not* like *c*-estimates.

As nearly as I can tell, the basic difference between the concepts of estimation and inference is that estimation yields a number (or possibly a mathematical function) while inference yields a statement. This difference does not seem especially profound, since any estimate can be used to form the hypothesis that the magnitude being estimated has the value yielded by the estimate. Moreover, truth values and truth frequencies can be treated numerically, so they too can be estimated. If this were the only distinction, there would be little to choose between saying that we estimate a magnitude or saying that we infer that it has a certain value. The same would hold for intervals. It would matter very little whether we make an estimate with an interval attached or infer that the value lies within an interval.

The concept of estimation is often introduced by the following type of consideration. In a certain practical situation, we might know what course of action to take if only we knew the value of some parameter. Since we do not know the value, we must make do with an estimate. A good estimate enables us sensibly to decide a course of action. The restaurant owner does not know how many people will patronize his establishment tomorrow, but he can make an estimate. The transit company does not know how many people will ride, but it can make an estimate. The gambler does not know how many times seven will occur in a given number of tosses of a pair of dice, but he can make an estimate. Since we should not claim to *know* the actual value of a magnitude unless we are fairly sure of it, the term 'estimate' conveys some lack of certainty. Nevertheless, an estimate is not just a blind guess; it is based upon evidence.

---

[1]　Jerzy Neyman, *Lectures and Conferences on Mathematical Statistics and Probability*, 2nd ed., Graduate School, U. S. Dept. of Agriculture, 1952, p. 158.

Some philosophers and statisticians seem to reserve the term 'inference' for deductive reasoning. According to this usage, we can infer the value only if we can deduce it from our data; otherwise, we should say that we make an estimate. Under this conception, the derivation of a probability from others by means of the calculus of probabilities (e.g., using Bayes' theorem to calculate a posterior probability from given prior probabilities and likelihoods) constitutes inference; attempting to determine a relative frequency in a population on the basis of the relative frequency in a sample does not qualify as inference. In this latter case, we would have estimation.

Hacking and Kyburg raise objections against my use of the term 'inference'. Hacking, at least, explicitly denies that he restricts the notion of inference to deduction [1]. Since he does not tell us what he means by 'inference' and 'estimation', it is impossible to be sure what basis he has for his objection. Apparently, it stems from ordinary language considerations (including, I imagine, the ordinary usage of statisticians). 'But who would dare infer that the long run frequency is exactly $\frac{17}{20}$, not say 0.8531 or 0.8351? No one. We are happy to estimate the long run frequency as $\frac{17}{20}$. But infer it? Not on your life.' [2] Two different issues may be involved. First, Hacking may possibly be suggesting that we should not call anything an inference unless we are fairly sure of it. He does not insist upon deductive necessity, but it should be more than a mere estimate. Second, a question of exactness may be involved. If an inference yields a statement, the result is something that is either true or false – there are no matters of degree. If your inferred value is off by the slightest amount, the inference has a false conclusion and that is all there is to it. If, however, an estimate yields a number, that number may approximate more or less closely the true value of the magnitude. Thus, there may seem to be degrees of accuracy associated with estimation which do not exist in the case of inference.

In using the term 'inference', I was concerned only to reject

---

[1]   *This volume*, p. 45.
[2]   *This volume*, p. 46.

the notion of c-estimation, not the ordinary notion of estimation.
I never intended to suggest that we could be very sure of our
inferred values of limiting frequencies, nor did I intend to suggest
that an inferred value is useless if it is ever so slightly inaccurate.
In these senses, I am certainly discussing methods of estimating
limiting frequencies. But the fundamental logical question remains.
Call it what you will, 'estimation' or 'inference', what kinds of
conditions are we justified in imposing upon the methods or rules?
In particular, can consistency conditions, such as the *normalizing
conditions* and the *criterion of linguistic invariance*, be demanded?
I believe Hacking and I are in complete agreement that this is
the issue.

If I am asked to bet or take other action in terms of the unknown
value of some magnitude, it may, upon occasion, be wise to choose
the best estimate of that magnitude and behave as if that were,
in fact, the actual value. It would be absurd, however, to bet
that a logically impossible value is the true value. The question
I am raising is just this: what value do you pick when you have
to say what you think the true value is? That is what I meant by
an inferred value; that is what we have in an ordinary kind of
estimate, though not in a c-estimate.

It is an immediate consequence of Carnap's definition of 'c-mean
estimate' that it need not be a logically possible value of the
magnitude in question. The c-estimate of the number of children
in a family may not be an integer; the c-estimate of gain on a
wager may be an amount it is logically impossible to win under
the conditions of the bet. This consequence does not give rise to
explicit contradictions *because c-estimates cannot be detached and
asserted* as synthetic statements about the magnitude. Ordinary
estimates can sometimes be asserted; this is what gives them their
practical import. Though the *average* number of children in some
class of families may be fractional, the *estimate* of the number
in a given family must be integral. Though the *expectation* of gain
on a bet may be an impossible amount to win, the *estimate* of the
winnings must be a possible amount. It is to avoid logical absurdity
that I have insisted upon the consistency conditions. They apply
to rules of inference and methods of estimation. They may not

apply to c-estimates, but Hacking clearly has some other sort of estimation in mind. Thus, it is not clear to me that he has shown the dispensability of conditions such as additivity for estimation. This cannot be shown, I think, without a much clearer statement of the conditions under which estimated values can be treated as actual values. An enormous virtue of Carnap's treatment of c-estimation lies in the fact that he has given us an unequivocal answer to the question.

One further remark is appropriate in this context. Kyburg is correct in pointing out that there are certain kinds of statements about limiting frequencies which can be known to be false, and on which bets can, therefore, be settled [1]. Self-contradictory statements – e.g., the limit of the relative frequency has two distinct values, or the value is greater than one – fall into that category. It is just such statements that the consistency requirements are designed to block. Demonstrably false statements about limits can be made, but I do not believe that an explicit contradiction in the form of the lottery paradox arises in connection with the inductive rule which enables us to assert values for limits of relative frequencies. Since the lottery paradox has been one of the most important reasons for rejecting inductive acceptance rules, it is significant to note how the paradox can be avoided without abandoning acceptance rules for synthetic probability statements.

5.   Corroboration. In my initial paper, I attempted to confront Popper's conception of the logic of science with a dilemma. Either science comprises knowledge of the unobserved, or it has no predictive import. If it does embody knowledge of the unobserved, it is inductive; if not, it is barren. Watkins states unequivocally that Popper rejects the first alternative, and thus escapes the need for any nondemonstrative ampliative inference. A set of accepted basic statements may have factual content, but '. . . corroboration-appraisal *is* analytic and does *not* have predictive implications' [2].

---

[1]   *This volume*, p. 74.
[2]   *This volume*, p. 63.

According to Popper, the aim of (theoretical) science is *not* to establish far-reaching knowledge of the world, but rather, to provide (conjectural) explanations which are as far as possible from being *ad hoc*. While I have no doubt that Watkins accurately characterizes Popper's view, I am unconvinced that the view is acceptable.

When someone is said to know physics, most of us would suppose he knows some general laws or theories – e.g., classical electrodynamics, special relativity, the first and second laws of thermodynamics, etc. Taken at face value, such laws or theories make statements about unobserved matters of fact. On Popper's account, it seems, we cannot claim to know any such things. We can know the attempts that have been made to falsify them. This enables us to know something about the corroboration of the hypotheses in question, but it certainly does not permit us to know these hypotheses in any sense. Since the corroboration-appraisal is analytic, all we know are the observed results of the tests – no more. Hypotheses are used for the purpose of explanation, but they are not accepted, asserted, or known; rather, their corroboration is appraised. The conclusion seems inescapable: science does not embody any knowledge beyond observation. The 'growth' of knowledge appears to consist in the accumulation of additional observations. According to crude inductivism, scientific knowledge grows by accumulating observations and generalizing upon them; according to deductivism, scientific knowledge grows by accumulating observations and refusing to generalize upon them. Our theorizing activity will determine to some extent the observations we actually make, for the attempt to falsify a hypothesis may lead us to perform an experiment or make an observation we otherwise would not have. But the hypotheses themselves form no part of the corpus of our knowledge, and the corroboration statements merely reformulate the content of our observations.

In order to come to terms with the undeniable fact that science has a predictive function, Popper must make a deep and sharp separation between theoretical and applied science. The distinction itself is very difficult to accept in such a radical form. But even if it is tenable, the logic of science would be seriously incomplete if it did not account for the predictive aspect of applied science as well as the explanatory aspect of theoretical science. Indeed, one wonders whether we would continue to prize explanatory hypotheses of theoretical science if we became convinced that their predictive import could not be accepted at least tentatively.

Watkins acknowledges, in the final paragraph of his paper, that corroboration does have predictive import in practical decision making. In speaking of a predictive problem, he writes, '. . . it would be rational for him to choose the better corroborated one, the one which has withstood the more severe criticism, since he has nothing else to go on' [1]. I cannot avoid concluding that applied science is, indeed, inductive in the fundamental and important sense of that term. Either corroboration has an inductive aspect, or there is no logic of prediction. If there is no logic of prediction, it is hard to see how any choice would be 'rational'.

There is, I believe, an extremely important conclusion to be drawn from this entire symposium. The attempts of Ayer and Strawson, on the one hand, and of Popper, on the other, to do away with the problem of induction have not succeeded. Carnap's attempt to furnish an inductive logic encounters deep philosophical problems. The Reichenbach attempt to provide a vindication of induction, supplemented by my attempts to plug some of the gaps, still faces enormous difficulties. In short, *there still is a philosophical problem of induction.*

---

[1]   *This volume,* p. 66.

THE RULE OF DETACHMENT IN INDUCTIVE LOGIC *

HENRY E. KYBURG, Jr.

University of Rochester

1. What is a rule of detachment in inductive logic? [1] Such a rule has been mentioned time and again in the literature of induction but it has seldom been given a precise characterization. Sometimes particular rules are spelled out (as in my own work, or in Isaac Levi's *Gambling with Truth*), but that kind of thing provides us with no handles by which to take hold of the general problem of the existence (or suitability) of any rule of detachment in inductive logic.

A rule of detachment in general may be regarded as a permissive rule allowing the detachment of a conclusion from a particular set of premises. The premises, in induction, are usually regarded as simple observable facts; observations themselves; or statements or propositions based directly upon those observations. It is possible that sometimes the premises will be taken to include general statements, or statistical generalizations. The nature of the conclusion of an inductive argument is both more important and more problematic than the nature of the premises. There are three quite distinct things that such a conclusion might be:

(1) An analytic, logically true, probability statement, such as $c(h, e) = p$, where e consists of observation statements or protocol statements and satisfies a principle of total evidence, and where h is simply the hypothesis in question; c represents a logical confir-

---

* The author is indebted to the National Science Foundation for support of research on this subject.

[1] Bar–Hillel claims that the only 'rule of detachment' is *modus ponens*; I have taken the phrase only in a general sense of any rule which allows the detachment of a conclusion from premises. If 'rule of acceptance' is regarded as more suitable, I am agreeable to a change of terminology.

mation function. More generally, *any* analytic conclusion of the form: in the light of e, expect h.

(2) The factual statement h itself, which may be particular or general – though, as we shall see, this can be a hard distinction to draw.

(3) A decision as to a course of action, or the course of action itself. Conclusions of this type may be trickily disguised as hypotheses: when there is one course of action, a, that is obviously appropriate, given that h is true, then one can misleadingly express the directive: 'perform a' in the words 'accept hypothesis h'.

Some logical probability theorists (e.g. Carnap) adopt *both* views (1) and (3) – and in either case it seems to make good sense to talk about a 'rule of detachment' though in neither case does it appear to be a controversial sort of rule. In the first instance I can see no more difficulty in detaching the analytic conclusion $c(h, e) = p$ from the inductive premises e, than in detaching the conclusion $X \rightarrow X$ from its premises $X \rightarrow XX$ and $XX \rightarrow X$ in a proof in Hilbert and Ackermann's system of logic. This is still not quite the deductive 'detachment', for the premises, deductively speaking, of $c(h, e) = p$ are of course the axioms or definitions that give the function c its meaning. But there is still a perfectly clear sense in which, when e represents our body of relevant knowledge and we assert $c(h, e) = p$, e may be regarded as the evidence on which our assertion is based. It is, at any rate, what gives our assertion its pragmatic justification. The schematic form of the argument so justified is

$$\frac{e}{c(h, e) = p}.$$

An alternative and perhaps better schematization (due to R. Jeffrey) is

$$e \text{ is total evidence}$$
$$c(h, e) = p$$
$$\overline{\text{believe } h \text{ to degree } p.}$$

Not only logical probability theorists, but also (and particularly)

statisticians and decision theorists of all camps would look on (3)
as appropriately characterizing the *conclusion* of an inductive
argument; or, since 'arguments' are verbal entities, perhaps we
should say: an appropriate conclusion to the inductive phase of
a piece of behavior. In this sense, too, I cannot see how anyone
would object to a rule of detachment – i.e. a rule that says: in
such and such circumstances, given such and such evidence, make
such and such a decision. The decision, in a clear and obvious
sense, is detached from the evidence in the light of which it is
made. The decision or the action, once it has been made or embarked
upon, no longer carries with it any reference to the evidence which
led to it, or on which it is based. This is obviously true of *explicit*
reference; it is also true of implicit reference, since a decision *d*
may be based on any one member of a whole class of bodies of
evidence, and *d* carries with it no way of determining which of
these bodies of evidence was in fact the one which led to it.

Again, in this case, I think a rule of detachment is fairly unproblematic. I can think of no one who would seriously object to
a rule which would allow a course of action or a decision as to a
course of action to be detached from (regarded independently of)
the evidence that led to it. Such a rule is neither very problematic,
nor, I think, very interesting.

It is only when an inductive conclusion is regarded as a straightforward factual statement or proposition, that the question of the
possibility of an inductive rule of detachment becomes serious and
interesting. This is the case, it should be noted, whether the conclusion in question is general ('All crows are black') or particular
('Sam is black').

Let us take inductive conclusions in this sense: they are to be
statements of fact, propositions, perhaps even declarative sentences.
I am not concerned about the particular character of these entities,
but only to distinguish them from their analytic counterparts (as
offered by Carnap, for example) and to distinguish them from
decisions, actions, recommendations, etc. as offered by decision
theorists and (in another sense) also by Carnap.

Call the declarative, factual, inductive conclusion *h*. Then an
inductive rule of detachment will be a rule that says: under such

and such circumstances, *accept h.* How will the 'such and such' circumstances be circumscribed? In a wide variety of ways. Most obviously in terms of the probability of *h*, relative to the total evidence we have for it. That is the one natural criterion that enters into most rules. But there are others that are also important, such as information content. Indeed, some writers, such as Popper, regard information content as supremely important. Both probability and content may be regarded as ingredients of scientific utility (epistemic utility, to use Hempel's neat phrase), but there are others – for example, the harmoniousness of *h* with the rest of our scientific principles. And of course it is not only scientific utility that we may take into account in considering whether or not to accept a statement *h*. We may consider the emotional utility of accepting *h* (does it make us *feel* good?), its political utility (is it conductive to the stability of the state?), and its practical utility (will its acceptance add to our scientific stature? our income? our academic rank?). (I am not suggesting that these utilities *should* be considered, but only that they *might* be.)

But notice that we may not consider pragmatic utility. It is not accepting *h* that has pragmatic consequences (narrowly construed), but acting on *h*. And, at least for the discussion here, we must sharply distinguish between accepting *h* and acting on *h*, even though we may regard acceptance of *h* as taking on a *disposition* to act on *h*. A *strictly* behavioristic interpretation of acceptance *may* be put forward; but then the distinction between (2) and (3) collapses and it becomes difficult to see how anyone could oppose a rule of detachment: if to *accept h* is *merely* to act on it, then how could anyone ever claim that we do not accept inductive conclusions?

A rule of detachment, then, if there is one, will be construed as a rule that permits the acceptance of a statement *h* representing a factual inductive conclusion, given that certain criteria are satisfied. These criteria will be expressed in terms referring to one or more of the following:

(1)   a body of statements regarded as evidence, and satisfying some principle of acceptability, and also a condition of total evidence;

(2) the probability of h, relative to this body of statements;
(3) the information content of h (this may also be relativized to the body of statements mentioned in (1));
(4) the simplicity and fruitfulness of h;
(5) other factors not generally regarded as relevant by philosophers of science, such as political or moral utility.

2. What difference does it make whether or not we allow a rule of detachment? In the first place, the content of science will differ immensely on the two views: if we allow no rule of detachment, then science – so far as it consists of a body of statements at all – will consist of a set of observation statements or protocol statements: 'On September 10, 1963, Jones observed the thermometer t, and made the reading 10.3 °C'. The question as to just what statements are to be regarded as protocol statements is a deep and difficult one; I shall have to worry the edges of it later on, but right at the moment we need only observe that *whatever* protocol statements may be, they certainly do not include Newton's laws, or Hooke's law, or Avogadro's law, or the Quantum Theory, or even 'All crows are black'. And it is just these generalizations, laws and theories that most of us regard as the distinctive *content* of science. Does chemistry consist of the observations of particular chemists at particular times? Or does it not rather consist of the general principles, laws, etc. that have been put forth by these chemists (on the basis of their particular experiences) and have withstood repeated tests, confirmations, attempts at falsification, etc.? Are the protocol statements that correspond to the observations of physicists the content of physics? Or is it not the set of physical laws and generalizations that have best withstood the test of time? To be sure, on the former interpretation, we have a kind of linear and ineluctable progress: physics grows as (quantitatively *as*) more physicists make more observations. On the view that takes physics to include laws and generalizations physics will only progress *significantly* when the laws and generalizations and theories are replaced by new ones that go beyond the old. Indeed it may appear to regress when old laws are refuted before there are new ones to replace them. Isn't this too just about what common sense makes of the matter? Do

we not regard the creator of a new theory that becomes a part of the accepted body of theory of physics as making a *real* contribution to the science, while his brother who records observations that are little more than just *mere* observations we regard as not making much of a contribution? But on the view that there is no rule of detachment, we should have just the opposite attitude: we should regard the observer as expanding the body of physics, while the theorizer plays with concepts that are simply *irrelevant* to physics. The last statement needs support: it sounds too strong. But let us put the matter in its simplest terms, and pursue it briefly.

Let us suppose that there is no rule of detachment. This presupposes a clear-cut distinction between observation statements and non-observation statements. Let us call the latter, *very loosely*, theoretical. Then we may classify the statements asserted professionally by physicists as follows: there is a set E of statements e which are the protocol, observation, evidence – statements, certified by actual observation, on which physics is based. There is a set G of statements g not of this sort, but which are (perhaps only loosely speaking) also asserted by physicists. I claim that under the hypothesis that there is no rule of detachment in induction, statements g are totally redundant and unnecessary. It is well known that theoretical terms are in a certain sense redundant: in the sense that the set of observational statements characteristic of a general theory can be generated by a recursive procedure that does not involve any theoretical terms. But here we only arrive at the non-theoretical characterization by beginning with the theory; the theory (though in principle dispensable) is pragmatically essential.

This is precisely what is not true of the role of general statements on the view of science that I am describing; the only scientific statements that have direct practical importance are (like the evidence statements for science) protocol statements; they are statements that are just like the members of E, except that they have not (yet) been certified by observation. Their importance lies in the fact that they will or will not be so certified in the future – so let us call the set of such statements F, and the individual statements f. The only statements that can be definitively confirmed or refuted are statements in E and statements in F; those in E *have* been definitively confirmed. (There may well be protocol statements neither in E nor in F - e.g. statements about the past, or denials of statements in E.)

Now we are to take probability (no doubt in the logical sense) as a guide in life – that is, we are to order our lives by the (logical) probabilities of the statements of F. These probabilities must be relative, and what they must be relative *to*, are the elements of E. Take the pragmatic principle of total evidence in its strongest sense, and regard all probabilities as relative to the conjunction of all the elements of E – denote it by CE. In calculating the probability of an element of F, one often *seems* to make use of elements of G: thus to calculate the probability of heads on the next toss of this coin (f_h) one will take into account the (probable) fact that about half the tosses of the coin, in the long run, will yield heads (g_h). We have, then, *apparently*:

(1) $p(f_h/g_h) = \frac{1}{2}$ or $p(f_h/g_h \cdot CE) = \frac{1}{2}$.

But on the view that I am discussing this must be interpreted as short-hand for:

(2) $p(f_h/CE) = \frac{1}{2}$, *because*

(3) $p(f_h/g_h \cdot CE) = \frac{1}{2}$ and $p(g_h/CE) = 1$.

The whole point of using (1) rather than (2) directly must be that it is *easier* to calculate $p(g_h/CE)$ and $p(f_h/g_h \cdot CE)$ than $p(f_h/CE)$. It is certainly not a question of possibility, as the relation provided by Bayes' theorem shows:

$$p(f_h/CE) = \frac{p(g_h/CE)\, p(f_h/g_h \cdot CE)}{p(g_h/f_h \cdot CE)}.$$

But it seems highly questionable to me – particularly in the light of Carnap's researches – that it should be easier to calculate $p(g_h/CE)$ than $p(f_h/CE)$. The same is certainly as true of far-reaching, elegant, and powerful theories as it is of simple statistical generalizations such as g_h. The sole difference is that in the case of theories (sometimes – not always: consider the quantum theory) we have $p(f/g \cdot CE) = 1$, in view of the analyticity of $g \supset f$.

Thus one result, anyway, of the view of science that rejects a rule of detachment for induction, is that general statements (statements other than protocol statements) play no logical role either in the pursuit of science or in its applications; and it is at least doubtful that they play a pragmatic role.

It is no help, incidentally, to regard the analytic probability statements as themselves a part of the corpus of physics. In itself it is peculiar to do so – why regard $p(f/CE) = r$ as any more a part of physics than $p(f/CK) = r$, where K is any set of statements at all, logically possible or not, physically possible or not? And why should $p(f/CE) = 1$ or $p(f/CE) = \frac{1}{4}$ be any more a part of physics than $2 + 2 = 7$?

Nor, finally, can we make sense of the use of generalizations and laws in science (on the supposition that there is no inductive rule of detachment), if we interpret probability differently. Suppose $p(h/e)$, is regarded as having empirical content – through a frequency interpretation or an interpretation that takes probability to be an 'abstract counterpart' of observable frequencies. In this case, on the view I am discussing, it is not probability statements that we can accept as guides in life, because probability statements, being general empirical statements, cannot be *accepted*. What we *can* accept, on this view, and what do serve as a guide in life, are statements which are *estimates* of probabilities. Such statements of estimates of probabilities, however, are quite in the same boat as the analytic probability statements considered above. This is something that proponents of empirical interpretations of probability curiously often seem to overlook. To say that the estimate of the (empirical) probability that *so and so* is *p*, is just about the same as to assert that the logical probability of *s* (corresponding to 'so and so') given CE, is *p*, where CE is unspecified. In order that the estimate in question be taken as a guide in life, we must go beyond the assertion that it is our best estimate, and *accept* it as characterizing the future.

To sum up, if we do have a rule of detachment, science may consist of a body of statements, including general statements, about the world; on the view which does not countenance a rule of detachment, science must consist of a set of observation statements together with analytic probability statements (or statements of estimates of statistical parameters, say, which estimation statements, even on a frequency view of probability are just as analytic and empty as Carnap's degree-of-confirmation statements). The connection between scientific fact and human decision and action will be just as different in the two views as the content of science. If there is a rule of detachment, the process of arriving at a decision will often be predominantly deductive in character (as it seems to be in real life), taking as premises those general statements that constitute the essential body of scientific knowledge as well as other statements. If there is no such rule, each decision, each prediction, is itself irreducibly inductive in character – even though deductive short-cuts may be found that assist us in our computations. Indeed, on the view that allows no rule of detachment, this is the *sole* scientific function of generalization and theory building.

Bar–Hillel suggests that in employing a rule of detachment we are throwing away information, as when we record the mean of a series of observations in lieu of the distinct observations. He is wrong on two counts: on the usual assumptions the mean and number of observations of a measurement represent *sufficient* statistics, and thus contain precisely as much information as the sequence of observations; and the sort of rule of detachment I am talking about does not involve *replacing* the evidence by a hypothesis, but *supplementing* the evidence statements by a hypothesis statement.

3.   Still and all, though the proposal to do without a rule of detachment leads to results that are surprising or even a bit shocking, there is a certain appealing simplicity and purity about the proposal. It is worth while then to see what else, besides this shock to our common sensibilities, we are led to.

One thing which is required, I have mentioned already: we must make a sharp classification of statements into those that *may* be accepted (on an appropriate observational basis) and those that may not be. In the terms used earlier, we must accept a sharp distinction between protocol statements and general statements.

It is well known that there are certain difficulties with this kind
of distinction; some of them have been pointed out (in another
context) by Quine. Quine points out that there is no statement
that, by itself, we would hold to, come what may. Even our logic
might be changed; but certainly not only might we reject statements
alleged to be based on direct observation, but in point of fact we
often *do* just that when the alleged observation conflicts with a
body of well-founded knowledge that we regard as more certain
than we regard hallucination, temporary derangement, or simple
error as unlikely. To make things quite specific, consider such a
simple and typical sequence of events as the tosses of a coin. When
I used this example before, I took the appropriate protocol statements to be entirely unproblematic – 'heads on the next toss' – f_h;
elements of E: 'heads on the first toss'; 'tails on the fifth toss', etc.

But surely one can make an error: an error of counting; even
an error of judging. 'Tails on the third toss.' 'What? That was the
coin with two heads? I must have been wrong.' Observe that if
we eschew a rule of detachment, then it does us no good to retreat
further into phenomenalism. We might try the gambit of dealing
only with 'seemings'. Half the times the coin seemed to be tossed,
it seemed to land heads; therefore the probability that the next
time the coin seems to be tossed it will seem to land heads is one
half. What is the matter with this approach? For one thing it
makes further hash out of science. Now the content of science is
not even observation reports of occurrences, but observation reports
of observations. But we can go one step further. Now the observation cannot be in error – if the coin *seems* to us to land heads
that's what it seems to us to do and there is an end of the matter.
But the immediate seeming cannot enter into science as it is – it
must be in some kind of propositional or sentential form as an
observation report: 'On what seemed to be the fifth toss, the coin
seemed to land heads.' But this observation *report* may just
as well be in error as the original report 'On the fifth toss the
coin landed heads'. Not because the *observation* might have
been in error, but because the *report* might be in error. (This
source of error infects the less phenomenalistic species of protocol
statements, too.)

Furthermore, it behoves us to reflect on the grounds that we will take as adequate to cause us to reject an observation statement that we have accepted. It is silly to speak of error in observation statements, unless we have some way (sometimes) of deciding when error is present in a particular case. Sometimes it is just a question of new or closer observation. 'No, that's not a crow after all; it's a blackbird.' 'Sorry, I *meant* to say *one* hundred ten degrees, not two hundred ten.' But it is also often the case that we reject an observation statement because of its relation, *not directly to other observation statements*, but to non-observational statements: 'No, that's not a crow; it's blue, and all crows are black.' 'That reading can't be two hundred ten degrees; the thermometer is in boiling 5 % saline solution and it couldn't be that hot; five per cent saline solution always boils at about 110 °C.' This kind of correction of observation statements seems altogether ruled out on the view that takes protocol statements to be incorrigible and eschews a rule of detachment. Without a rule of detachment there can be no accepted general statements (such as 'All crows are black', '5 % saline solution boils around 110 °C') with which observation statements can come into conflict. We simply have no reason other than its improbability, to reject the statement: 'I just saw a blue crow': or the statement, 'This 5 % saline solution is boiling at 210 °C'. And even the prior improbability of these statements is no greater than the prior improbability of any measurement observation: the prior probability that this small object will be observed to weigh 5.0731 grams is of course vanishingly small. But when we make that observation, we accept the corresponding protocol statement. Why is it that the same principles don't apply to 'Nothing (almost nothing) that seems to be a crow seems to be blue' and 'This seems to be a blue crow'?

An even more serious problem is brought up by the fact that the very *meaning* of the terms we use as observational predicates is modified by the theoretical framework we accept. This is obvious on the level of classifying a whale as a fish or a mammal; but it applies also on a deeper and more important level in chemistry and physics.

Perhaps the most telling argument of all in this context is that there is a body of background knowledge that must be *accepted* before an experiment becomes an experiment. A measurement is meaningless unless we know the physical characteristics of the measuring instrument. Even the Compleat Bayesian must accept such statements as, 'This sequence is symmetric', before he can start tossing coins.

Some of these difficulties have been discussed by those whose position I am attacking. The general answer is that we are concerned with an idealization (which must indeed be admitted), and at that only with an idealization that applies to one context at a time. Thus it would be claimed that *in a particular situation*, the distinction between observation statements and other statements could be taken as absolute; and *in that context* observation statements may be taken as incorrigible; and so on. This proposal has a ring of plausibility to it – after all one should no more ask for universal applicability in a theory of this sort than one should ask for a pailful of a universal solvent. And yet the form of the limitation here imposes severe restrictions on the regulative force of the whole approach. It should be the case in philosophical idealization that while the particular compromises with reality that you make may lead to a theory which fails to settle some extreme differences of opinion, there is a broad range of common situations in which the residual differences of opinion are relatively minor. For example, in formalizing particular deductive arguments there is plenty of room for variation in detail, though one has to stretch things pretty far to get formalizations that will lead to opposite judgments about validity. This does not seem to be the case for inductive arguments; according to whether you accept 'rat a learns quickly', 'rat b learns quickly', . . ., as protocol statements, or only 'on trial number j rat a solved the maze in k seconds', you will arrive at very different probabilities for the statement 'rat z learns quickly'. (In the former case the probability may be quite respectable; in the latter it is presumably close to zero.)

Jeffrey's brilliant suggestion at this conference takes care of the difficulty I am discussing here. It does so in a heroic way, however: his demonstration that we need consider only the probabilities of evidence statements has two extraordinary consequences. First, not only is science empty of general statements, but it now becomes empty of *observation* statements as well! What *is* the content of science? *Second*, observe that while Jeffrey's formula tells us how the probability of A changes when uncertain evidence is added to our body of knowledge, there seems to be no neat way to regard that probability as a conditional probability in Carnap's sense. The credence function changes, but leaves no trace of the path by which it got to where it is.

One problem that has bothered the logical probability theorists, such as Carnap, has been the problem that on most logical interpretations of probability, universal generalizations turn out to have 0 probability. There are interpretations in which this is not the case: see recent work of Hintikka and Carnap, older work of H. Jeffreys. In a sense, the problem is an irrelevant one anyway: if there is no rule of detachment, then however probable generalizations may become, we can never simply *accept* them, and hence we can never use them as a basis for deductive arguments of the sort that we imagine engineers to use. Nevertheless it will be instructive to consider an example of the sort that (it has been claimed) the concept of instance confirmation can handle.

The claim has been made (whether or not there is anyone who still makes this claim, I don't know) that the improbability of generalizations is unimportant, since it is only the instances of generalizations that we need be concerned with in planning our lives and dealing with our environments. It is not the probability of the generalization, 'All crows are black' that is important to us, but the probability of the instantial statement 'The next crow I see will be black.'

The concept of instance confirmation may serve well enough in such a simple context as this; but it will not fare so well in more complicated cases. Suppose we want to design a bridge. We design it with the help of various general physical laws. It has been said that we do not have to have high probabilities for these general laws – we need only have good reasons to believe that these general laws will hold *in this instance*. That is, it will suffice for our engineering work to have high degrees of instance confirmation.

But what is the instance? Is it the bridge itself? There's a curious notion: how do we understand a bridge as an *instance* of a general law? What is the law? The law that bridges constructed in such and such a manner won't collapse? That would be an odd law of nature, and not at all the sort of law that the engineer uses. He uses laws from Newtonian Mechanics; Hooke's Law connecting stress and strain; various laws embodied in the physical constants characterizing the material with which he works: coefficients of thermal expansion, of elasticity, of thermal conductivity, etc. But if these are the laws he uses, then at best each instance (the instance that is highly confirmed) is a particular aspect of the behavior of a particular beam or a particular rivet. And the probability (degree of confirmation) that the bridge will stand is of the order of the *product* of all these instance confirmations. (Multiply, if you wish, by a safety factor of four or ten and the degree of confirmation that the bridge will stand is still very small.)

Even so, we aren't through. For let us take a particular rivet. The general laws (the equations for plastic flow; the relevant coefficients) lead to the conclusion that if a shearing stress of S pounds is imposed on that rivet, it will not shear. Now stress is put on that rivet every time a car passes across the bridge; so that what has a high instance confirmation here is not the generalization, 'This rivet will *never* give way', but only 'On its next test, this rivet will not give way'. Of course the engineer is not concerned with the *next* test, but with a large number of future tests – and the large number of future tests will come to have only a small degree of confirmation, since (again) its order of magnitude will be the nth power of the order of magnitude of the single-instance confirmation.

There is one more step to be taken: the engineer's calculations should perhaps be understood as containing an implicit reference to time: 'For every t, if beam B is subjected to stress S at t, then it will exhibit strain R at t.' But if this is the case our instance confirmations must all be taken to be *instant* confirmations as well, and to arrive at the credibility conclusion that will hold for a finite stretch of time, we must somehow form the infinite product of the credibilities that hold for each of the infinitely many instants that compose that finite period of time!

The example that I have just been discussing of the engineer and the bridge is relevant to more than the question of instance confirmations versus respectable degrees of confirmation for generalizations. It is relevant to this whole question of whether or not one should detach inductive conclusions. The same comments about the engineer's procedure hold whether we are dealing with instance confirmations or any other sort of confirmations; the advantage offered by being able to count on having high credibilities for *some* generalizations is minor, for there are so many generalizations involved, in so many ways, in the design of a bridge, that in sum it must be *incredible* that the bridge should stand. And if it is very improbable that the bridge will stand for the next ten years, then surely the mathematical expectation of the act of investing in materials and labor to build the bridge is negative, and we should not do it.

Let it be noted that what I have been saying is not a list of particular objections to particular proposals to do without a rule of detachment for inductive logic. It is perfectly general. What I have been saying applies directly to the *general* proposal to do without a rule of detachment; it applies to any scheme according to which scientific acceptance is confined to (at *most*) (a) protocol statements, (b) analytic probability statements, and (c) decisions or courses of action. These are deep theoretical problems that arise whatever alternative to a rule of detachment is proposed:

(1) The problem of identifying a particular class of statements to serve as incorrigible protocol statements.

(2) The problem of establishing general principles which will allow us to come to an agreement as to what will count as a protocol statement in a particular context.

(3) The problem of handling statements that appear on the ordinary view to be based on a whole complex network of laws and generalizations.

(4) The related problem of what to count as an *instance* of a generalization.

(5) The problem of the disparity between the view of science to which this kind of proposal leads, and the general ordinary view of science as consisting of a body of general statements and laws and even theories, as well as of observation statements.

4. How does a proposal to establish an inductive rule of detachment fare on these questions? It depends of course, on the particular rule that you have in mind. But it is possible to make some general remarks.

To begin with, the fifth problem is no problem at all. If we have a rule of detachment that allows the incorporation of laws and generalizations into our scientific body of knowledge, then our reconstruction will conform perfectly to our intuitive and naive views of the content of scientific knowledge. Indeed it is perhaps this fact more than any other that has led such philosophers of science as Popper and Dewey (to name two quite different philosophers of science) to take for granted that a rule of inductive detachment is implicit in scientific practice. And scientists certainly look on themselves as providing theories and generalizations that are to be accepted – if only until further notice and subject to future tests. Note that even when a scientist reports on the magnitude of a physical constant, and does so in probabilistic terms, he is offering for acceptance a general statement about the world. 'Compound X melts at 137.3 ± 0.15 °C'. The '0.15' presumably represents a standard deviation, so that the assertion has this full form: 'Observations (past, present, and future) of the melting point of X are normally distributed with a mean of 137.3 °C and a standard deviation of 0.15 °C'. This is a perfectly general statistical statement. (Sometimes 'standard error' will replace 'standard deviation'; but conversion from one to the other is simple.)

Problems (3) and (4) also become pretty trivial if we have a suitable rule of detachment at our disposal. Statements (such as: 'The bridge will not fall down') that appear on the ordinary common-sense view to be based on a complex network of laws and generalization, turn out to be in fact based on a network of acceptable laws and generalizations.

The engineer who designs the bridge does just what we think of him as doing: he begins with a large number of laws and generalizations which are so well supported by evidence as to be accepted (acceptable) as a part of the body of science. He adds to these his knowledge of certain physical constants – again, knowledge that, though in a certain sense only probable, satisfies criteria which

allow its detachment from the evidence that supports it and allow
its separate inclusion as part of his body of scientific knowledge.

(Certain of the propositions with which the engineer must deal
may still be directly inductive: for example there is no table that
will tell him how many cars will use the bridge on weekdays between 4.30 and 6.30 p.m. But he can find inductive evidence that
will give him a [possibly vague] probability distribution for this
number; and the *distribution* will be such as to allow him to detach
an upper limit for the number in question.)

Thus problem (3) is handled in the most conventional and natural
way possible. Most of the reasonings and calculations of the engineer are perfectly deductive in character, on this reconstruction,
as they are in real life. The problem of what to count as an 'instance'
does not arise – anything counts, because the statement about
the instance is obtained *deductively* by universal instantiation,
rather than inductively. And that takes care of problem (4).

The first two problems *may* still exist, even if we have a rule of
inductive detachment – and on Jeffrey's view they need not exist
even *without* a rule of detachment –, though on my own view they
need not. Consider the first problem: can we avoid the necessity
of identifying a certain class of statements as incorrigible protocol
statements? If we allow a rule of inductive detachment, there is
no reason why the answer shouldn't be 'yes'. In allowing a rule of
detachment we have already abandoned the irrational ideal of a
rational corpus containing only divinely certified certainties. It is
perfectly possible that something we accept, for perfectly good
reasons, will turn out to be false after all. Now there is no reason
at all why we cannot extend this same reasonable attitude to
include observation statements as well as generalizations and the
like. Instead of seeking an error-proof phenomenalistic basis for
our body of scientific knowledge, we can take the common-sense
assertions of scientists at face value: we do not have to tell them
that when they think they are observing thermometers and volt-
meters, they are really only observing their apparent observations.
An observation may be in error – even when our observational
rule of detachment has directed us to accept it. But it can be
corrected – either by a more accurate observation of the same

thing, or (and this is extremely important; it is a kind of correction not allowed at all on the alternative view) by an examination of the way the observation fits into our body of accepted knowledge. When a man tells us that there is a pink elephant in the next room, we do not have to search the room to tell him that his observation is in error.

I referred to an 'observational' rule of detachment as distinct from an inductive rule of detachment. I did so, because we might well want to state the two rules separately. But both are alike in the sense that they depend on probabilities, as well perhaps as on other things. We accept the proposition 'There is a dog sleeping by the fire' even though all we can be sure of is the half of the dog that is toward us, and even that half might turn out to be an hallucination or a post-hypnotic suggestion. Nevertheless we accept the statement on the basis of *direct observation*: 'How do you know?' 'I can see him there!' It requires an *argument* to cause us to reject the observation statement: 'The dog turned into a butterfly; *so* it wasn't really a dog in the first place.' Ha, ha! Fooled you! It's just a suggestion we gave you while you were under hypnosis . . .' etc.

I do not mean to say that there are no problems that will arise in working out an observational rule of detachment, but I conjecture that they will be essentially technical problems: the technical problems of working out the specific criteria appropriate to such a rule.

The second problem on the list *appears* to be irrelevant, if we have a rule of detachment, but this is not necessarily the case. In my own work, I take independence of context to be something of a criterion: that is, a rule of detachment, to be adequate, must be such that in case there is question about its operation in a given context, the question can be resolved to the satisfaction of both parties by proceeding to a larger context. Not all of those who have worked on rules of detachment have adopted this principle: Isaac Levi, for example, has worked on acceptance rules which are context dependent in a sense which violates the above criterion.

If having an inductive rule of detachment is so natural and simple, and solves all these problems, even suggesting a solution for the problem of the corrigibility of observation statements, why is there any question but that we should formalize and reconstruct science in such a way as to allow an inductive rule of detachment? The most telling answer to this question is simply that no rule of detachment yet formulated has had any wide degree of acceptance. Many writers have proposed such rules, or at least have made suggestions as to the nature of 'corroboration', 'factual support', 'partial implication', etc. on which (among other things, perhaps) a rule of detachment might be based; but all of the rules that have been proposed have had defects. Still, the defects seem to stem from certain technical difficulties and therefore to be rectifiable by certain technical dodges. In the past few years we have found out quite a bit about both the difficulties and the dodges.

One difficulty that arises in the case of every rule that takes as one of its criteria probability, is: what probability? 0.6? 0.99999? Something in between? Something that may vary with context? If the latter, what will determine the probability? The degree of caution of the most cautious participant in the discussion?

My approach to this problem was to define a whole sequence of rational corpora of different *levels*. Each rational corpus consisted of a set of statements whose probability exceeded a certain minimum value characteristic of that level of rational corpus. The problem of choosing a level of rational corpus in which to operate in a given context was left open; but I think it could reasonably be determined as the rational corpus of the most skeptical of the participants in a debate. (That would be a kind of minimal rational corpus for that context.) Furthermore it could be shown that the choice of level was not crucial, because the sequence of rational corpora built on a given observational base fit together in a coherent fashion.

Another difficulty is Goodman's: if we have evidence which allows us to accept '*a* is green', then we also have evidence that allows us to accept '*a* is grue'; and these two statements, together with certain other natural ingredients of our rational corpora, lead to a contradiction. The problem here is not introduced by a rule of detachment, and there are independent reasons for wanting to solve it. But to suppose our rule of detachment to be formulated explicitly is to suppose Goodman's problem solved.

More than this, however, there are related problems which may be just as hard to handle; at least they have been dealt with by statisticians under the heading of criteria for the choice of hypotheses [1]. I can illustrate these problems by an example. Consider a set A of objects, some of which also belong to a set B. We wish to accept a hypothesis as to the proportion of A's that are B's, on the basis of a sample of n A's, of which m are B's. Let r be the proportion of B's in the sample and p the proportion of B's among A's in general. It is well known that we can calculate the minimum proportion of samples consisting of n A's that are such that $|r-p|<\varepsilon$. If this proportion is high enough, and our sample is a random one in the appropriate sense, we simply *accept* the proposition that *in our sample*

$$|r-p|<\varepsilon, \text{ or } r-\varepsilon<p<r+\varepsilon.$$

Now the problem is this: we can find any number of pairs of numbers ε_1 and ε_2 such that the proportion of samples of n A's for which the relation $r-\varepsilon_1<p<r+\varepsilon_2$ holds is as high as in the former case. (ε_1 and ε_2 need not be equal, of course.) Since we want probabilities to be based on accepted statistical statements we don't want to accept all of these statistical statements of the form and so we must establish a criterion that selects exactly one of these statistical statements as the prime candidate for acceptance. There might be another reason that we would want to accept only one of these statistical statements: if we accepted them all, and if we also accepted the conjunction of any statements that we accepted individually, then, as I showed in my Jerusalem paper [2], we would be led to a contradiction.

This brings me to another problem for a rule of detachment; a problem which is one of the most curious to come to light in recent years. The question is this: should we expect our inductive rule of detachment to lead to bodies of knowledge that are logically

---

[1]   But philosophers have acted as if they were totally unaware of them.

[2]   'Probability, rationality, and a rule of detachment', *Logic, Methodology and Philosophy of Science*; *Proceedings of the 1964 International Congress*, Y. Bar–Hillel, ed., North-Holland Publishing Company, Amsterdam, 1965, pp. 301–310.

closed? That is, if we have reason to accept X and reason to accept Y, will we have reason also to accept the conjunction of X and Y? Natural as this might seem, I think (though there are those who think otherwise) that the evidence suggests that we cannot expect logical closure in our bodies of scientific knowledge. This is surely the case if we formulate our rule of detachment purely in terms of probabilities: in general it need not be the case that if the probability of X is greater than r and the probability of Y is greater than r, then the probability of their *conjunction, X and Y,* will be greater than r. (Inductive logicians seem to be well aware of this fact; but, oddly enough, writers on epistemology such as Chisholm seem to forget it.)

The lottery paradox shows that one cannot simply *impose* logical closure on bodies of belief. Let r be the level of probability at which we allow acceptance. Consider a fair lottery, in which we know there will be one winner, and which contains more than $1/(1-r)$ tickets. Then for any i, the probability that ticket number i will not win is greater than r, and we may *accept* the statement: 'Ticket i will not win'. But to accept the *conjunction* of all statements of the form 'Ticket i will not win' is just to accept the statement that no ticket will win, contradicting the statement that one ticket will win.

I have used this paradox to argue that the principle of logical closure for bodies of rational belief must be abandoned; others (notably Isaac Levi) have used the same paradox to argue that we must abandon hope of finding a purely probabilistic rule of detachment. In the latter case we have the new problem of formulating criteria for the rule of detachment which will seem natural and which will not lead to problems like that of the lottery paradox. In the former case, we must show that getting along without logical closure causes no hardship.

Salmon has suggested that perhaps the distinction between singular statements and general hypotheses may provide the key: if we never *accept* singular predictions we can avoid the lottery paradox while maintaining logical closure in our body of beliefs; and yet this does not at all entail that we cannot formulate acceptance rules for general statistical statements. (With respect to universal statements even Carnap has recently written as if plausible acceptance rules might be formulated [1]. But the distinction between universal or statistical generalizations and singular statements is not easy to draw. 'This bridge will not collapse today', is the same as 'For every time t greater than t_0 and less than t_1, the bridge will not collapse at time t.' And 'For every x, if x is a crow, then x is black' is the same as 'The species *crow* is monochrome' (or 'has such and such a genetic constitution'). And, as I have suggested elsewhere [2], even if the distinction can be made, it may not do away with lottery *type* paradoxes.

All of *these* problems, observe, are fairly straight-forward technical problems; nothing of deep philosophical significance is involved. And that is why I think it is more fruitful and easier to continue the attempt to formulate an intuitively adequate rule of detachment, than to beat our brains out trying to find philosophical ruses – or deep philosophical truths – that will make plausible the austere point of view that denies the acceptability of most of the statements of modern science.

---

[1] Cf. his 'Replies and systematic expositions', in *The Philosophy of Rudolf Carnap*, P. A. Schilpp, ed., Library of Living Philosophers, Open Court, La Salle, Illinois, 1964, pp. 859–1013.

[2] *Op. cit.*

Y. Bar–Hillel: *On alleged rules of detachment in inductive logic.*

1. In footnote 2 on p. 98 of his paper, Kyburg quotes my objection (in the original, oral version of my talk) to the use of the
expression 'rule of detachment' for inductive logic and expresses
his willingness to change his terminology to, say, 'rules of acceptance' (though he has not yet done so in the printed version of
his talk). I am afraid I am still not satisfied. In the very same note
he explains his attempt to extend the original use of this phrase
in deductive logic as due to his taking the phrase 'only in a general
sense of any rule which allows the detachment of a conclusion
from premises'. But I must again protest against this 'general
sense'. The relationship between the conclusion and the premise(s)
of an argument is customarily described with the help of such verbs
as 'follow', 'derive', 'deduce', 'infer', and their cognates. It is difficult
to see the need for any further innovation. But the use of 'detach'
for this purpose should certainly be discouraged, since it would
obfuscate a mnemonically useful picture and replace it by a confused one. When the Polish logicians introduced this term (or
rather its Polish and German equivalents) in the early twenties – I
was unable to trace this innovation to some particular person, but
it likely that it was either Leśniewski or Łukasiewicz or Chwistek
who used it for the first time – their intention was presumably
just to replace the Latin *modus ponens* by an expression in the
vernacular. When they called the rule often depicted as

$$\frac{\begin{array}{l} p \to q \\ p \end{array}}{q.}$$

Abtrennungsregel, their pedagogical aim was to impress the student
with the fact that from two premises of which the first had the
form of an implication and the second that of the antecedent of
this implication one can deduce the consequent of the implication,

as it were by 'detaching' it from the antecedent, since the antecedent is asserted in the second premise. At no point, to my knowledge, was their intention, or that of anybody else who adopted their proposal, to encourage the at best useless and at worst harmful picture of 'detaching the conclusion from the premises'. It must have been due to a misunderstanding that Kyburg was led to adopt this unfortunate mode of speech which then led him on to the still less fortunate metaphor of 'detaching decisions from the evidence in the light of which they were made' and detaching 'a course of action from the evidence that led to it', locutions which far from having 'a clear and obvious sense' (as claimed by Kyburg) can only lead to confusion.

2. We now proceed to Kyburg's arguments for the existence of a rule of detachment in inductive logic (where 'rule of detachment' now means 'rule of inference in some as yet unspecified sense'). He offers two schematic formulations, with the second one treated as 'an alternative and perhaps better schematization'. The first form is:

(A)
$$\frac{e}{c(h,\, e) = p}$$

and the second is:

(B)
$$\frac{\begin{array}{l} e \text{ is total evidence} \\ c(h,\, e) = p \end{array}}{\text{believe } h \text{ to degree } p.}$$

But the 'conclusion' of (A) (to be read in accordance with Carnap's usage, to which Kyburg evidently adheres here, as 'the degree of confirmation of the hypothesis h on the evidence e is p') is an analytic statement (in an appropriate system of inductive logic) and, whatever can be said about how this particular c-value was arrived at, it certainly makes no sense to say that the assertion of this statement was based on the evidence e. But here is what Kyburg says: 'But there is still a perfectly clear sense in which, when e represents our body of relevant knowledge and we assert

$c(h, e) = p$, e may be regarded as the evidence on which our assertion is based.' I can only voice my utter lack of comprehension.

Now what about (B)? It should be clear that (B), far from being an 'alternative' to (A), is *toto coelo* different from it; the only common feature is that the conclusion of (A) is a premise of (B). As such, (B) looks like an eminently reasonable rule. When the degree of confirmation of an hypothesis h on the total evidence e is p, it is indeed good advice to believe in h to the degree p, i.e. to attach to h a subjective (absolute) probability p (though I shall later question the practical usefulness of this notion of 'total evidence'). If this were all that Kyburg meant by an 'inductive rule of detachment' (misleading as his way of expressing it would be), we could close the case. Unfortunately, and rather surprisingly, it turns out after all that (B) is not really the rule Kyburg is looking for. The rule he is after 'will be a rule that says: under such and such circumstances, *accept h*'. We are back, after a long and confusing detour, to the by now almost classical problem of the existence of *rules of acceptance* in inductive logic. As Carnap puts it: 'According to a widely accepted view, it is the proper aim of inductive logic to supply *rules of acceptance*, i.e. rules which determine for given h and e either that h is to be accepted or that it is to be rejected or that it is to be left suspended' [1]. But Carnap goes on to state his disagreement with this view. His position is rather that 'rules of acceptance as ultimate rules for inductive reasoning are inadequate' and he then briefly indicates his reasons for this position. Kyburg, unfortunately, altogether fails to come to grips with Carnap's arguments. Carnap's *Replies* in the Schilpp volume are not mentioned at all in Kyburg's rather exhaustive bibliography to his critical review of *Recent Work in Inductive Logic* [2], nor are they mentioned in his 1964 talk [3], and apparently

---

[1] R. Carnap, 'Replies and systematic expositions', in *The Philosophy of Rudolf Carnap*, P. A. Schilpp, ed., Library of Living Philosophers, Open Court, La Salle, Illinois, 1963, p. 972.

[2] *American Philosophical Quarterly*, 1, 1964, pp. 1–39.

[3] Henry E. Kyburg, Jr., 'Probability, rationality, and a rule of detachment', *Logic, Methodology and Philosophy of Science*; *Proceedings of the 1964 International Congress*, Y. Bar–Hillel, ed., North-Holland Publishing Company, Amsterdam, 1965, pp. 301–310.

came too late to his attention even for his present paper since he refers to them in just one sentence in parentheses, obviously as a kind of afterthought during revision.

Carnap's reasons are that rules of acceptance yield in one respect too much, and in another respect too little [1]. When a rule of acceptance advises somebody to accept an hypothesis h in a case where the degree of confirmation of h on the total evidence e is less than 1, i.e. to act as if he knew that h were true, then in certain cases such an action may be entirely unreasonable, since in general rational advice for practical action will have to take utilities into account. On the other hand, in certain situations, rules of acceptance will give no advice on how to act – since they would advise one to suspend judgment – while other rules of rational inductive behaviour will give better advice.

Now sometimes the hypothesis in question may be of such a theoretical nature that it makes no sense to talk about any action that someone might perform just by assuming h to be true. It appears that in this case Carnap has 'no compelling objection against' using rules of acceptance, 'provided the reconstruction is merely meant as a rough delineation of scientific procedure in a purely *theoretical field*, and especially if the reconstruction is applied only to the acceptance of universal laws' [2]. I must confess that I do not quite understand this passage. Scientists, of course, very often speak about accepting and rejecting theories and laws,

---

[1] It was this 'yielding too little' I had in mind when I said (see Kyburg's report, *this volume*, p. 106) 'that in employing a rule of detachment in inductive logic we are throwing away information', and, if I remember correctly, this intention of mine should have been quite clear. At any rate, I am entirely at a loss to understand the first count on which I am supposed to be wrong in this remark. A rule of detachment, in Kyburg's sense, has absolutely nothing to do with sufficient statistics which he invokes here. As to the second count, it was Kyburg who put so much stress on the ability of a conclusion of an inductive argument to stand by itself, after having been 'detached' from its premises. Kyburg's new meta-rule, 'Employ rules of inference only so long as they don't land you into trouble, otherwise forget about them', is a very interesting one but might need some further investigation before being accepted.

[2] *Op. cit.* p. 973.

and it is possible that Carnap, out of deference to this mode of speech, has some fruitful explication in mind. I, however, know no such explication, not even 'as a rough delineation of scientific procedure'. A scientist may mean by his talk of accepting theories that he regards these theories as true in some final sense ('God's truth') so that he will no longer accept any empirical findings as evidence against them. I do not think that inductive methodology should provide rules of acceptance of this nature. Accepting a theory may also mean basing one's research on the assumption that the theory is true; but again I have grave doubts whether general rules are needed to advise one on which theories to base one's research, and I have no idea what their exact form could be. Finally (or rather, 'finally', since there are probably many other meanings to this phrase), accepting a theory may also mean something like dedicating more time to the exposition of the theory in one's classroom teaching than to competing ones, or perhaps teaching it to the exclusion of all others. A professor may not be able to acquaint his students with all the theories that have been offered in a given field, and perhaps some kind of general advice could be given to enable him to overcome the pedagogical dilemma in which he may find himself. However, this type of advisory function is surely not the business of inductive logic, though I would not want to deny that degrees of confirmation might play some role here. Then there is also, of course, the well-known highly idiosyncratic usage of 'acceptance of theories' by Popper and his followers, but they would be the last to look for rules to this effect (particularly rules that refer to degree of confirmation and total evidence).

In his later discussion, Kyburg succeeds in confusing the issue still more. He starts at a certain point, without warning, to talk about construing a rule of detachment 'as a rule that permits the acceptance of a statement h representing a factual inductive conclusion, given that certain criteria are satisfied'. How seriously are we supposed to take this word 'permits'? If 'permits' is supposed to be understood in anything like its ordinary sense, we are presumably also permitted *not* to accept h in the given circumstances, but this interpretation would play havoc with the whole course of the subsequent argument. But what other meaning 'permits' could have is not clear to me. That it is not just a slip of the pen is obvious since a few lines later the term 'principle of acceptability' shows up, there being apparently some connection between 'acceptability' and 'permission to accept'.

But let us now turn to the criteria whose satisfaction would 'permit the acceptance of a statement h'. According to Kyburg, they 'will be expressed in terms referring to one or more of the following:

(1) a body of statements regarded as evidence, and satisfying some principle of acceptability, and also a condition of total evidence;
(2) the probability of h, relative to this body of statements;
(3) the information content of h (this may also be relativized to the body of statements mentioned in (1));
(4) the simplicity and fruitfulness of h;
(5) other factors not generally regarded as relevant by philosophers of science, such as political and moral utility.'

Now this is an encyclopedic enough list, though the connection of its items with 'detachment' and 'inductive logic' is certainly far beyond what even the most imaginative stretching of terminology would allow. (What, incidentally, are the 'principles of acceptability'? Are they the same as the 'rules of acceptance'? If not, are they somehow connected with them?) Now, I do not wish to deny that in weighing scientific theories one against the other, the factors (2), (3) and (4) are indeed often taken into account, though of course only in a very rough way, since in the absence of a well-developed inductive logic (2) and (3) cannot realistically be evaluated, while (4) is in a still worse state. (1), if I understand its somewhat peculiar formulation at all, is best incorporated into (2), which should then read: 'the probability of h, relative to the total evidence'; (5), as Kyburg remarks, is generally regarded by philosophers of science as irrelevant, though it certainly played a role in the rejection of certain scientific hypotheses by the church, by church-controlled governments, by totalitarian regimes, etc., and in the acceptance of certain hypotheses, such as those regarding race, etc. (Incidentally, the reason why philosophers of science have tended to disregard this factor and, I hope, will continue to do so – though historians and sociologists of science will of course be highly interested in it – is that the 'political and moral utility' mentioned in it cannot be assigned to the theory but only to its 'acceptance' – or rejection – by an appropriate body. A theory of, say, racial superiority of whites over coloureds has no political or moral utility as such. The theory is true or false, well-confirmed or ill-confirmed. It is the belief in the truth of the theory which, in addition to being true or false, justified or unjustified, can be politically useful, morally despicable, etc.)

But nevertheless I do not find it particularly useful to formulate the outcome of the weighing process as 'acceptance, rejection, or leaving in suspense'. Weighing of theories is a process of comparison that, at best, will establish a partial order between them that could be called, say, 'has greater appeal than' or, if one insists, 'is more acceptable than'. But in view of the partiality of this ordering relation, i.e. in view of the fact that there is nothing that would enable us to determine, in all cases, whether theory A has greater appeal than theory B, it is utterly utopian to entertain the possibility of establishing a 'degree of acceptability' of theories such that theories with a degree of acceptability higher than some number would be regarded as 'acceptable'.

We do need further development of inductive logic, and further investigation into scientific methodology, in particular into the comparability of scientific theories, but nobody needs rules of acceptance of any kind. Applied to directly testable statements such rules would lead to irrational behavior, while with regard to theoretical statements, they would just be bad methodology.

3. During the course of his contribution, Kyburg makes three claims on behalf of the alleged need for a rule of detachment: (i) 'if we allow no rule of detachment, then science – so far as it consists of a body of statements at all – will consist of a set of observation statements or protocol statements' (the 'Baconian nightmare'); (ii) the supposition 'that there is no rule of detachment ... presupposes a clear-cut distinction between observation statements and non-observation statements'; (iii) 'under the hypothesis that there is no rule of detachment in induction, statements g [theoretical statements] are totally redundant and unnecessary'. I am afraid that in spite of Kyburg's lengthy discussion, I could find (in his words) no justification at all for any of these three claims. Since I believe, in addition, that no justification could possibly be found for them, I shall just state categorically that all three claims are wrong.

4.   However, as happens so often, beneath Kyburg's worries – which led him to seek salvation in an inductive rule of detachment – there lies a serious problem which has not been sufficiently discussed so far, in general, and unfortunately not by Kyburg either. This problem centers around the notion of total evidence.

This notion plays a decisive role in the applicability of Carnap's (or anybody else's) inductive logic (and Kyburg voices no objections against this role). But it is idealized to such a degree that absolutely no direct application could ever be made of it in practice – and I think that Carnap would agree to that. For practical purposes, such as computing utilities in order to come to rational decisions, only that part of the total observational evidence that is deemed to be relevant will be taken into account. This may perhaps be feasible for situations where no theory is (seriously) involved, but I can think of no such situations beyond certain simple games of chance. In general, however, whether some observational statement is or is not relevant to some other statement (in the pre-systematic sense of 'relevant') will be very much theory-dependent (and I am inclined to believe that the computation of degrees of confirmation relative to the total observational evidence will yield different results according to the theories taken into account), but no inductive logic exists or is in view that seems to be able to handle this case.

This does not mean, of course, that 'the requirement of total evidence' or rather 'the requirement of total relevant evidence' is totally useless. But its chief use seems to be its limiting character: if you can point out to somebody that his decisions are based on neglecting a certain body of relevant evidence, you will have undermined the appropriateness of the decisions; and if you succeed in showing that they were based on a neglect of conceivably relevant evidence, you will have thrown serious objective doubts on the appropriateness. For all practical applications the 'requirement of total evidence' should be replaced by the advice never to neglect evidence whose relevance is known [1].

5.   One final remark: the concept of a class of statements, say G, whose degree of confirmation relative to some given class of statements, say F, is greater than $1 - \varepsilon$, where ε is some real number between 0 and 1 (and rather close to 0, for most intended applications), plays a central role in Kyburg's thinking and forms the basis of his construction of what he calls 'rational corpora'. However, in view of the fact, pointed out by many authors – notably Isaac Levi – and stressed by Kyburg himself, that G is not closed under conjunction, it seems obvious to me, as it seems to Levi and others (but not to Kyburg), that this concept is not of particular interest, in spite of some initial attractiveness. Kyburg's own attempts to preserve this attractiveness, as well as those by Salmon and others, seem to me doomed to failure. And this is not a *technical* problem, as Kyburg seems to think. On the contrary, the attempts to save this notion, after the peculiarity of its behavior under conjunction has been pointed out, seem to me so irrational that only the professed fear that without such a move, i.e. without 'accepting' the additional statements into the new rational corpus, one must arrive at 'the austere point of view that denies the acceptability of most of the statements of modern science' – a bleak prospect indeed – can explain it. But let me assure Kyburg and whoever else is so desperately looking for inductive rules of acceptance: science will go on as usual without such rules, scientific theories will continue to be proposed, tested, weighed against competing theories, discarded, forgotten, revived, hailed as breakthroughs and viciously opposed, even on occasion 'accepted', with or without rules. But rules for their acceptance (without quotation marks) are definitely unwanted.

---

[1]   See Carnap's *Logical Foundations of Probability*, p. 211.

P. SUPPES: *Two rules of detachment in inductive logic.*

I must confess that I find the papers by Kyburg and Bar–Hillel difficult to assess. In this brief set of remarks I argue that there is at least one clear sense in which the existence of a rule of detachment is indisputable. (What I have to say here is treated more fully in 'Probabilistic inference and the concept of total evidence', published in *Aspects of Inductive Logic*, Amsterdam, 1967, edited jointly by Hintikka and me.)

Let A and B be events or propositions. The proposition $A \rightarrow B$ is the usual conditional proposition and $P(B|A)$ is the usual conditional probability. One probabilistic rule of detachment, easily derived within the standard mathematical theory of probability, and thus valid for either logical or statistical theories of probability, is the following.

(1)
$$\begin{array}{ll} P(A \rightarrow B) \geqslant 1 - \varepsilon & \text{Premise} \\ \underline{\quad P(A) \geqslant 1 - \varepsilon \quad} & \text{Premise} \\ P(B) \geqslant 1 - 2\varepsilon & \text{Conclusion} \end{array}$$

A second distinct but related rule uses a conditional probability assertion rather than a conditional proposition as the major premise.

(2)
$$\begin{array}{ll} P(B|A) \geqslant 1 - \varepsilon & \text{Premise} \\ \underline{\quad P(A) \geqslant 1 - \varepsilon \quad} & \text{Premise} \\ P(B) \geqslant (1 - \varepsilon)^2 & \text{Conclusion} \end{array}$$

There is, it seems to me, a quite clear sense in which (1) and (2) are rules of detachment, and I am sure that no contributor to this symposium would deny the elementary mathematical proofs of their validity. It would consequently seem to follow that Kyburg and Bar–Hillel are discussing rules of detachment which are meant to have a different sort of meaning.

One drift of the discussion is to replace the relatively well-defined idea of a rule of detachment by the concept of a rule of acceptance. The problem of characterizing rules of acceptance is an important one, but it involves much broader issues than does the discussion of rules of detachment. I would argue for first trying to settle the narrower question of the nature of rules of detachment in inductive logic.

I find myself in agreement with most of Bar–Hillel's particular criticisms of Kyburg's positive arguments for a rule of detachment in inductive logic. But in response to Bar–Hillel's own arguments I would argue that (1) and (2), or their more general forms

$$(1') \qquad \begin{array}{ll} P(A \to B) \geqslant r & \text{Premise} \\ \underline{P(A) \geqslant s} & \text{Premise} \\ P(B) \geqslant r+s-1 & \text{Conclusion} \end{array}$$

and

$$(2') \qquad \begin{array}{ll} P(B|A) \geqslant r & \text{Premise} \\ \underline{P(A) \geqslant s} & \text{Premise} \\ P(B) \geqslant r \cdot s & \text{Conclusion} \end{array}$$

provide natural generalizations of *ponendo ponens* in deductive logic, and are used in much the same way.

Because of the lack of a sharp distinction between inductive and deductive logic in ordinary talk, even in ordinary scientific talk, the presence of rules of detachment in inductive logic which generalize *ponendo ponens* seems wholly natural. When $\varepsilon > 0$ (or r and s are less than 1), there is a degradation or decrease of probability as we pass from the premises to the conclusion of (1) or (2), but the spectre of the lottery 'paradox' does not disturb me. It is to be emphasized that this is not a paradox derivable within probability theory, but rather its derivation depends wholly on a quite special concept of rules of acceptance.

What does need examining, but is beyond the scope of the present discussion, is the relation between the extensive use of Bayes' theorem and other methods of statistical inference, such as the method of maximum likelihood, to the concept of rules of detachment in deductive and inductive logic.

K. R. POPPER: *On rules of detachment and so-called inductive logic.*

As I understand it, the problem of detachment in inductive logic arises because inductive logicians have made the following invalid inference:

Premise 1   Inductive logic is a generalization of deductive logic.

Premise 2   Probability logic is a generalization of deductive logic.

Conclusion   Inductive logic is probability logic.

I shall begin by explaining premise 2, which I believe to be true, at least if put in the following form: the probability calculus has an interpretation (the 'logical interpretation') in which it may be regarded as a generalization of deductive logic.

1.   The probability calculus is capable of several interpretations. In the expression

$$p(a, b) = r,$$

a and *b* can be several different things. For example, *a* can be an event like tossing a penny, and *b* can be a description of the conditions under which the event takes place. If *a* is the event that a toss of a penny shows heads uppermost, and *b* describes *the usual experimental conditions*, then $p(a, b) = \frac{1}{2}$. But the conditions may be changed, and the probability will change: if I toss the penny on to a slotted table then the probability of heads may still be equal to that of tails, but it will not be $\frac{1}{2}$, because the penny may get stuck in a slot of the table and show neither heads nor tails uppermost. In this interpretation of probability, *a* and *b* are events, or experimental arrangements. I call it the *'propensity interpretation of probability'* [1], and I believe that it is by far the most important interpretation.

Now, one of the interesting things about the formal calculus of probability is that it can be given a second interpretation which may be called the *'logical interpretation'*, in which it becomes *a*

---

[1]   See especially my three papers (a) 'The propensity interpretation of the calculus of probability, and the quantum theory', in *Observation and Interpretation*, S. Körner, ed., 1957, pp. 65–70 and 88 f.; (b) 'The propensity interpretation of probability', *British Journal for the Philosophy of Science* **10**, 1959, pp. 25–42; and (c) 'Quantum Mechanics without "The Observer" ', in *Quantum Theory and Reality*, Mario Bunge, ed., 1967.

genuine generalization of deductive logic. If I write '*a* follows from *b*' as '*b* ⊢ *a*', then we might try to express this, in the probability calculus, as $p(a, b) = 1$, where *a* and *b* now represent *statements*. Actually, this does not really express *b* ⊢ *a* as we shall see. In order to express *b* ⊢ *a* accurately in probabilistic terms we have to write it:

(1)   for every x, $p(a, b \cdot x) = 1$,

that is to say, *a* follows from *b* if and only if the probability of *a* given *b* remains 1 whatever additional information *x* you may add to *b*. What we have in probabilistic terms here is analogous to what I have called the *rule of augmentation of premises* in deductive logic: if *a* follows from *b*, then *a* also follows from *b* in conjunction with any further premise *x* which you may add to *b*. This rule is of great practical significance; without it valid deductive inference would not guarantee the transmission of truth from the premise to the conclusion. If we have a valid inference we can say that if the premises are true, then the conclusion is true, *whatever else may be the case*. If the rule of augmentation of premises did not hold, then we could *invalidate* inferences by adding new premises; and all we could say of a valid inference, *b* ⊢ *a*, would be that if the premise *b* is true *and* there is nothing else – no true *x* – that in- validates the inference, then the conclusion is true.

Now, the reason why *b* ⊢ *a* does not correspond to $p(a, b) = 1$ is this: even if we have $p(a, b) = 1$, we may for certain values of *a* and *b* find some information (or premise) *x* which changes the probability when added to *b*. We can even find examples of $p(a, b) = 1$ such that, if some *x* is added to *b* as an additional premise, then the probability changes from 1 to 0. (This may happen in an infinite universe. For example, let *a* be the statement that a number drawn from an infinite collection of natural numbers is odd and *b* the statement that the number drawn is prime, and let *x* be the information that the number drawn is the number 2; then $p(a, b) = 1$ and $p(a, bx) = 0$ [1].) So $p(a, b) = 1$ does not correspond to validity

---

[1] We can formulate the following *principle of stability for probability* 1: if $p(a, c) = 1$ then for every *b*, $p(a, bc) = 1$, *unless* $p(b, c) = 0$ while *bc* is consistent.

of the inference from b to a. To express the valid inference $b \vdash a$ in probabilistic terms, we have to incorporate the augmentation of premises into our probabilistic formulation, as done for example by formula (1).

It is easy to see that:

(2)   if, for every x, $p(a, bx) = p(a, b)$, then $p(a, b) = 1$.

This may be expressed as follows: if no additional premise x, or no additional condition x, is able to change the probability of a given b, then b fully, or completely, determines a. On the logical interpretation of $p(a, b)$, this means that

(3)   for every x, $p(a, bx) = p(a, b)$

is a necessary and sufficient condition for the validity of the inference $b \vdash a$. On the objective 'propensity interpretation of probability' in which a and b are interpreted as events, (3) means that b is a completely sufficient condition for a to happen (whatever else may be the case) or a *full deterministic cause* of a. And vice versa: if we take (3) as asserting a deterministic causal relation between b and a, then we are (obviously) bound to interpret

$$p(a, b) = r$$

in general (and especially for r not far from 1) as the degree of the causal, (or almost-causal) bond between b and a; or in other words, we are bound to interpret p in the sense of the *propensity interpretation of probability* [1].

Formula (3) expresses among other things that it is unnecessary for the link between b and a to stipulate 'other things being equal' ('*ceteris paribus*'). It says: 'Whatever else may happen – even if the additional conditions are completely 'unequal' – the occurrence of b is sufficient to guarantee that of a'. On the other hand, if (3) is not true, so that we have

(4)   there exists at least one x such that $p(a, bx) \neq p(a, b)$,

---

[1] See my three papers mentioned in the note on p. 131, especially (a) pp. 65 (7), 67 ff., and 70; (b) pp. 27 (2), 30 (2), and 35 ff; and (c) p. 39.

then even if $p(a, b) = 1$, the presence of b does not guarantee that of a. In fact it can easily be shown that whenever (4) holds, there will exist an x such that

$$p(a, bx) = 0,$$

even if $p(a, b) = 1$.

Thus if we wish to interpret

$$p(a, b) = r,$$

for $r = 1$, or for r near to 1, as indicating a kind of causal connection between b (cause) and a (effect), then we are *always* bound to include, explicitly or tacitly, a condition like 'other things being equal' (*'ceteris paribus'*), unless indeed (3) is satisfied, which is the necessary and sufficient condition for full causal determination of a by b. (Incidentally we can, if we like, give a general definition of 'b fully determines a (either positively or negatively)' by using the following formula (5) as definiens:

(5)   for every x, either $p(a, bx) = 1$ or $p(x, ab) = 1$.

For the first of these expresses that b positively determines a, and the second that the occurrence of b excludes that of a.)

2.   Thus it becomes plausible that the probability calculus can be interpreted as a gen·ralization of deductive logic, because in a very special case [which may be written $(x) \ p(a, bx) = p(a, b)$, or $p(a, b\bar{a}) = 1$ [1]] a probabilistic formula corresponds exactly to valid

---

[1] I am using '(x)' to mean 'for every x'; we can then say $b \vdash a$ if and only if $(x) \ p(a, bx) = 1$. In my *Logic of Scientific Discovery* I also expressed 'a follows from b' by '$p(a, b\bar{a}) = 1$' which dispenses with the use of bound variables. This is a special case of the definition given in the text: it arises from augmenting the premises with the most unfavourable information, namely the negation of the conclusion a. If this does not affect the probability 1, then a follows from b. On the interpretation of the probability calculus as a generalization of deductive logic, see *ibid.*, pp. 356 ff. (Incidentally, it is there shown – see p. 350 – that the rule '$0 \leqslant p(a, b) \leqslant 1$' is not a convention, as is often supposed, but is actually a consequence of the multiplication and addition theorems for probabilities; and it is also shown, in several places, that $p(a, b) = r$ remains a meaningful formula even if $p(b) = 0$.)

inference. (Incidentally, the formula '$(x)\, p(a,\, bx) = r$' can hold only for $r = 1$; in all other cases, we can always find some x whose addition to b will change r.) Deductive logic is *generalized* by probability logic because in the probability calculus (a) the bound variable 'x' can be omitted and (b) r can vary from 0 to 1 (whereas in deductive logic we only have the special case when r is 1). And the intuitive interpretation of this generalization – the 'logical interpretation' (as opposed to the propensity interpretation) – is pretty clear: when a follows from b, then a says not more than b; that is to say, the informative content of a is included in that of b. But when $r = p(a,\, b)$ lies *between* 0 and 1 then we have in r (or better, in $1 - r$) a 'measure' of how much of the informative content of a is not included in that of b.

Now to turn to the problem of the rule of detachment. In deductive logic we have two rules of detachment:

(a) the *modus ponens*: $((b \supset a) \cdot b) \vdash a$

(b) the metalinguistic rule: if $b \vdash a$ and $b \in T$ then $a \in T$,
where '$\in T$' is an abbreviation for 'is true'.

Each of these rules can be translated, obviously, into probabilistic terms:

(a′) $(x)\, p(a,\, (b \supset a) \cdot bx) = 1$

(b′) if $(x)\, p(a,\, bx) = 1$ and $b \in T$ then $a \in T$.

But these are of course not the rules of detachment of which inductive logicians dream. Rather, what they have in mind is something like the following '*ideal rule of inductivist detachment*':

$$\text{if } p(a,\, b) = r \text{ and } b \in T \text{ then } p(a) = r.$$

(Actually, there exists the following somewhat similar valid rule:

$$\text{if } p(a,\, b) = r \text{ and } p(b) = 1, \text{ then } p(a) = r;$$

but this rule is rather trivial because $p(b) = 1$ means that the informative content of b is nil. Thus the rule says only that, if the probability of a equals r, given information with nil content, it also equals r without any information [1].)

Inductive logicians dream of the 'ideal rule of detachment' because if it held then they could apply the calculus of probability to betting situations: if $p(a, b) = r$ and we are given the information b (or the information $b \in T$), then, they wish or dream, we would be rational to bet on a with odds given by r. Or, suppose a is a scientific theory and b the evidence. Then if they interpret science as a sort of 'gamble against nature', they can, with the aid of their rule, tell scientists how much confidence they should place in their theories if the evidence is true. In their dream the logic of science becomes the 'logic' of 'betting against nature', i.e. inductive logic, i.e. probability logic.

Unfortunately, the 'ideal rule of detachment' is invalid, precisely because of the problem of the augmentation of premises. The truth of b does not assure me that there is not some x which is also true and which, if added to the 'premise' b, would affect r, even to the extent of reducing r from 1 to 0. We might try to improve the 'ideal rule' as follows:

$$\text{if } (x)\ p(a, bx) = r \text{ and } b \in T, \text{ then } p(a) = r;$$

but this is nonsense, because as we have seen it could hold only

---

[1] (*Added in proof.*) This formula can be generalized as follows:

Let h be a hypothesis, e evidence and b background knowledge (which may be zero, in which case b is tautological and may be simply omitted from the formulae). Inductivists may wish e to be reasonably probable (given b); or in other words that $p(e, b) = 1 - \varepsilon$ where ε is some small number. They will be interested in the increase of the probability $p(h, b)$ if e is added to the second argument. This increase however will be very small for we have (neglecting ε^2 and higher powers)

$$\text{if } p(e, b) = 1 - \varepsilon, \text{ then } p(h, b) + \varepsilon \geqslant p(h, eb) \geqslant p(h, b) - \varepsilon.$$

If in the implicate of this formula 'ε' is replaced by '2ε', then the formula becomes universally valid in the calculus of probability.

This shows that (1) to increase the probability of a hypothesis, one would have to shift the improbability to the evidence; and (2) one could not go on (without infinite regress) basing beliefs on probabilities, that is, on so-called *rational* beliefs: rather one would have to base probabilities, logically speaking, on *faith*, pure and simple.

for $r = 1$. So the ideal rule of detachment cannot possibly be valid in any form.

Now, what have inductive logicians done about it? Carnap says this rule is valid (not in a semantic but in a pragmatic sense [1]) if and only if b is *all* you know, your *'total knowledge'*. And indeed, if b is your 'total knowledge' then there is no further x to be afraid of.

Various things can be said about this. It introduces subjective elements: the idea of total knowledge contains a temporal element, for it may change through time – so we must speak of total knowledge at time t. But the moment we allow time to enter logical considerations, we must ask questions like: 'What if b was your total knowledge at time t but in the second it takes you to draw the inference you receive further information?'. A more serious objection is, of course, that I cannot know what my total knowledge is. We are actually led to a kind of infinite regress. Suppose b is my total knowledge; then in order to *know* that b is my total knowledge I should have to add to b the knowledge that b is my total knowledge. But this addition is of course likely to change the probability, since it is, according to Carnap, relevant knowledge. If b is my total knowledge, then I must know this fact before I can use the rule: but if I *know* that b is my total knowledge, then b was *not* my total knowledge, because my total knowledge was actually b plus the knowledge that b is my total knowledge. This

---

[1] See points I_6 and I_7 on p. 201 of his *Logical Foundations of Probability*, 2nd. ed., 1962, where he says (I have italicized *'nothing else'*; everything else, including the square brackets, is Carnap's):

I_6 'If e and *nothing else* is *known* by X at t, then h is confirmed by X at t to the degree $\frac{2}{3}$.' [Here, the term 'confirmed' does not mean the logical (semantical) concept of degree of confirmation occurring in D_1 but a corresponding pragmatical concept; the latter is, however, not identical with the concept of degree of (actual) belief but means rather the degree of belief justified by the observational knowledge of X at t.] The phrase 'and nothing else' in I_6 is essential; see § 45B concerning the requirement of total evidence.

I_7 'If e and nothing else is known by X at t, then a decision of X at t based on the assumption of the degree of certainty $\frac{2}{3}$ for h is rationally justified (e.g., the decision to accept a bet on h with a betting quotient not higher than $\frac{2}{3}$).'

may sound a little absurd, but the whole idea of total knowledge is absurd: it seems to me to be clearly absurd to demand, in a theory of practical action, that before you can act practically you should always have total knowledge. Bringing in total knowledge is so absurd from a practical point of view that I feel justified in answering it with such almost absurd subtleties as the infinite regress of total knowledge.

Carnap's famous so-called *'requirement of total knowledge'* is thus a completely *ad hoc* attempt to save the rule of (pragmatic) detachment in inductive logic. It has no justification, practical or theoretical, other than that.

What is the real situation about the rule of detachment? The probability calculus *is* a genuine generalization of deductive logic and, as it is a generalization, the rule of detachment of deductive logic is only applicable in a particular case, where $r = 1$ and instead of b we have bx for every x. The place where the rule of detachment is applicable is just where we would expect, namely where we have valid deductive inference. We have a rule of detachment where it belongs, and no generally applicable generalized rule of detachment where it does not belong. And that is the end of it [1].

---

[1]   Believing as I do that there is a probability logic which is a generalization of deductive logic, but that 'inductive logic' is nonexistent, I do of course disagree with Suppes' statement (at the beginning of the penultimate paragraph of his contribution to the present discussion), 'Because of the lack of a sharp distinction between inductive and deductive logic in ordinary talk, even in ordinary scientific talk, the presence of rules of detachment in inductive logic which generalize *ponendo ponens* seems wholly natural.' His formulae are correct, and no doubt may be described as 'generalized rules of detachment'. But although generally valid, they are not generally applicable; and indeed he has given no indication how they are to be used. (His second formula – of which mine is a special case – is most easily interpreted thus: if B almost follows from A, and if the content of A is fairly small, then the content of B is also fairly small; or in other words: if the informative content of B considerably exceeds that of A, then $P(B, A)$ cannot be great.) In every attempted application of his rule, he would have to assume that his information contains *'total knowledge'* (or, what amounts to the same, that no unfavourable knowledge x has been omitted from his information). In other words, the problem of *'augmentation of premises'* would have to be dealt with in every case of practical application. See also the previous footnote.

But how then can the probability calculus be applied? The answer is that in physics we know exactly how to apply it. In physics we do not 'detach' a from the conditions, but we try experimentally to realize the conditions. In physics $p(a, b) = r$ has a definite meaning: it says that under the experimental conditions b the probability of a will be r. We do not say that the experimental conditions are realized and that therefore the probability of a will be r. In fact we never *know* whether the experimental conditions are fully realized; and we do not need in physics any rule of detachment to detach the probability of a from the information b.

We see from all this that though probability logic *is* a generalization of deductive logic, it cannot be *that* generalization of deductive logic which inductivists wish inductive logic to be. As for inductive logic, I do not believe that it exists. There is, of course, a logic of science, but that is part of an applied deductive logic: the logic of testing theories, or the logic of the growth of knowledge.

Moreover, scientists would have little use for an inductive logic, even if inductivists could provide them with one. For the central problem of inductive logic is the problem of acceptance: Under what circumstances should I accept a theory? The inductivist answer is: Accept the most probable theory! I believe that this is a completely mistaken solution to a comparatively unimportant problem. The problems which confront scientists have little to do with acceptance, since they are problems connected with the growth of science; that is to say with *the comparison of the merits of competing theories*. Scientists would not (and should not) worry about whether a theory should be accepted because it has probability 0.73 while another one only has probability 0.72; quite apart from the fact that there does not exist so far any probability theory in which it has been established of any scientific theory that it has more than zero probability.

I think that inductive logic is really just a red herring – or perhaps, in view of the amount of paper it devours, a white elephant.

W. C. Salmon: *Who needs inductive acceptance rules?*

On this occasion, as on others, Professor Bar–Hillel has asserted that a system of inductive logic can be constructed, without doing basic violence to our conception of science, which embodies no rules of acceptance. He asks implicitly just what he asked explicitly on another occasion: Who needs inductive acceptance rules? (On that occasion, *he* called them 'rules of detachment' [1].) I use the verb 'to assert' deliberately, for he does not consider Kyburg's substantial arguments designed to show, for example, that an inductive logic with no rules of acceptance renders theoretical statements 'totally redundant and unnecessary'. Instead, he is content 'just [to] state categorically' that this and others of Kyburg's conclusions are 'wrong'. Bar–Hillel's closing reassurance, that science will go on without explicitly formulated rules of acceptance, is irrelevant to the question at issue. We may be quite sure that science will proceed entirely oblivious to philosophers' worries about inductive logic, much as mathematicians before Peano, Frege and Russell established lots of important theorems of number theory. Science can and does proceed without waiting for completed foundations. This does not show that the foundations can be completed without introducing rules of acceptance. My sympathies, in this discussion, are largely with Kyburg, though I endorse neither his conception of a hierarchy of rational corpora nor his logical interpretation of probability. I do think, however, that rules of acceptance are indispensable to inductive logic, and I should like to offer a couple of reasons for this view.

(1) While the proper analysis of scientific explanation is still an open issue, it seems widely acknowledged that providing explanations is a basic function of science. One of the most influential accounts of explanation is the 'covering law model'. According to this conception, a deductive explanation of a particular event requires the deduction of the explanandum-statement from true (or highly confirmed) premises that include a universal generalization. Within Carnap's system based upon c^* we could never claim to have any such explanation simply because no general statement could ever get a degree of confirmation other than zero. This property of c^* has, however, been regarded by everyone, including Carnap himself, as a defect. It is not true of every possible confir-

---

[1]   Henry E. Kyburg Jr. and Ernest Nagel eds., *Induction: Some Current Issues*, Wesleyan University Press, 1963, p. 46.

mation function, so it is not a necessary consequence of the view that inductive logic does not require rules of acceptance.

Leaving aside this peculiarity of a comprehensive class of confirmation functions, a problem remains. Without rules of acceptance, it is difficult to see how we can have any general hypothesis, regardless of its degree of confirmation, that can be employed as the general premise from which the explanandum-statement is to be deduced. If we try to replace the general premise with a degree of confirmation statement, we cannot satisfy the requirement that the explanandum-statement be deducible from the explanans-statements. Letting i be the statements of initial conditions, a the explanandum-statement, h a general hypothesis, and e evidence statements relevant to that hypothesis, none of the following arguments is a valid deduction:

$$
\begin{array}{lll}
i & i & i \\
c(h,\, e) = p & c(h,\, e) = p & c(h,\, e) = p \\
\hline
a & e & e \\
\quad\quad\text{, nor} & \overline{} & e \text{ is total evidence} \\
 & a & \overline{} \\
 & \quad\quad\text{, nor} & a,
\end{array}
$$

(unless e entails a, in which case the argument is completely trivial and not an explanation at all). What we need is:

$$
\begin{array}{c}
i \\
h \\
\hline
a\, ,
\end{array}
$$

but we are never able to assert the premises of this argument unless we have acceptance rules. Of course, we might regard this schema as a criterion of satisfactory deductive explanation, provided $c(h,\, e)$ is large enough, even though we cannot assert the premises. It seems strange, however, to regard as an appropriate explanation an argument whose premises are in principle unassertable, and whose conclusion is assertable only on grounds independent of the 'explanatory' argument.

The situation for inductive explanation is even worse. According to the corresponding account, inductive explanations have at least the following two characteristics in common with deductive explanations:

(I) The explanans must contain at least one general statement as an essential premise. (In inductive explanations, the general premise is a statistical generalization.)

(II) The explanandum-statement must be the conclusion of a logically correct inference. (In inductive explanations, the inference must be a correct induction.)

Each of these characteristics gives rise to a difficulty. A statistical generalization, unlike a degree of confirmation statement, is synthetic, so it raises exactly the same problems about acceptance as does the general hypothesis required in the deductive case. Moreover, since the explanandum-statement is also synthetic, characteristic (II) requires that the argument that constitutes the explanation conform to a correct rule of acceptance for inductive logic.

It appears that a leading conception of scientific explanation presupposes inductive acceptance rules, and becomes radically untenable without them. I do not mean to say that this view of explanation is the correct one, but it does seem to me that anyone who denies acceptance rules a place in the explication of the logic of science, needs to show in some detail how the theory of explanation can be modified or replaced so as not to depend upon the acceptance of synthetic statements as conclusions of inductive inferences.

Who needs acceptance rules? Anyone who wants to embrace a conception of scientific explanation resembling the covering law model for deductive and inductive explanation.

(2) Everyone acknowledges, I think, that we must have rules enabling us to accept probability statements; the question is whether these statements are analytic or synthetic. Carnap's answer to this question is well-known. He maintains that degree of confirmation statements are analytic. They can, therefore, be asserted on the basis of acceptance rules of *deductive* logic; so inductive logic needs no rules of acceptance. Deductive logic provides the rules for accepting the probability statements we need to assert. A necessary condition for maintaining that acceptance rules for

inductive logic are dispensable is adoption of the view that analytic probability statements taken in conjunction with observational evidence constitute an adequate 'guide of life'.

I have argued elsewhere in this volume that analytic degree of confirmation statements cannot bear this burden; synthetic probability statements are required. There is no need to repeat the argument here. It is sufficient to point out that synthetic probability statements can be established, if at all, only as conclusions of inductive inferences. Their acceptance requires precisely the kind of inductive acceptance rules whose utility is at issue.

Once more, *who needs acceptance rules?* Anyone who holds that analytic probability statements do not provide a satisfactory guide of life, and that synthetic probability statements are needed for this purpose. I think I am not alone in this view.

Various protests may be raised against this position. First, it may be argued, although frequency considerations are of fundamental importance in practical behavior, we do not need to *infer* values of limiting frequencies. It is enough to have *estimates* of these values, and estimate statements are analytic. In reply to this objection, I should say that it is precisely because estimate statements are analytic that we need something more. We need factual assertions. All the reasons we have for denying that analytic degree of confirmation statements provide an adequate guide of life are equally reasons for denying that analytic estimate statements do so, either. If, on the other hand, estimate statements are construed as synthetic, then we need inductive acceptance rules to make them available as a basis for action.

Another possible objection takes issue with the acceptance of synthetic frequency statements on the ground that we can never be certain whether any such statement is true. Such statements can never be finally known as 'God's truth'. My answer is that certainty and finality constitute nothing more than a red herring in this context. To accept a hypothesis is *not* necessarily to accept it irrevocably. It is entirely possible to conceive acceptance in a way that leaves open the matter of subsequent rejection. If, for example, induction by enumeration is an inductive acceptance rule, then it has its own correlative rejection rule: Whenever additional observations become available to augment your sample, reject the former inferred value of the limiting frequency and replace it by a value inferred from the larger sample.

One more objection needs attention. If we are going to accept on a provisional basis statements of which we are not completely certain – it might be said – we shall have to assign them probabilities. This will give rise to the lottery paradox or related difficulties. I should say in reply that the consequence by no means follows. It is essential, I believe, to assert synthetic probability statements, but it is not necessary to attach higher level probabilities to them. Statements about limiting frequencies can simply be accepted provisionally – posited in Reichenbach's sense – without attaching any particular weight to them. The acceptance is provisional, not because probabilities are assigned to them, but because there are clearly specified rules for subsequent rejection if certain kinds of evidence appear. The lottery paradox does not arise, as I explain elsewhere in this volume, because this positing procedure is confined to statistical generalizations and is not extended to statements about individual events.

J. Hintikka: *The possibility of rules of acceptance.*

I should like to comment on the controversy between Professor Kyburg and Professor Bar–Hillel. I have been impressed by the arguments of both – so much so that I have a considerable difficulty in making up my mind as to which one of them is right. In this truly philosophical predicament, I am moved to ask whether part of the issue could be reduced to a more manageable technical problem.

There is in fact such a problem ready at hand. We may ask: Are rules of acceptance possible? Is it possible to define, if only in some artificially simple languages, rules of acceptance (detachment) which would be like the ones Kyburg has been pleading for? More specifically, can one find probability measures on the statements of some simple language and define by their means a probabilistic rule of acceptance which satisfies the minimum requirements of consistency and logical closure which every well-behaved rule of acceptance clearly should satisfy? A negative answer to this question would give me a very strong reason for siding with Bar–Hillel; a positive answer might give some new hope to Kyburg.

That this problem is not trivial is shown by the paradoxes (especially by the 'lottery paradox') into which earlier attempts to set up rules of acceptance have led. In spite of these difficulties, my problem admits of a fairly clear-cut positive solution. Using the probability measures outlined in my own contribution to this colloquium, one can define very simple rules of acceptance which satisfy the requirement that the set of acceptable statements is consistent and closed with respect to logical implication.

In a sense, my proposed rules of acceptance are precisely as you would expect them to be. The paradoxes have shown that high probability alone does not work as a standard of acceptance. Now what is the simplest additional thing you feel like requiring of an acceptable theory or hypothesis over and above high probability? Surely, we want to require that the high probability in question is not due to *a priori* considerations alone, but is based on a sufficiently large amount of evidence. In a recently published paper (jointly with Risto Hilpinen) I showed that this one additional requirement, interpreted in the simplest possible way, gives a rule of acceptance for general (closed) statements in an applied monadic first-order language. (This simple interpretation takes the requirement to say that the generalization is to be based on a sufficiently large number of completely known instances.) As far as singular statements are concerned, we can accept them if and only if they are implied by acceptable generalizations.

Thus there really is something to be discussed in a symposium on rules of acceptance. There are no deep philosophical problems about the possibility of such rules, although considerable technical problems still face us when we try to extend the positive result just mentioned to more complicated languages. Whether you argue for them or against them, your arguments concerning acceptance rules will have to turn on interpretational questions or on presuppositions like the so-called requirement of complete evidence.

The arguments which Kyburg has marshalled in his contribution and in his earlier work have convinced me that in order to discuss some of the most important theories of scientific method, we would have to invent rules of acceptance, even if they did not exist, in our actual scientific practice. This is the motivation for the work which I have just reported on and which does give us respectable rules of acceptance. I leave it to others to find out whether this constitutes an invention or, as I suspect, a genuine discovery.

R. CARNAP: *On rules of acceptance.*

1. When I say that the end result of inductive reasoning is not the acceptance of a hypothesis, but rather the assignment of a probability to the hypothesis, this is not meant as a description of what is usually done, but rather as a proposal for a rational reconstruction. Therefore, although in the present controversy I agree essentially with Professor Bar–Hillel against Professor Kyburg, I am quite doubtful about one view in which they seem to agree, that here we have to choose between two irreconcilable positions. I do not think, as Kyburg does, that our using or not using rules of acceptance (or detachment) makes a vast difference in our philosophy of science. Nor would I, like Bar–Hillel, totally condemn such rules.

There is especially one reason that should dissuade us from severely condemning the acceptance of hypotheses. This reason lies in the fact, usually not noticed, that practically all of us who use a concept of probability dependent upon evidence implicitly think in terms of acceptance. When we speak about the determination of the probability, the rational degree of belief in a hypothesis with respect to evidence, we take the evidence as 'given'; we treat it as if we knew it with perfect certainty; and this is clearly the same as taking it as 'accepted', no matter whether we use this term or not. And we do this although most of us, when we discuss not inductive logic but epistemology, declare that we can never have perfect certainty for any synthetic proposition. For many years I have tried in vain to correct this flaw in the customary procedure in inductive logic, in other words to find a way of dealing with *uncertain evidence*. Then Richard Jeffrey indicated in his doctoral thesis a solution for the simplest case (one observation proposition) [1]; and now he has generalized this solution for any number n of observation propositions [2]. Although – as always – some points here are still in need of further clarification, this is a significant step forward.

It seems to me that our present question, like many other problems in methodology, is not so much a question of right or wrong, but rather of primitive or more refined procedures. Working with acceptance rules is a simple procedure that is practically quite useful in many situations. But I regard it as one of the tasks of inductive logic to develop more efficient procedures. And, in particular, the present problem situation appears to me as a special case of the distinction between three kinds of concepts, namely, classificatory, comparative, and quantitative concepts.

Suppose an examiner is asked to find out for each person on a given list whether he has a specified ability, e.g. driving a car, or solving problems in geometry. The form of the report is prescribed to him. In the simplest case he is asked to indicate those persons whom he judges as good, by marking their names by '+'. In a slightly refined version of the first procedure, he is to mark by '+', '−', and '0' the names of those he judges good, or bad, or still undecided, respectively; in this version the bipartition is replaced by a triple classification. Another, more efficient, procedure would use the comparative concept 'x is superior to y (in the specified respect)'; in other words, the examiner gives a rank order of the persons. A report of this form gives obviously more information about the persons' abilities than the mere classification. Still more would be supplied by a quantitative report, provided the examiner has or develops an adequate quantitative concept, a way of measuring degrees of the ability in question. Here the report assigns a number to each person.

Now the situation seems to me quite analogous when a research worker is asked to test a list of hypotheses about a particular subject matter in a special field of science. These hypotheses may concern particular objects, say a medical diagnosis concerning a

---

[1] *Contributions to the theory of inductive probability*, Ph. D. Thesis, Princeton University, 1957 (unpublished).

[2] *The Logic of Decision*, New York, 1965, ch. 11.

group of persons with respect to a specified disease; or they may be more general, e.g., concerning the physiological effects of a family of chemical compounds. From time to time he is to report on his results about the status of the hypotheses. Here again we have the three possible forms. A report of the simplest form indicates which of the hypotheses have been accepted; or, in the slightly improved version, each hypothesis is marked as accepted, or as rejected, or as not yet decided. Another form of the report may give a rank order of the hypotheses with respect to probability (or maybe with respect to acceptability, if this concept is defined). A report of the third form gives for each hypothesis a numerical value, say the degree of confirmation on the basis of the given evidence. This numerical value is relevant for our further work with these hypotheses, e.g. for determining estimates, betting quotients, and many other things, maybe even acceptance. [In the latter case, however, not only the degree of confirmation should be considered but also the prior amount of information or content measure [1]. For competing hypotheses with equal amounts of information, the one with the highest degree of confirmation is to be preferred. If those amounts are not equal, both degree of confirmation and amount of information should be taken into consideration. If you look for a quantitative concept of acceptability, it should be a function of both those magnitudes (you might try their product).]

From what I have said you will understand that I would not raise any objections of principle against the use of rules of acceptance. In one special case it seems to me even quite natural to talk in terms of acceptance, namely with respect to the postulates of a theoretical system, e.g. those of the classical electromagnetic theory, or of the kinetic theory of gases, or of quantum mechanics. In the context of such a theory, in contrast to empirical generalizations, the very meaning of the theoretical terms is dependent on the postulates. Thus within each particular research project, a certain set of postulates is usually presupposed, either

---

[1] Cf. 'Probability and content measure', in *Mind, Matter, and Method: Essays in Philosophy and Science in Honor of Herbert Feigl*, P. K. Feyerabend and G. Maxwell eds., Minneapolis, 1966.

explicitly or implicitly. Here we may well say that, within the context of the project, the postulates are 'accepted'. But, aside from hypotheses of this particular kind, it seems to me preferable to use a quantitative procedure of reporting, provided the required quantitative concepts of inductive logic have been developed.

In particular, it seems to me inadvisable to use rules of acceptance in situations where the results of the investigation are not sought for purely cognitive aims, but are intended also to be used for practical decisions. Here the utilities of the possible outcomes of decisions are relevant, and therefore rules of acceptance of the usual kind – all those not involving utilities – would be inadequate.

2. Now I should like to comment on Professor Salmon's views about rules of acceptance and, in particular, on two arguments he offers in support of his assertion that rules of acceptance for synthetic hypotheses are indispensable both for science and for practical decisions.

His first argument is directed against my view that inductive logic can serve as a guide in life, that is to say, as an instrument in our search for rational decisions. In my schema for decision making, I use sentences of the form: 'The degree of confirmation (or logical probability) for the hypothesis H on the basis of the propositions E and A is so-and-so much', where E consists of the given observational results, A is the assumption that I carry out a certain act, and H is the prediction that a certain outcome will result. Salmon thinks that statements of this kind cannot fulfil their intended function, because they are purely analytic. Therefore he proposes to replace them by synthetic probability statements which give values, not of logical but of statistical probability. Now I agree with Salmon in the view that decision making must be based on knowledge of facts, and hence the deliberation which is to lead to the choice of a decision must use synthetic statements. But this requirement is clearly fulfilled in my schema of decision making, because it uses the premise: 'E consists of all the observational results which I have at the present moment and which are relevant for H'. I have pointed this out at an earlier occasion [1].

___
[1] Cf. my paper, 'The aim of inductive logic', in *Logic, Methodol-*

Another argument of Salmon's is based on the view that a scientific explanation of observed facts is not possible without the use of accepted laws. As I see it, this holds indeed for deductive explanations, but not for *inductive* explanations. While a deductive explanation deduces the explanandum from the premises which include at least one law, an inductive explanation shows only that the explanandum has a sufficiently high probability on the basis of the premises (compare Hempel's analysis of inductive explanation [1]). In an explanation of this kind it is not necessary that the laws referred to are accepted, that is, known with certainty (or near certainty). It is sufficient if the law has, on the basis of the given evidence, a fairly high probability. In my view, the inductive explanation can be carried out even if a system of inductive logic is used which assigns probability zero to all universal laws; it is sufficient that the instance probability is sufficiently high (cf. my *Logical Foundations of Probability*, Chicago, 1950, pp. 572f.). Let us consider a simple example. From the premises (1) 'This solid body A is heated' and the universal law (2) 'Whenever a solid body is heated, it expands', we can deduce the explanandum (3) 'A expands'. For the deduction of (3) it would suffice to have, instead of the law (2), the much weaker instance statement (2') 'If the body A is heated, it expands'. Similarly, in an inductive explanation, it will (under suitable circumstances) be possible to show, on the given evidence, a sufficiently high probability for (3), not only if we have a high probability for the law (2), but even if we have a high probability only for the instance (2').

Y. BAR–HILLEL: *The acceptance syndrome.*

1. Of the contributors to the discussion on our symposium and of the many other participants in the colloquium who in their talks or discussion remarks referred, sometimes even prominently and decisively, to 'acceptance' and its rules, none gave much indication that he regarded the notion of acceptance as being in

---

ogy and Philosophy of Science; Proceedings of the 1960 International Congress, E. Nagel, P. Suppes, A. Tarski, eds., Stanford, California, 1962, pp. 303–318.

[1] In his *Aspects of Scientific Explanation and Other Essays*, New York, 1965, pp. 331–496.

need of clarification. I regard this as remarkable and rather disappointing, since it was so clear to me – and I tried to stress this point in my first comment [1] – that the term 'accept' (as well as, of course, 'reject') is highly ambiguous both in our ordinary speech and in our informal scientific discourse. I called attention to at least three quite different, though not necessarily totally independent, uses of this term, in addition to the idiosyncratic one sometimes used by Professor Popper and his followers. (In the meantime, I had no trouble, after a modicum of soulsearching, introspection and discussion with friends and colleagues, discovering a not inconsiderable number of further frequent uses.) The general underlying assumption that 'to accept' has but one, unique meaning (up to vagueness) in all contexts (i.e. for statements, generalizations, hypotheses, theories, etc.), which is furthermore so clear as to be in need of no clarification, is truly amazing in its lack of sophistication.

Without this preliminary clarification, any discussion of the rationality, justifiability, or 'logicality' of acceptance is doomed to futility. I myself shall doubtless go on talking, informally, about accepting and rejecting this or that, and so will everybody else. But before I am ready to embark upon an investigation into the justifiability of, say, accepting theories (and I mean here exclusively scientific theories and not 'theories' of the kind that it was the butler and not the maid who did the lord in) and, even more so, upon a discussion of the existence of 'rules of acceptance' in any reconstruction of scientific thinking, I am afraid that I would have to insist on such prior clarification, up to a certain degree, whose exact nature I had better leave open for the time being.

One has to distinguish at least between the following questions:
(1) In which senses do people (and, in particular, scientists) accept (or reject) (a) observational statements, (b) observational generalizations, (c) hypotheses, (d) theories, (e) . . . ?
(2) Can these types of behaviour be justified, and in what sense?
(3) Can the justification be reconstructed as being in accordance with certain 'rules of acceptance', and what would be their nature?

---

[1] 'On alleged rules of detachment in inductive logic', *this volume*, pp. 120–128.

2. I indeed 'totally condemned' any non-deductive rules of acceptance (or 'rules of acceptance in inductive logic', as they have also been called) of any kind discussed so far in the literature or even of any future kind in which the term 'acceptance' preserves any of its customary meanings. But I did not 'severely condemn' or even condemn at all 'acceptance of hypotheses'. Carnap seems to regard these two kinds of acts as identical or to have understood me as regarding them as identical. Let me therefore repeat (what I have already said rather clearly, I hope) that I myself and all scientists (I previously said 'science', in accordance with the customary anthropomorphic mode of speech) will continue to accept hypotheses, in some appropriate sense of this phrase, but that no rule of inductive or probability logic is conceivable, not even one that takes into account also the pragmatic features mentioned by Kyburg as criteria (4) and (5) – though Kyburg shows no awareness there that by invoking those criteria he is well beyond 'inductive logic'.

It seems to me, therefore, that Carnap was wrong in trying to show, as is his custom in many similar situations, that the views of Kyburg and myself were not really as irreconcilable as they were presented by us. Moreover I think that the particular way in which he attempted to show this, *viz.*, by applying his well-known and often extremely effective distinction between classificatory, comparative and quantitative concepts, was not really to the point.

'Working with acceptance rules' is never, *pace* Carnap, 'a simple procedure that is practically quite useful in many situations', though accepting, say, the testimony of a reliable witness, indeed may be. (Notice that the rule, 'Accept – in the sense of "regard as true" – the testimony of a witness whom you have every reason to regard as reliable!', is not a 'rule of acceptance', in any of the many senses used in the discussion, as far as I could make out. It would be a bad rule, anyway. In the case of two reliable witnesses who happen to contradict each other, it would lead to schizophrenia.)

Incidentally, there is no good reason to believe with Carnap [1]

---

[1] *This volume*, p. 148.

that the concept 'has a higher probability than' is the comparative concept corresponding to the qualitative concept 'is accepted' (and not only for the trivial, though still not unimportant, reason that 'accepted' and 'acceptable' are, at least *prima facie*, different concepts). Carnap, of course, is in general fully aware of this, as becomes quite clear from his subsequent remarks in parentheses, though on occasion he slips into formulations inherited from older times. But more importantly: it should by now be clear that the relation 'is more acceptable than', if this concept is ever explicated with a reasonable amount of adequacy, will most certainly not turn out to be a rank-ordering, i.e., a quasi-order, but, at most, a partial order, so that not every two competing theories will always be comparable. And this is so because in the evaluation of, say, theories for 'acceptance', in some appropriate sense, one will usually take into account not only their degrees of confirmation – relative to the total available evidence –, as Carnap tended to believe many years ago, and some of his followers still tend to believe today (should such a function ever become seriously definable for theories relative to observational evidence, something I doubt very much), nor their content measures alone, as Popper seems to have believed at times, nor a function of these two magnitudes alone, as Carnap seems to believe today [1].

I don't understand, though, Watkins' misgivings about this point. He says that '[Carnap] adds that for acceptance we should *also* employ a measure of content. But this would vary *inversely* with a probabilistic measure of confirmation' [2]. The 'but' is strange. It is, of course, exactly Carnap's point that the acceptability of a theory should vary both directly with its degree of (posterior) confirmation as well as inversely with its degree of (prior) confirmation. It would be nice if this simple point – as a matter of fact, far too simple for its aims – would be grasped by the Popperians. A lot of pointless controversy could be saved.

Carnap's point is still an oversimplification since no functions that will not take into account a large number of pragmatic factors,

---

[1] *This volume*, p. 148.
[2] *This volume*, p. 275.

largely unanalyzed and poorly understood so far, though sufficiently
understood to throw the gravest doubts on their quantizability,
have any chance of being an even moderately adequate explicans
for any of the senses in which we talk about accepting theories.
Of course, if one becomes enamored of one of the factors, as Popper
became of prior content measure, and insists on regarding this
factor as the only important one in the explication of the high-
prestige term 'accept', the only choice left is to invent a new sense
of this term, a 'very unsolemn sense', to misuse an expression of
Watkins [1], i.e. the sense in which to 'accept one out of a number
of competing scientific hypotheses is to select it as the one most
worth superseding by a better one'. I don't think this makes much
sense altogether. At the best, it means something like 'never be
satisfied with what you have, always try for something better',
which is sound, though somewhat banal advice. The important
point is, of course, an explication of what it is to be a 'better
hypothesis'. And here I hope that Popper would agree that prior
content is not the only factor to be taken into consideration, but
I wish he would say so clearly and explicitly. I hope he would
agree that posterior confirmation is an equally important factor
(if it could be adequately defined at all), in spite of the fact that
he claims the opposite, since his well-known counter-arguments
only show either that this concept is very hard to explicate adequately, certainly for high-level theories (which I grant, of course),
or that it could not be the only factor (which Carnap grants). I
would be still happier if Popper (and Carnap) would agree that
not even both of these measures together could, even in principle,
suffice as the only factors for 'the comparison of the merits of
competing theories'. And I, for one, am not satisfied with taking
into account also the 'verisimilitude' of a hypothesis, its closeness
to truth, as the only third factor. Not because I believe that this
factor is so far still ill-defined, which I do, but because it is still
clearly a purely semantic one, while 'to accept' is not only a
definitely pragmatic term in ordinary usage but also one which
it is not worthwhile, or possible, adequately to explicate as a

---

[1] *This volume*, p. 281.

purely semantic term. What about such features as ease of learning (and/or teaching), elegance, and – well, let's get it out of our system – simplicity? (It should by now be clear that all attempts to explicate simplicity in purely semantic terms have utterly failed.) What about generalizability, picturizability, ease of computation, etc.?

I must also take exception to Carnap's statement – made in connection with his insistence that one should not severely condemn the acceptance of hypotheses – 'that practically all of us who use a concept of probability dependent upon evidence implicitly think in terms of acceptance. When we speak about the determination of the probability, the rational degree of belief in a hypothesis with respect to evidence, we take the evidence as "given"; we treat it as if we knew it with perfect certainty; and this is clearly the same as taking it as "accepted", no matter whether we use this term or not' [1]. That many of us often indeed think in these terms, I would not want to deny for a minute. I also admit that I understand the reason for which Carnap believes that some rational justification for this behaviour must be found, namely, that otherwise the practical applicability of inductive logic would seem to be gravely jeopardized. But it surely could not possibly be the business of inductive logic, in the sense in which Carnap himself uses this term, i.e. as distinguished from methodology and epistemology, to say anything at all, not to speak about 'rules', as to when evidence is to be treated as 'given', to be treated as known with perfect certainty, to be accepted. I am happy to learn that, partly due to the efforts of Jeffrey (from whom and, of course, from Carnap himself I got my allergy towards acceptance, to begin with), Carnap now sees a way to give up this assumption which should never have been made at all, not even in despair.

I agree, of course, with Carnap that within some given research project certain theories are 'presupposed, either explicitly or implicitly', and therefore, in this sense, 'accepted'. But I fail to see that in any such situation 'rules of acceptance' are used (and this, of course, does not mean at all that the presupposed theories are

---

[1] *This volume*, p. 146.

selected arbitrarily). 'When starting a research project, tell your research assistants that they should proceed on the basis of certain theories, whose validity they should not question (unless they really see no other way)', may be excellent advice in a manual for principal investigators, but I doubt whether such a rule has ever been called a 'rule of acceptance' or should be called so without confusing still further an already sufficiently confused issue.

Carnap has made it many times very clear in which sense 'inductive logic serves as a guide in life', and I find it very puzzling that so many authors, including this time Salmon, Watkins and Kneale [1], keep harping on the theme that there must be something wrong with a view that assigns to an analytic tool a role in decision making. Let's hope that Carnap's remarks [2] will finally put the issue to rest. (I have some more specific comments on this point elsewhere in this volume [3]).

But I am unhappy with Carnap's treatment of another argument of Salmon's for the necessity of 'accepting' theories, namely that otherwise 'a scientific explanation of observed facts is not possible' [4]. Carnap is ready to grant this for deductive explanations but not for inductive ones. I see no justification for this admission. It seems to be based on the standard non-distinction between the ordinary, pragmatic use of the term 'explanation' and its extraordinary, semantic use by some scientists and philosophers of science, as well as on the non-distinction between sound (satisfactory, etc.) explanation and explanation, period. (This second distinction is, of course, often noticed and explicitly mentioned, e.g., by Hempel, but seldom heeded to, in practice, probably because of the fact that 'explain' is a part-time achievement verb so that 'He gave an explanation for F' is often automatically understood as 'He gave a satisfactory explanation for F'.) Whether the laws used as premises in a deductive explanatory argument are accepted or not, makes no difference as to whether this argument is an ex-

---

[1] See W. Salmon, *The justification of inductive rules of inference*, and the comments upon it by W. C. Kneale and J. W. N. Watkins, in this volume.

[2] *This volume*, p. 149.

[3] *This volume*, pp. 66 ff.

[4] *This volume*, p. 150.

planatory one or not, though it of course makes a difference as to whether the explanation will be regarded as satisfactory.

Incidentally, Carnap seems to accept without much ado the identification of 'satisfactory inductive explanation' with 'providing the explanandum with a high probability', so prominent in Hempel's treatment. This is quite wrong. In innumerable cases, explanations – including scientific explanations – will be regarded as satisfactory even if the explanandum receives only a small probability, if only this posterior probability is sufficiently higher than the prior one.

3.   I do not know who exactly are the 'inductive logicians' whose sweet dreams of having at their disposal an 'ideal rule of detachment' of a form something like

$$\text{if } p(a, b) = r \text{ and } b \text{ is true, then } p(a) = r,$$

Popper is out to shatter. His victory over them is a very easy one, since this 'rule' is nothing short of ridiculous.

But Popper also claims that 'Carnap says this rule is valid if . . . *b* is *all* you know, your *"total knowledge"* ' [1]. Popper provides no quotations. I bet my last shirt that Carnap never published anything of the kind and I regard it as extremely unlikely that he ever said such a thing, in a lecture, discussion or even in conversation. What he did say, on many occasions, was to the effect that if the inductive probability of some *h* on *X*'s total knowledge at some time *t* is *r*, then it is rational for *X* to bet on *h*, at time *t*, with a betting quotient not higher than *r* (under the customary qualifications as to utility, etc.). I regard this view as perfectly sound – as a matter of fact, I can hardly see any possible objections to it so long as one is ready to work, if only *per impossibile*, with 'total evidence'. And this, of course, has nothing to do with the 'ideal rule of detachment'.

Though I have my own objections against the practicality of the requirement of total evidence (some of which I voiced in my talk), I don't think that Popper's two objections are valid. The first one is pointless from the start, since Carnap himself is very explicit about the time dependency of the notion of 'total know-

---

[1]   *This volume*, p. 137.

ledge'. This does not mean that 'we allow time to enter logical considerations', as Popper claims.

Popper's second, 'more serious' objection is not much better founded. If b is X's total knowledge at time t, then I see no good reason why X's knowledge that b is X's total knowledge should not be included in b, and so *ad infinitum*. That Popper, of all people, should find this 'infinite regress' objectionable, is strange in view of his well-known, brilliantly witty defence of the innocence of self-reference (as such). These extra pieces of knowledge, if one has to go into these 'almost absurd subtleties', are not likely at all to influence the probabilities of hypotheses, and will in general be quite irrelevant. Why Popper should think differently, and in particular why he believes that Carnap thinks differently ('. . . since it [this addition] is, according to Carnap, relevant knowledge'), I don't know.

In the course of his argument, Popper uses one of his little twists which make arguing with him, on many occasions, somewhat exasperating. He says: 'it seems to me to be clearly absurd to demand, in a theory of practical action, that before you can act practically you should always have total knowledge' [1]. But, of course, nobody, absolutely nobody, and not only Carnap, has ever made *this* outrageous demand. The demand that one should, before acting, compute probabilities relative to *one's* total knowledge at the time is indeed impractical, as I have argued myself (and as Carnap admits, though perhaps not with sufficient force), but to twist this into a demand not to act before one has total knowledge... (In this connection, I think it is somewhat unfair to speak of 'Carnap's so-called "requirement of total knowledge" '. Though Carnap does use 'total knowledge' and 'total evidence' more or less interchangeably, he has never used, I am reasonably sure, the expression 'requirement of total knowledge' but only 'requirement of total evidence', and for good reasons. 'Requirement of total knowledge' has indeed a very unpleasant associative connotation, not only for Popper, but also for me, and probably also for Carnap. So why use it?)

---

[1]   *This volume*, p. 138.

Popper's next to last paragraph [1] is formulated so vaguely and unguardedly that I found myself at times oscillating in mid-sentence from violent disagreement to enthusiastic agreement. Who are those anonymous authors who stated that 'the central problem of inductive logic [of which discipline Popper himself does not "believe that it exists"] is the problem of acceptance: Under what circumstances should I accept a theory?' I agree, though, with Popper that this problem is 'comparatively unimportant'. I would go even further and say that it quite likely is only a pseudo-problem due to the utterly uncritical assumption that 'accepting a theory' has some clear, unique meaning, so that, after preliminary clarification, it would just vanish.

Though some 'inductivists' certainly said something to the effect that the most probable theory should be accepted (whatever they meant on that occasion by 'probable' and 'accepted'), Carnap – who is often regarded by Popper as the arch-inductivist – has recently made very explicit statements to the contrary, even before the colloquium. But I find myself enthusiastically agreeing with Popper that 'the comparison of the merits of competing theories' is indeed a major task of methodology of science. But, contrary to Popper, I think that scientists should worry (though perhaps not too much so) whether theory A has probability 0.73, relative to some body of evidence deemed to be relevant, while theory B has only probability 0.72 relative to the same body of evidence, exactly because in my view this difference is part of the comparison of these theories, one among the many other dimensions of comparison. Of course, no scientist would, or should, 'accept' theory A for this reason alone, in any of the various senses of 'accept'. But then, again, there does not exist so far any inductive logic that assigns numerical probability values at all to theories with respect to some body of observational evidence, and I for one have the gravest doubts that an adequate inductive logic will ever be forthcoming that will be able to do this.

4. The 'lottery paradox' and related paradoxes served for me only as an indicator that there is something fishy in the notion

---

[1] *This volume*, p. 139.

of rule of acceptance. But my denial of the need for such rules was not based on these paradoxes. Even if Hintikka has succeeded in showing how to avoid them, for extremely simple languages and for suitable probability measures – and I will have to study his announced precise treatment when it appears – this is only of limited relevance to the general question.

5. Suppes is, of course, right in assuming that neither Kyburg nor myself nor anybody else would want to deny the validity of the two rules of inference he regards as deserving the name of probabilistic rules of detachment. He is right in believing that Kyburg must have had some incomparably more exciting rules in mind and that I denied the possibility of those rules. I have no objection to calling Suppes' two rules, or the two other slightly more general ones he mentions, 'probabilistic rules of detachment'; for these rules, but not for Kyburg's ones, the generalization from *modus ponens* is indeed rather natural. I don't quite understand why Popper is worried that Suppes 'has given no indication how they [Suppes' probabilistic rules of detachment] are to be used' [1]. They will be used in the way probability logic, whose existence and usability Popper does not deny, is going to be used. Is it only the fact that Suppes was using the taboo term 'inductive logic' that caused Popper's worries?

6. It is hard to believe to what length the magic appeal of acceptance goes. Agassi has claimed – insightfully, I believe – that Popper concedes too much to the traditional view that science has to start with (provisionally) accepted statements, and that there is in particular no scientific explanation unless the explanandum is (provisionally) accepted, though Popper himself has pointed out that, on occasion, as a result of the explanation, the explanandum is not really explained but rather explained away, and therefore rejected. As I see it, it is just wrong that whatever calls for explanation has to be first accepted (even provisionally, whatever this may mean). On the contrary, quite often one will

---

[1] *This volume*, p. 138.

ask for a satisfactory explanation prior to 'acceptance' and let the 'acceptance' depend on how well this request will be satisfied. Though there surely are many people who 'accept' flying saucers before asking for an explanation, there are as surely other people who will suspend judgment until a satisfactory explanation for various pertinent phenomena is forthcoming. (May I add that I regard the second attitude as much more 'scientific'?) Watkins is so taken in by the magic appeal of the term 'accept' that he is ready to state, in criticizing Agassi, that 'after all, for there to be an explanatory task, *something* must be currently *accepted as calling for explanation*' [1] (my italics). So, if not 'really' accepted and not even 'provisionally' accepted, at least 'accepted as calling for explanation'!

7. There exists already a huge literature on rules of acceptance. No attempt has been made to deal with it explicitly either in my previous or in the present comment, Carnap's recent contribution being the only exception. But I did check a good amount of the literature, including contributions by philosophers of science as well as by statisticians and even by some scientists, and believe that nothing essential for our purposes has been overlooked. Nobody, though, has to rely on my judgment.

H. E. KYBURG JR.: *Reply.*

1. Carnap's arguments against the adequacy of rules of acceptance as ultimate rules for inductive reasoning [2] are very brief and cut very little ice except in the context of choosing among alternative actions. It is easy to imagine situations in which any ordinary probabilistic rule of acceptance dictates that h be accepted, and yet in which it is (in view of utility considerations), quite unreasonable to *act* on h. That is the first argument. The second argument is that it is easy to envisage situations in which we do not

---

[1] *This volume*, p. 277, footnote 3.

[2] See his 'Replies and systematic expositions', in *The Philosophy of Rudolf Carnap*, P. A. Schilpp, ed., 1963, pp. 972–973.

have enough evidence to *accept* h, but yet clearly ought to act upon it. I am not at all sure that there is any advantage in saying in this case that we are 'acting on hypothesis h' rather than simply that we are performing action a (what contribution does h make to the description of our act? or of our logic?), but in any case neither of these arguments has any bearing on beliefs which are not construed as directly as the bases of practical decisions. Even if beliefs are in general construed behavioristically (which they need not be), it seems to make perfectly good sense to talk about accepting h and at the same time acting, in a certain way, in a certain situation, as if $\sim h$ were true. The whole notion of 'acting on' a hypothesis is rather obscure.

On the other hand, in the context with which I was concerned, the 'rational reconstruction of scientific method' (Carnap's phrase), Carnap finds 'no compelling objection against this use [of acceptance rules], provided the reconstruction is merely meant as a rough delineation of scientific procedure in purely *theoretical* fields . . .' (*ibid.*, p. 973) or where the results of investigations are 'sought for purely cognitive aims' [1]. Practical applications where utility is of prime importance are another matter, and here in general I would agree with Carnap. But, alas, the quoted passage is just the passage that Bar–Hillel finds that he cannot quite understand. Or, at any rate, claims that he can't understand. For later on, in discussing the notion of total evidence, he appears to give me everything I ask for.

Carnap pointed out, in his contribution, and I have pointed out in more than one place, that any inductive logician of classical Carnapian stamp is committed to an acceptance rule for evidence statements. Bar–Hillel seems to find no fault with this sort of acceptance rule; he talks, like Carnap, of *taking into account* (a part of) the total observational evidence. But Bar–Hillel also recognizes, what is profoundly true, that 'whether some observational statement is or is not relevant to some other statement . . . will be very much theory-dependent (and I am inclined to believe that the computation of degrees of confirmation relative to the

---

[1]   *This volume*, p. 149.

total observational evidence will yield different results according to the theories taken into account)' [1]. What is it to 'take account of' a theory here? Isn't it the same as 'taking account of' a piece of observational evidence? i.e., accepting it? Clearly if degrees of confirmation are to serve as guides to action, we cannot tolerate a situation in which there is more than one degree of confirmation of a given hypothesis on given evidence, and therefore if taking account of different theories will lead to different degrees of confirmation, we can only take account of one theory. What is the difference between saying that we take account of at most one theory, and saying that we accept that theory?

With respect to observation statements, the situation has been profoundly changed by Jeffrey's work, as Carnap points out. But there are still difficulties, even in Jeffrey's theory, for the treatment of observation statements; and it is not clear just how Bar–Hillel's point, that degrees of confirmation should depend on theoretical background as well as observation statements, would fit into Jeffrey's theory.

Bar–Hillel claims that no inductive logic exists or is in view that seems to be able to handle the case of observation statements having an import that depends on the theoretical background. This, of course, is just what my *Probability and the Logic of Rational Belief* was intended to provide.

In 'The acceptance syndrome', Bar–Hillel seems to give in on almost every essential point. He says 'I did not . . . condemn at all "acceptance of hypotheses" ', and 'I myself and all scientists . . . will continue to accept hypotheses . . . but no rule of inductive or probability logic is conceivable' [2]. He here admits that acceptance of hypotheses is a fact, and denies only that it is subject to rules. Yet he produces not one shred of evidence that his failure to be able to conceive of such rules represents a characteristic of the concept rather than a characteristic of the conceiver. Apparently, however, while there is both a systematic psychological account of how we *do* draw deductive conclusions, and a systematic

---

[1] *This volume*, p. 127.
[2] *This volume*, p. 152.

normative account of how we *ought* to draw deductive conclusions, there is no corresponding normative account of how we ought to draw inductive conclusions, but only a purely descriptive psychological account. But this is absurd; there are many instances in which we have no trouble at all distinguishing between good scientific arguments and bad scientific arguments; this suggests that there is *some* sort of a standard for such arguments. As Salmon has pointed out in his paper 'The justification of inductive rules of inference' [1], even Popper's theory of corroboration constitutes a partial attempt to provide (or perhaps better, make explicit) such a standard of rational scientific acceptance.

In any event the issue that remains, after Bar–Hillel's final paper, seems simple enough: Bar–Hillel claims that there are no standards for scientific argument, other than deductive ones, and he supports his claim by citing the fact that he cannot conceive of such such standards. (Incidentally, this is clearly a non-demonstrative argument itself, but not, fortunately, a very cogent one.) I claim, on the other hand, that there are such standards of rational acceptance, and I support my claim by citing the standards I have produced. That my formulation may be defective does not argue for the non-existence of the standards; and Bar–Hillel has not even shown my formulation defective. That there are formulations that are not defective in the way that mine is, has been elegantly shown by Hintikka (see both his contribution to this colloquium and the bibliography therein), and also by Levi. The mere fact, which Bar–Hillel acknowledges, that there is 'already a huge literature on rules of acceptance' strongly suggests to me that such rules are not strictly inconceivable. The question remains whether there are any that adequately capture our presystematic view of scientific acceptance, and to that question Bar–Hillel has made, and clearly intends to make, no contribution.

2.   I have no arguments at all to pick with Salmon's ingenious argument for acceptance rules. In the deductive case of explanation, Carnap agrees that the covering law must be accepted. However,

---

[1]   *This volume*, pp. 24–43.

he argues that in the inductive case no problem arises, because 'It is sufficient if the law has, on the basis of the given evidence, a fairly high probability' [1]. Sufficient, that is, to show that 'The explanandum has a sufficiently high probability on the basis of the premises'. But this is not the case. From the fact that L has a high probability (e.g., from the fact that 'practically all airline passengers have uneventful trips' is highly probable,) together with the fact that we can accept – observation-type statements not being at issue here – 'Mrs. Jones is an airline passenger', nothing about Mrs. Jones follows deductively at all: in particular, the statement 'Mrs. Jones probably had an uneventful trip,' doesn't follow. It does follow (with suitable provisos concerning randomness) according to a perfectly conventional and sound rule of *inductive* inference:

> practically all A's are B's
> this (random) a is an A
> _____
> therefore (probably) this a is a B.

So this form of explanatory model requires not only (as does the deductive explanatory model) that certain general statements be accepted, but that both (a) certain general statements are accepted ('Practicably all airline passengers have uneventful trips'), and (b) that there are *rules* for the acceptance of the conclusions of non-demonstrative inferences.

What Carnap clearly has in mind is the fact that the instantial evidence that supports the general statement ('Practically all A's are B's'), will also and independently support the explanandum. But then we don't need the general statement at all, and indeed we have a rather different model of explanation from the conventional one. While it may have its own virtues, it is certainly not the Hempelian model.

Salmon's claim that the lottery paradox does not arise in connection with statistical generalizations, has been dealt with elsewhere in this volume [2].

---

[1] *This volume*, p. 150.
[2] *This volume*, p. 73.

PROBABLE KNOWLEDGE

RICHARD C. JEFFREY

The City University of New York

The central problem of epistemology is often taken to be that of explaining how we can know what we do, but the content of this problem changes from age to age with the scope of what we take ourselves to know; and philosophers who are impressed with this flux sometimes set themselves the problem of explaining how we can get along, knowing as little as we do. For knowledge is sure, and there seems to be little we can be sure of outside logic and mathematics and truths related immediately to experience. It is as if there were some propositions – that this paper is white, that two and two are four – on which we have a firm grip, while the rest, including most of the theses of science, are slippery or insubstantial or somehow inaccessible to us. Outside the realm of what we are sure of lies the puzzling region of probable knowledge – puzzling in part because the sense of the noun seems to be cancelled by that of the adjective.

The obvious move is to deny that the notion of knowledge has the importance generally attributed to it, and to try to make the concept of belief do the work that philosophers have generally assigned the grander concept. I shall argue that this is the right move.

1. *A pragmatic analysis of belief.* To begin, we must get clear about the relevant sense of 'belief'. Here I follow Ramsey: 'the kind of measurement of belief with which probability is concerned is ... a measurement of belief *qua* basis of action' [1].

---

[1] Frank P. Ramsey, 'Truth and probability', in *The Foundations of Mathematics and Other Logical Essays*, R. B. Braithwaite, ed., London and New York, 1931, p. 171.

Ramsey's basic idea was that the desirability of a gamble G is a weighted average of the desirabilities of winning and of losing in which the weights are the probabilities of winning and of losing. If the proposition gambled upon is A, if the prize for winning is the truth of a proposition W, and if the penalty for losing is the truth of a proposition L, we then have

(1) $$prob\ A = \frac{des\ G - des\ L}{des\ W - des\ L}.$$

Thus, if the desirabilities of losing and of winning happen to be 0 and 1, we have $prob\ A = des\ G$, as illustrated in Figure 1, for the case in which the probability of winning is thought to be $\frac{3}{4}$.

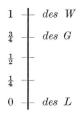

Figure 1.

On this basis, Ramsey [1] is able to give rules for deriving the gambler's subjective probability *and* desirability functions from his preference ranking of gambles, provided the preference ranking satisfies certain conditions of consistency. The probability function obtained in this way is a probability measure in the technical sense that, given any finite set of pairwise incompatible propositions which together exhaust all possibilities, their probabilities are non-negative real numbers that add up to 1. And in an obvious sense, probability so construed is a measure of the subject's willingness to act on his beliefs in propositions: it is a measure of degree of belief.

I propose to use what I take to be an improvement of Ramsey's scheme, in which the work that Ramsey does with the operation

---

[1] 'Truth and probability', F. P. Ramsey, *op. cit.*

of forming gambles is done with the usual truth-functional operations on propositions [1]. The basic move is to restrict attention to certain 'natural' gambles, in which the prize for winning is the truth of the proposition gambled upon, and the penalty for losing is the falsity of that proposition. In general, the situation in which the gambler takes himself to be gambling on A with prize W and loss L is one in which he believes the proposition

$$G = AW \vee \bar{A}L.$$

If G is a natural gamble we have $W = A$ and $L = \bar{A}$, so that G is the necessary proposition, $T = A \vee \bar{A}$:

$$G = AA \vee \bar{A}\bar{A} = T.$$

Now if A is a proposition which the subject thinks good (or bad) in the sense that he places it above T (or below T) in his preference ranking, we have

$$\text{(2)} \qquad prob\ A = \frac{des\ T - des\ \bar{A}}{des\ A - des\ \bar{A}},$$

corresponding to Ramsey's formula (1).

Here the basic idea is that if A_1, A_2, ..., A_n are an exhaustive set of incompatible ways in which the proposition A can come true, the desirability of A must be a weighted average of the desirabilities of the ways in which it can come true:

$$\text{(3)} \qquad des\ A = w_1\ des\ A_1 + w_2\ des\ A_2 + \ldots + w_n\ des\ A_n,$$

where the weights are the conditional probabilities,

$$\text{(4)} \qquad w_i = prob\ A_i / prob\ A.$$

Let us call a function *des* which attributes real numbers to propositions a *Bayesian desirability function* if there is a probability measure *prob* relative to which (3) holds for all suitable A, A_1,

---

[1] See Richard C. Jeffrey, *The Logic of Decision*, McGraw–Hill, 1965, the mathematical basis for which can be found in Ethan Bolker, *Functions Resembling Quotients of Measures*, Ph. D. Dissertation, Harvard University, 1965, and *Trans. Am. Math. Soc.*, **124**, 1966, pp. 293–312.

$A_2, \ldots, A_n$. And let us call a preference ranking of propositions *coherent* if there is a Bayesian desirability function which ranks those propositions in order of magnitude exactly as they are ranked in order of preference. One can show [1] that if certain weak conditions are met by a coherent preference ranking, the underlying desirability function is determined up to a fractional linear transformation, i.e., if *des* and *DES* both rank propositions in order of magnitude exactly as they are ranked in order of preference, there must be real numbers a, b, c, d such that for any proposition A in the ranking we have

$$(5) \qquad DES\ A = \frac{a\ des\ A + b}{c\ des\ A + d}.$$

The probability measure *prob* is then determined by (2) up to a certain quantization. In particular, if *des* is Bayesian relative to *prob*, then *DES* will be Bayesian relative to *PROB*, where

$$(6) \qquad PROB\ A = prob\ A\ (c\ des\ A + d).$$

Under further plausible conditions, (5) and (6) are given either exactly (as in Ramsey's theory) or approximately by

$$(7) \qquad DES\ A = a\ des\ A + b,$$

$$(8) \qquad PROB\ A = prob\ A.$$

I take the principal advantage of the present theory over Ramsey's to be that here we work with the subject's actual beliefs, whereas Ramsey needs to know what the subject's preference ranking of relevant propositions would be if his views of what the world is were to be changed by virtue of his having come to believe that various arbitrary and sometimes bizarre causal relationships had been established via gambles [2].

To see more directly how preferences may reflect beliefs in the present system, observe that by (2) we must have

---

[1]   Jeffrey, *op. cit.*, chs. 6, 8.
[2]   Jeffrey, *op. cit.*, pp. 145–150.

prob A > *prob B* if the relevant portion of the preference ranking is

$$A, \quad B$$
$$T$$
$$\bar{B}$$
$$\bar{A}$$

In particular, suppose that A and B are the propositions that the subject will get job 1 and that he will get job 2, respectively. Pay, working conditions, etc., are the same, so that he ranks A and B together. Now if he thinks himself more likely to get job 1 than job 2, he will prefer a guarantee of ($\bar{B}$) not getting job 2 to a guarantee of ($\bar{A}$) not getting job 1; for he thinks that an assurance of not getting job 2 leaves him more likely to get one or the other of the equally liked jobs than would an assurance of not getting job 1.

2. *Probabilistic acts and observations.* We might call a proposition *observational* for a certain person at a certain time if at that time he can make an observation of which the *direct* effect will be that his degree of belief in the proposition will change to 0 or to 1. Similarly, we might call a proposition *actual* for a certain person at a certain time if at that time he can perform an act of which the *direct* effect will be that his degree of belief in the proposition will change to 0 or to 1. Under ordinary circumstances, the proposition that the sun is shining is observational and the proposition that the agent blows his nose is actual. Performance of an act may give the agent what Anscombe calls [1] 'knowledge without observation' of the truth of an appropriate actual proposition. Apparently, a proposition can be actual or observational without the agent's knowing that it is; and the agent can be mistaken in thinking a proposition actual or observational.

The point and meaning of the requirement that the effect be 'direct', in the definitions of 'actual' and 'observational', can be illustrated by considering the case of a sleeper who awakens and

---

[1] G. E. M. Anscombe, *Intention*, § 8, Oxford, 1957; 2nd ed., Ithaca, N.Y., 1963.

sees that the sun is shining. Then one might take the observation to have shown him, directly, that the sun is shining, and to have shown him indirectly that it is daytime. In general, an observation will cause numerous changes in the observer's belief function, but many of these can be construed as consequences of others. If there is a proposition E such that the *direct* effect of the observation is to change the observer's degree of belief in E to 1, then for any proposition A in the observer's preference ranking, his degree of belief in A after the observation will be the conditional probability

$$(9) \qquad prob_E \ A = prob \ (A/E) = prob \ AE/prob \ E,$$

where *prob* is the observer's belief function before the observation. And conversely, if the observer's belief function after the observation is $prob_E$ and $prob_E$ is not identical with *prob*, then the *direct* effect of the observation will be to change the observer's degree of belief in E to 1. This completes a definition of *direct*.

But from a certain strict point of view, it is rarely or never that there is a proposition for which the direct effect of an observation is to change the observer's degree of belief in that proposition to 1; and from that point of view, the classes of propositions that count as observational or actual in the senses defined above are either empty or as good as empty for practical purposes. For if we care seriously to distinguish between 0.999 999 and 1.000 000 as degrees of belief, we may find that, after looking out the window, the observer's degree of belief in the proposition that the sun is shining is not quite 1, perhaps because he thinks there is one chance in a million that he is deluded or deceived in some way; and similarly for acts where we can generally take ourselves to be at best *trying* (perhaps with very high probability of success) to make a certain proposition true.

One way in which philosophers have tried to resolve this difficulty is to postulate a phenomenalistic language in which an appropriate proposition E can always be expressed, as a report on the immediate content of experience; but for excellent reasons, this move is now in low repute [1]. The crucial point is not that 0.999 999 is so close

---

[1] See, e.g., J. L. Austin, *Sense and Sensibilia*, Oxford, 1962.

to 1.000 000 as to make no odds, practically speaking, for situations abound in which the gap is more like one half than one millionth. Thus, in examining a piece of cloth by candlelight one might come to attribute probabilities 0.6 and 0.4 to the propositions G that the cloth is green and B that it is blue, without there being any proposition E for which the direct effect of the observation is anything near changing the observer's degree of belief in E to 1. One might think of some such proposition as that (E) *the cloth looks green or possibly blue*, but this is far too vague to yield *prob* $(G/E) = 0.6$ and *prob* $(B/E) = 0.4$. Certainly, there is *something* about what the observer sees that leads him to have the indicated degrees of belief in G and in B, but there is no reason to think the observer can express this something by a statement in his language. And physicalistically, there is some perfectly definite pattern of stimulation of the rods and cones of the observer's retina which prompts his belief, but there is no reason to expect him to be able to describe that pattern or to recognize a true description of it, should it be suggested.

As Austin [1] points out, the crucial mistake is to speak seriously of the *evidence* of the senses. Indeed the relevant experiences have perfectly definite characteristics by virtue of which the observer comes to believe as he does, and by virtue of which in our example he comes to have degree of belief 0.6 in G. But it does not follow that there is a proposition E of which the observer is certain after the observation and for which we have *prob* $(G/E) = 0.6$, *prob* $(B/E) = 0.4$, etc.

In part, the quest for such phenomenological certainty seems to have been prompted by an inability to see how uncertain evidence can be used. Thus C. I. Lewis:

> If anything is to be probable, then something must be certain. The data which themselves support a genuine probability, must themselves be certainties. We do have such absolute certainties, in the sense data initiating belief and in those passages of experience which later may confirm it. But neither such initial data nor such later verifying passages of experience

---

[1] Austin, *op. cit.*, ch. 10.

can be phrased in the language of objective statement – because what can be so phrased is never more than probable. Our sense certainties can only be formulated by the expressive use of language, in which what is signified is a content of experience and what is asserted is the givenness of this content [1].

But this motive for the quest is easily disposed of [2]. Thus, in the example of observation by candlelight, we may take the direct result of the observation (in a modified sense of 'direct') to be, that the observer's degrees of belief in G and B change to 0.6 and 0.4. Then his degree of belief in any proposition A in his preference ranking will change from $prob\ A$ to

$$PROB\ A = 0.6\ prob\ (A/G) + 0.4\ prob\ (A/B).$$

In general, suppose that there are propositions $E_1, E_2, ..., E_n$, in which the observer's degrees of belief after the observation are $p_1, p_2, ..., p_n$; where the E's are pairwise incompatible and collectively exhaustive; where for each i, $prob\ E_i$ is neither 0 nor 1; and where for each proposition A in the preference ranking and for each i the conditional probability of A on E_i is unaffected by the observation:

(10) $$PROB\ (A/E_i) = prob\ (A/E_i).$$

Then the belief function after the observation may be taken to be $PROB$, where

(11) $$PROB\ A = p_1\ prob\ (A/E_1) + p_2\ prob\ (A/E_2) + ...$$
$$+ p_n\ prob\ (A/E_n),$$

if the observer's preference rankings before and after the observation are both coherent. Where these conditions are met, the propositions $E_1, E_2, ..., E_n$, may be said to form a *basis* for the observation; and the notion of a basis will play the role vacated by the notion of *directness*.

---

[1] C. I. Lewis, *An Analysis of Knowledge and Valuation*, La Salle, Illinois, 1946, p. 186.

[2] Jeffrey, *op. cit.*, ch. 11.

The situation is similar in the case of acts. A marksman may have a fairly definite idea of his chances of hitting a distant target, e.g. he may have degree of belief 0.3 in the proposition H that he will hit it. The basis for this belief may be his impressions of wind conditions, quality of the rifle, etc.; but there need be no reason to suppose that the marksman can express the relevant data; nor need there be any proposition E in his preference ranking in which the marksman's degree of belief changes to 1 upon deciding to fire at the target, and for which we have $prob$ $(H/E) = 0.3$. But the pair H, $\bar{H}$ may constitute a *basis* for the act, in the sense that for any proposition A in the marksman's preference ranking, his degree of belief after his decision is

$$PROB \ A = 0.3 \ prob \ (A/H) + 0.7 \ prob \ (A/\bar{H}).$$

It is correct to describe the marksman as *trying* to hit the target; but the proposition that he is trying to hit the target can not play the role of E above. Similarly, it was correct to describe the cloth as *looking* green or possibly blue; but the proposition that the cloth looks green or possibly blue does not satisfy the conditions for directness.

The notion of directness is useful as well for the resolution of unphilosophical posers about probabilities, in which the puzzling element sometimes consists in failure to think of an appropriate proposition E such that the direct effect of an observation is to change degree of belief in E to 1, e.g. in the following problem reported by Mosteller [1].

Three prisoners, a, b, and c, with apparently equally good records have applied for parole. The parole board has decided to release two of the three, and the prisoners know this but not which two. A warder friend of prisoner a knows who are to be released. Prisoner a realizes that it would be unethical to ask the warder if he, a, is to be released, but thinks of asking for the name of *one* prisoner *other than himself* who is to be

[1] Problem 13 of Frederick Mosteller, *Fifty Challenging Problems in Probability*, Reading, Mass., Palo Alto, and London, 1965.

released. He thinks that before he asks, his chances of release are $\frac{2}{3}$. He thinks that if the warder says 'b will be released,' his own chances have now gone down to $\frac{1}{2}$, because either a and b or b and c are to be released. And so a decides not to reduce his chances by asking. However, a is mistaken in his calculations. Explain.

Here indeed the possible cases (in a self-explanatory notation) are

$$AB, \ AC, \ BC,$$

and these are viewed by a as equiprobable. Then $prob \ A$ is $\frac{2}{3}$ but $prob \ (A/B) = prob \ (A/C) = \frac{1}{2}$, and, since the warder must answer either 'b' or 'c' to a's question, it looks as if the direct result of the 'observation' will be that a comes to attribute probability 1 either to the proposition B that b will be released, or to the proposition C that c will be released. But this is incorrect. The relevant evidence-proposition would be more like the proposition *that the warder says, 'b'*, or *that the warder says, 'c'*, even though neither of these will quite do. For it is only in cases AB and AC that the warder's reply is dictated by the facts: in case BC, where b and c are both to be released, the warder must somehow choose *one* of the two true answers. If a expects the warder to make the choice by some such random device as tossing a coin, then we have $prob \ (A/\text{the warder says, '}b\text{'}) = prob \ (A/\text{the warder says, '}c\text{'}) = \ = prob \ A = \frac{2}{3}$; while if a is sure that the warder will say 'b' if he can, we have $prob \ (A/\text{the warder says '}b\text{'}) = \frac{1}{2}$ but $prob \ (A/\text{the warder says '}c\text{'}) = 1$.

3. *Belief: reasons vs. causes.* Indeed it is desirable, where possible, to incorporate the results of observation into the structure of one's beliefs via a basis of form E, $\bar{E}$ where the probability of E after the observation is nearly 1. For practical purposes, E then satisfies the conditions of directness, and the 'direct' effect of the observation can be described as informing the observer of the truth of E. Where this is possible, the relevant passage of sense experience *causes* the observer to believe E; and if $prob \ (A/E)$ is high, his belief in E may be a *reason* for his believing A, and E

may be spoken of as (inconclusive) *evidence* for A. But the sense experience is evidence neither for E nor for A. Nor does the situation change when we speak physicalistically in terms of patterns of irritation of our sensory surfaces, instead of in terms of sense experience: such patterns of irritation *cause* us to believe various propositions to various degrees; and sometimes the situation can be helpfully analyzed into one in which we are caused to believe $E_1, E_2, ..., E_n$, to degrees $p_1, p_2, ..., p_n$, whereupon those beliefs provide *reasons* for believing other propositions to other degrees. But patterns of irritation of our sensory surfaces are not reasons or evidence for any of our beliefs, any more than irritation of the mucous membrane of the nose is a *reason* for sneezing.

When I stand blinking in bright sunlight, I can no more believe that the hour is midnight than I can fly. My degree of belief in the proposition that the sun is shining has two distinct characteristics. (a) It is 1, as close as makes no odds. (b) It is compulsory. Here I want to emphasize the second characteristic, which is most often found in conjunction with the first, but not always. Thus, if I examine a normal coin at great length, and experiment with it at length, my degree of belief in the proposition that the next toss will yield a head will have two characteristics. (a) It is $\frac{1}{2}$. (b) It is compulsory. In the case of the coin as in the case of the sun, I cannot decide to have a different degree of belief in the proposition, any more than I can decide to walk on air.

In my scientific and practical undertakings I must make use of such compulsory beliefs. In attempting to understand or to affect the world, I cannot escape the fact that I am part of it: I must rather make use of that fact as best I can. Now where epistemologists have spoken of observation as a source of *knowledge*, I want to speak of observation as a source of compulsory *belief* to one or another degree. I do not propose to identify a very high degree of belief with knowledge, any more than I propose to identify the property of being near 1 with the property of being compulsory.

Nor do I postulate any *general* positive or negative connection between the characteristic of being compulsory and the characteristic of being sound or appropriate in the light of the believer's experience. Nor, finally, do I take a compulsory belief to be necessarily a permanent one: new experience or new reflection (perhaps, prompted by the arguments of others) may loosen the bonds oɪ compulsion, and may then establish new bonds; and the effect may be that the new state of belief is sounder than the old, or less sound.

Then why should we trust our beliefs? According to K. R. Popper,

> ... the decision to accept a basic statement, and to be satisfied with it, is causally connected with our experiences – especially with our *perceptual experiences*. But we do not attempt to *justify* basic statements by these experiences. Experiences can *motivate a decision*, and hence an acceptance or a rejection of a statement, but a basic statement cannot be *justified* by them – no more than by thumping the table [1].

I take this objection to be defective, principally in attempting to deal with basic statements (observation reports) in terms of *decisions* to *accept* or to *reject* them. Here acceptance parallels belief, rejection parallels disbelief (belief in the denial), and tentativeness or reversibility of the decision parallels *degree* of belief. Because logical relations hold between statements, but not between events and statements, the relationship between a perceptual experience (an event of a certain sort) and a basic statement cannot be a logical one, and therefore, Popper believes, cannot be of a sort that would justify the statement:

> Basic statements are accepted as the result of a decision or agreement; and to that extent they are conventions [2].

But in the absence of a positive account of the nature of acceptance and rejection, parallel to the account of partial belief given in section **1**, it is impossible to evaluate this view. Acceptance and rejection are apparently acts undertaken as results of decisions; but somehow the decisions are conventional – perhaps only in the sense that they may be *motivated* by experience, but not *adequately* motivated, if adequacy entails justification.

---

[1] K. R. Popper, *The Logic of Scientific Discovery*, London, 1959, p. 105.
[2] Popper, *op. cit.*, p. 106.

To return to the question, 'Why should we trust our beliefs?' one must ask what would be involved in *not* trusting one's beliefs, if belief is analyzed as in section **1** in terms of one's preference structure. One way of mistrusting a belief is declining to act on it, but this appears to consist merely in lowering the degree of that belief: to mistrust a partial belief is then to alter its degree to a new, more suitable value.

A more hopeful analysis of such mistrust might introduce the notion of sensitivity to further evidence or experience. Thus, agents 1 and 2 might have the same degree of belief – $\frac{1}{2}$ – in the proposition H_1 that the first toss of a certain coin will yield a head, but agent 1 might have this degree of belief because he is convinced that the coin is normal, while agent 2 is convinced that it is either two-headed or two-tailed, he knows not which [1]. There is no question here of agent 2's expressing his mistrust of the figure $\frac{1}{2}$ by lowering or raising it, but he can express that mistrust quite handily by aspects of his belief function. Thus, if H_i is the proposition that the coin lands head up the ith time it is tossed, agent 2's beliefs about the coin are accurately expressed by the function $prob_2$ where

$$prob_2 \; H_i = \tfrac{1}{2}, \; prob_2 \; (H_i/H_j) = 1,$$

while agent 1's beliefs are equally accurately expressed by the function $prob_1$ where

$$prob_1 \; (H_{i_1}, H_{i_2}, ..., H_{i_n}) = 2^{-n},$$

if $i_1 < i_2 < ... < i_n$. In an obvious sense, agent 1's beliefs are *firm* in the sense that he will not change them in the light of further evidence, since we have

$$prob_1 \; (H_{n+1}/H_1, H_2, ..., H_n) = prob_1 \; H_{n+1} = \tfrac{1}{2},$$

while agent 2's beliefs are quite tentative and in that sense, mistrusted by their holder. Still, $prob_1 \; H_i = prob_2 \; H_i = \tfrac{1}{2}$.

After these defensive remarks, let me say how and why I take

---

[1] This is a simplified version of 'the paradox of ideal evidence', Popper, *op. cit.*, pp. 407–409.

compulsive belief to be sound, under appropriate circumstances. Bemused with syntax, the early logical positivists were chary of the notion of truth; and then, bemused with Tarski's account of truth, analytic philosophers neglected to inquire how we come to believe or disbelieve simple propositions. Quite simply put, the point is: coming to have suitable degrees of belief in response to experience is a matter of training – a *skill* which we begin acquiring in early childhood, and are never quite done polishing. The skill consists not only in coming to have appropriate degrees of belief in appropriate propositions under paradigmatically good conditions of observation, but also in coming to have appropriate degrees of belief between zero and one when conditions are less than ideal.

Thus, in learning to use English color words correctly, a child not only learns to acquire degree of belief 1 in the proposition that the cloth is blue, when in bright sunlight he observes a piece of cloth of uniform hue, the hue being squarely in the middle of the blue interval of the color spectrum: he also learns to acquire appropriate degrees of belief between 0 and 1 in response to observation under bad lighting conditions, and when the hue is near one or the other end of the blue region. Furthermore, his understanding of the English color words will not be complete until he understands, in effect, that blue is between green and violet in the color spectrum: his understanding of this point or his lack of it will be evinced in the sorts of mistakes he does and does not make, e.g. in mistaking green for violet he may be evincing confusion between the meanings of 'blue' and of 'violet', in the sense that his mistake is linguistic, not perceptual.

Clearly, the borderline between factual and linguistic error becomes cloudy, here: but cloudy in a perfectly realistic way, corresponding to the intimate connection between the ways in which we experience the world and the ways in which we speak. It is for this sort of reason that having the right language can be as important as (and can be in part identical with) having the right theory.

Then learning to use a language properly is in large part like learning such skills as riding bicycles and flying aeroplanes. One must train oneself to have the right sorts of responses to various sorts of experiences, where the responses are degrees of belief in propositions. This may, but need not, show itself in willingness to utter or assent to corresponding sentences. Need not, because e.g. my cat is quite capable of showing that it thinks it is about to be fed, just as it is capable of showing what its preference ranking is, for hamburger, tuna fish, and oat meal, without saying or understanding a word. With people as with cats, evidence for belief and preference is behavioral; and speech is far from exhausting behavior [1].

Our degrees of beliefs in various propositions are determined jointly by our training and our experience, in complicated ways that I cannot hope to describe. And similarly for conditional subjective probabilities, which are certain ratios of degrees of belief: to some extent, these are what they are because of our training – because we speak the languages we speak. And to this extent, conditional subjective probabilities reflect *meanings*. And in this sense, there can be a theory of degree of confirmation which is based on analysis of meanings of sentences. Confirmation theory is therefore semantical and, if you like, logical [2].

---

[1]   Jeffrey, *op. cit.*, pp. 57–59.

[2]   Support of U.S. Air Force Office of Scientific Research is acknowledged, under Grant AF–AFOSR–529–65.

L. HURWICZ: *Richard Jeffrey on the three prisoners.*

I would like to make a comment which I think is along the lines of Professor Jeffrey's discussion of the three prisoners. I would like to make the situation a little more explicit than it was earlier, although I shall not contradict anything that has been said: I think this will help us to see to what extent, if any, there is anything surprising or paradoxical in the situation.

First of all let me say this: there were three possible decisions by the warden – AB, BC and AC; then, as against that, there was also the question of what the warden would say to a who asked the question who else was being freed, and clearly the warden could only answer 'b' or 'c'. What I'm going to put down here is simply the bivariate or two-way probability distribution, and it doesn't matter at all at this stage whether we interpret it as a frequency or as a subjective probability, because it's just a matter of applying the mechanics of the Bayes theorem.

One other remark I'd like to make is this: the case that was considered by Professor Jeffrey was one where the *a priori* probabilities of AB, BC and AC were each one-third. This actually does not at all affect the reasoning, and I will stick with it just because it is close to my limitations in arithmetic.

So the marginal frequencies or probabilities are all equal to one-third. If the decision had been AB, then of course the warden could only answer 'b', and similarly if the decision had been AC, he could only answer 'c'. So the joint frequency or probability of the following event is one-third: the people chosen for freeing are a and b, and when the warden is asked, 'Who is the person other than a who is about to be freed?', his answer is 'b'. The joint probability is also one-third that the choice was AC and that the warden answered 'c'.

We now come to the only case where the warden has a choice of what he will say, namely, the case where the decision was BC.

The question was raised, quite properly, of how he goes about making this choice.

Let me here say the following. In a sense what I'm doing here is a sally into enemy territory, because I personally am not particularly Bayesian in my approach to decision theory, so I would not myself assert that the only method is to describe the warden's decision, the warden's principle of choice, as a probabilistic one. However, if it is not probabilistic, then of course the prisoner, our a, would have to be using some other principle of choice on his part in order to decide what to do. Being an unrepentant conservative on this, I might choose, or A might choose, the minimax principle. However, in order to follow the spirit of the discussion here, I will assume that the whole thing is being done in a completely Bayesian or probabilistic way; in this case, to compute the remaining joint distribution we must make some probabilistic assumption about how the warden will behave when asked the question.

So let the principle be this, that he has a certain random device such that if the people to be freed are b and c, his answer to the question will be 'b' with probability β and 'c' with of course probability $1-\beta$. All I will assume for the moment about β is that it is between zero and one, and that's probably one of the few uncontroversial points so far.

It is clear that the sum of the two joint probabilities (BC and 'b', and BC and 'c') will be one-third; so the first will be $\frac{1}{3}\beta$, and the second $\frac{1}{3}(1-\beta)$. The marginal (or absolute) probabilities of 'b' and 'c' will be $\frac{1}{3}(1+\beta)$ and $\frac{1}{3}(2-\beta)$ respectively.

Inf. → Dec. ↓	'b'	'c'	Marginal
AB	$\frac{1}{3}$	0	$\frac{1}{3}$
BC	$\beta/3$	$(1-\beta)/3$	$\frac{1}{3}$
AC	0	$\frac{1}{3}$	$\frac{1}{3}$
Marginal	$(1+\beta)/3$	$(2-\beta)/3$	1

Now what are the probabilities after the warden has given his answer? Suppose that the answer that the warden gave is 'b': the problem now is, what is the probability that a is to be freed, given that the warden said that b is to be freed? This probability, which I will denote by 'π_b', I obtain in the following way using what I hope is a self-explanatory notation:

$$\pi_b = p(A/\text{'}b\text{'})$$

$$= \frac{p(A \cdot \text{'}b\text{'})}{p(\text{'}b\text{'})}$$

$$= \frac{p(AB \cdot \text{'}b\text{'}) + p(AC \cdot \text{'}b\text{'})}{p(AB \cdot \text{'}b\text{'}) + p(AC \cdot \text{'}b\text{'}) + p(BC \cdot \text{'}b\text{'})}$$

$$= \frac{\frac{1}{3} + 0}{\frac{1}{3} + 0 + \beta/3}$$

$$= 1/(1 + \beta).$$

Similarly I get π_c (the probability that a is to be freed, given that the warden said that b is to be freed) as follows:

$$\pi_c = p(A/\text{'}c\text{'})$$

$$= \frac{p(A \cdot \text{'}c\text{'})}{p(\text{'}c\text{'})}$$

$$= \frac{p(AB \cdot \text{'}c\text{'}) + p(AC \cdot \text{'}c\text{'})}{p(AB \cdot \text{'}c\text{'}) + p(AC \cdot \text{'}c\text{'}) + p(BC \cdot \text{'}c\text{'})}$$

$$= \frac{0 + \frac{1}{3}}{0 + \frac{1}{3} + (1 - \beta)/3}$$

$$= 1/(2 - \beta).$$

Now the question which we now have to ask is this: are these conditional probabilities, π, different from the marginal (absolute) probability that a is to be freed, $p(a)$? And the answer is that they are except when β happens to be equal to one-half, in which case the probability remains at its marginal value of two-thirds. But except in this special case the probabilities π_b and π_c can vary from one-half to one [1].

---

[1] In the problem as reported by Mosteller, it might be reasonable to take $\beta = \frac{1}{2}$. In that case, let us note, $\pi_b = 1/(1 + \frac{1}{2}) = \frac{2}{3}$ (not $\frac{1}{2}$ as suggested

As I indicated before, there is no quarrel between us, but I do want to explore just one step further, and that is this. You remember when we were told this anecdote there was a wave of laughter and I now want to see what it was that was so funny. It is that this prisoner became doubtful about asking for this extra information, because he thought his probability of being released would go down after getting it. So it seemed that having this extra information would make him less happy, even though he didn't have to pay for it. That really was the paradox, not the fact that the probabilities changed. Clearly, the change in probabilities is itself not at all surprising; for example, if the warden had told a the names of *two* people other than himself who would be freed, his optimism would have gone down very drastically [1].

What is surprising is that a thought he would be less happy with the *prospect* of having the extra piece of information than without this prospect. What I want to show now is that a was just wrong to think this; in other words, if this information was free, he should have been prepared to hear it.

Suppose for instance β is different from one-half: I think it is implicit in this little anecdote that the probability of a's being released either before or after getting the information, in some sense corresponds to his level of satisfaction. If his chances are good he is happy; if his chances are bad he is miserable. So these π's, though they happen to have been obtained as probabilities, may at the same time be interpreted as utilities or what Professor Jeffrey called desirabilities. Good. Now if a proceeds in the Bayesian

---

in the statement of the problem!) and also $\pi_c = 1/(2-\beta) = 1/(2-\frac{1}{2}) = \frac{2}{3}$. Hence (for $\beta = \frac{1}{2}$) a was wrong to expect the probabilities to change. But, on the other hand, the warden's reply would give him no additional information.

[1] Or suppose, that $\beta = 1$ (and a knows this). Then if a hears the warden tell him that c is one of the persons to be released, he will have good reason to feel happy. For when $\beta = 1$, the warden will tell a about having selected c only if the selected pair was AC. On the other hand, still with $\beta = 1$, if the warden says that b is one of the persons to be released, this means (with equal probabilities) that either AB or BC has been chosen, but *not* AC. Hence, with the latter piece of information, a will be justifiably less optimistic about his chances of release. (With β close to one, a similar situation prevails.)

way he has to do the following: he has to look at all these numbers, because before he asks for the information he does not know whether the answer will be 'b' or 'c'. Then he must ask himself the following: How happy will I be if he says 'b'? How happy will I be if he says 'c'? And then in the Bayesian (or de Finetti or Ramsey) spirit he multiplies the utilities, say $u('b')$ and $u('c')$ associated with hearing the warden say 'b' or 'c' by the respective probabilities, say $p('b')$ and $p('c')$, of hearing these answers. He thus obtains an expression for his expected [1] utility associated with getting the extra information, say

$$Eu^* = p('b') \cdot u('b') + p('c') \cdot u('c').$$

Now the required probabilities are the marginal probabilities at the bottom of the table, i.e.,

$$p('b') = \frac{1+\beta}{3}, \quad p('c') = \frac{2-\beta}{3}.$$

As for utilities, it is implicit in the argument that they are linear [2] functions of the probabilities that a will be released given the warden's answer. So

$$u('b') = \pi_b = \frac{1}{1+\beta}, \quad u('c') = \pi_c = \frac{1}{2-\beta}.$$

Hence the (expected) utility associated with getting the extra information from the warden is

$$Eu^* = \frac{1+\beta}{3} \cdot \frac{1}{1+\beta} + \frac{2-\beta}{3} \cdot \frac{1}{2-\beta} = \tfrac{2}{3}.$$

On the other hand, the expected utility Eu°, associated with *not* asking the warden for extra information is simply equal to the original probability $p(a)$ that a will be released,

$$Eu^\circ = p(a) = \tfrac{2}{3}.$$

---

[1]   In the sense of the mathematical expectation of a random variable.
[2]   See footnote 2 on the next page.

Hence it so happens that (for a utility function linear in probabilities of release)

$$Eu^* = Eu^\circ,$$

i.e., the expected utility with extra information (Eu^*) is the same as without extra information (Eu°). Thus a should be willing (but not eager) to ask for extra information (if it is free of charge). 'On the average' [1], it won't do him any harm; nor will it help him [2].

P. SUPPES: *Rational changes of belief.*

I am generally very much in agreement with Professor Jeffrey's viewpoint on belief and knowledge as expressed in his paper. The focus of my brief remarks is to point out how central and difficult are the problems concerning *changes* of belief. Jeffrey remarks that the familiar method of changing probable beliefs by explicitly conditionalizing the relevant probability measure is not adequate in many situations – in fact, in all those situations that involve a change in the probability assigned to evidence, but a change that does not make the probability of possible evidence 0 or 1.

My point is that once we acknowledge this fact about the probable character of evidence we open Pandora's box of puzzles for any theory of rational behavior. I would like to mention three problems. These problems are not dealt with explicitly by Jeffrey, but the focus I place on them is certainly consistent with his own expressed views.

1. *Attention and selection.* I begin with the problem of characterizing how a man attempting to behave rationally is to go about selecting and attending to what seems to be the right kind of evidence. Formulations of the problem of evidence within a logically well-defined language or sample space have already passed over

---

[1] 'On the average' expresses the fact that the decision is made on the basis of mathematical expectation. It need not imply a frequency interpretation of probabilities.

[2] When utilities are *non-linear* with respect to probabilities of release, the prospect of additional information may be helpful or harmful.

the problem of evaluating their appropriateness. Any man has highly limited capacities for attention and observation. Given a characterization of his powers and limitations what is a rational way to behave? Consider the familiar coin-flipping example. When is it appropriate to stop concentrating on the outcomes of the flips and to start observing closely the behavior of the gambler doing the flipping? To take another sort of example, how do we characterize the behavior of detectives who act on subthreshold cues and conjectures that can scarcely even be verbalized, let alone supported by explicit evidence? Put more generally, what is the rational way to go about discovering facts as opposed to verifying them? It is easy to claim that for a wide variety of situations rational discovery is considerably more important than rational verification. In these cases of discovery we need to understand much better the information-processing capacities of human beings in order to be able to characterize in a serious way *rational* information-processing. Above all, it is certainly not clear to me what proportion of rational information-processing should be verbalized or is even verbalizable.

2. *Finite memory.* The second problem concerns the rational use of our inevitably restricted memory capacities. A full-blown theory of rationality should furnish guidelines for the kinds of things that should be remembered and the kind that should not. Again a solution, but certainly not a solution whose optimality can be seriously defended, is at least partly given by the choice of a language or a sample space for dealing with a given set of phenomena. But the amount of information impinging on any man in a day or a week or a month is phenomenal and what is accessible if he chooses to make it so is even more so. What tiny fraction of this vast potential should be absorbed and stored for ready access and use? Within the highly limited context of mathematical statistics, certain answers have been proposed. For example, information about the outcome of an experiment can be stored efficiently and with little loss of information in the form of the likelihood function or some other sufficient statistic, but this approach is not of much use in most situations, although elements of the approach

can perhaps be generalized to less restricted circumstances. Perhaps even more importantly, it is not clear what logical structure is the most rational to impose on memory. The attempts at constructing associative computer memories, as they are often called, show how little we are able as yet to characterize explicitly a memory with the power and flexibility of a normal man's, not to speak of the memory of a normal man who is using his powers with utmost efficiency. Perhaps one of the most important weaknesses of confirmation theory and the Ramsey-sort of theory developed by Jeffrey and others is that little is said about imposing a logical structure on evidence. Part of the reason for this is that the treatment of evidence is fundamentally static rather than dynamic and temporal. In real life, evidence accumulates over time and we tend to pay more attention to later than earlier data, but the appropriate logical mechanisms for storing, organizing and compressing temporally ordered data are as yet far from being understood.

3. *Concept formation.* The most fundamental and the most far-reaching cognitive changes in belief undoubtedly take place when a new concept is introduced. The history of science and technology is replete with examples ranging from the wheel to the computer, and from arithmetic to quantum mechanics. Perhaps the deepest problem of rational behavior, at least from a cognitive or epistemological standpoint, is to characterize when a man should turn from using the concepts he has available to solve a given problem to the search not just for new evidence but for new concepts with which to analyze the evidence. Perhaps the best current example of the difficulty of characterizing the kinds of concepts we apply to the solution of problems is the floundering and vain searching as yet typical of the literature on artificial intelligence. We cannot program a computer to think conceptually because we do not understand how men think conceptually, and the problem seems too difficult to conceive of highly nonhuman approaches. For those of us interested in rational behavior the lesson to be learned from the tantalizing yet unsatisfactory literature on artificial intelligence is that we are a long way from being able to say what a rational set of concepts for dealing with a given body of experience should be like, for we do not have a clear idea of what conceptual apparatus we actually use in any real sense.

To the problems about rationality I have raised in these remarks there is the pat answer that these are not problems of the theory of rational behavior but only of the theory of actual behavior. This I deny. A theory of rationality that does not take account of the specific human powers and limitations of attention, memory and conceptualization may have interesting things to say but not about human rationality.

R. C. JEFFREY: *Reply.*

Suppes' and Hurwicz' comments are interesting and instructive, and I find I have little to add to them. But perhaps a brief post-script is in order, in response to Suppes' closing remark:

> A theory of rationality that does not take account of the specific human powers and limitations of attention may have interesting things to say, but not about human rationality.

It may be that there is no real issue between us here, but the emphasis makes me uncomfortable. In my view, the logic of partial belief is a branch of decision theory, and I take decision theory to have the same sort of relevance to human rationality that (say) quantification theory has: the relevance is there, even though neither theory is directly about human rationality, and neither theory takes any account of the specific powers and limitations of human beings.

For definiteness, consider the following preference ranking of four sentences s, s', t, t', where s and s' are logically inconsistent, as are t and t'.

$$s$$
$$s'$$
$$t$$
$$t'$$

This ranking is *incoherent*: it violates at least one of the following two requirements. (a) Logically equivalent sentences are ranked together. (b) The disjunction of two logically incompatible sentences is ranked somewhere in the interval between them, endpoints included. Requirements (a) and (b) are part of (or anyway, implied by) a definition of 'incoherent'. To see that the given ranking is incoherent, notice that (a) implies that the disjunction of the sentences s, s' is ranked with the disjunction of the sentences t, t', while (b) implies that in the given ranking, the first disjunction is higher than the second. In my view, the point of classifying this ranking as incoherent is much like the point of classifying the pair s, s' as logically inconsistent: the two classifications have the same sort of relevance to human rationality. In the two cases, a rational man who made the classification would therefore decline to own the incoherent preference ranking or to believe both of the inconsistent sentences. (For simplicity I speak of belief here as an all-or-none affair.)

True enough: since there is no effective decision procedure for quantificational consistency there is no routine procedure a man can use – be he ever so rational – to correctly classify arbitrary rankings of sentences as incoherent or arbitrary sets of sentences as inconsistent. The relevance of incoherence and inconsistency to human rationality is rather that a rational man, once he comes to see that his preferences are incoherent or that his beliefs are inconsistent, will proceed to revise them. In carrying out the revision he may use decision theory or quantification theory as an aid; but neither theory fully determines how the revision shall go.

In fine, I take Bayesian decision theory to comprise a sort of *logic* of decision: the notion of coherence has much the same sort of relationship to human ideals of rationality that the notion of consistency has. But this is not to deny Suppes' point. The Bayesian theory is rather like a book of rules for chess which tells the reader what constitutes winning: there remains the question of ways and means.

INDUCTION BY ENUMERATION AND
INDUCTION BY ELIMINATION

JAAKKO HINTIKKA

Stanford University and University of Helsinki

The most striking general feature of the theory of induction at the present moment is the division of the field into several different schools of thought [1]. The best known contrast between different points of view is undoubtedly the difference between the views of Professor Carnap and of Sir Karl Popper [2]. There are other discrepancies between different approaches, however, which are not unrelated to the Carnap–Popper debate but which also have other ramifications and other sources. A well-known case in point is the contrast between those theories of induction in which some sort of rule of acceptance is used or argued to be unavoidable and those in which such rules play no part and in which one is instead supposed to be content with assigning different degrees of probability (on evidence) to the statements one considers [3]. There is

---

[1] For general surveys, see Henry E. Kyburg, 'Recent work in inductive logic', *American Philosophical Quarterly* 1, 1964, pp. 1–39, and S. F. Barker, *Induction and Hypothesis*, Cornell University Press, Ithaca, New York, 1957.

[2] The basic works are: Rudolf Carnap, *Logical Foundations of Probability*, University of Chicago Press, Chicago, 1950, 2nd ed., 1962, and Karl R. Popper, *The Logic of Scientific Discovery*, Hutchinson and Co., London, 1959. See also Karl R. Popper, *Conjectures and Refutations*, Routledge and Kegan Paul, London, 1963; Rudolf Carnap, *The Continuum of Inductive Methods*, University of Chicago Press, Chicago, 1952, and the relevant parts of P. A. Schilpp, ed., *The Philosophy of Rudolf Carnap*, The Library of Living Philosophers, Open Court Publishing Company, La Salle, Illinois, 1963.

[3] Cf. e.g. Isaac Levi, 'Corroboration and rules of acceptance', *The British Journal for the Philosophy of Science* 13, 1963, pp. 307–313, and Henry E. Kyburg, 'Probability, rationality, and a rule of detachment', *Logic, Methodology and Philosophy of Science, Proceedings of the 1964 International Congress for Logic, Methodology and Philosophy of Science*, Y. Bar–Hillel ed., North-Holland Publishing Company, Amsterdam, 1965, pp. 301–310.

also the older contrast between those approaches to induction in which a premium is put on the variety of observed instances and on a process of elimination among a number of competing hypotheses, and those which rely primarily on the mere number of positive instances. Theories of the former sort are said to stress induction by means of elimination, and those of the latter sort induction by enumeration [1].

In this current situation, the possibility is often overlooked that some of these contrasts may in the last analysis be more apparent than real. It seems to me that this possibility is to be taken seriously. As far as I can see, there exists no clear-cut proof that a reconciliation of the opposing views is really impossible in some important sense in any of the three cases mentioned. It is of course true that there are plenty of difficulties confronting serious efforts at compromise here. These difficulties are exemplified by the troubles, sometimes amounting to outright inconsistencies, into which attempts to set up a sound and interesting rule of acceptance on a probabilistic basis have recently run [2]. There are also several results which show that a reunion in the philosophy of induction is impossible to achieve in certain particular ways. I cannot set great store on these results, however, for usually everything depends on the precise construction which is put on the contrasting views. These are often so vague as to allow several alternative interpretations. For instance, it may be shown that an entirely natural interpretation of the idea of 'allowing so many possibilities' may convert Popper's adage 'the more possibilities a statement allows, the more probable and the less informative it is' from a tautology into a falsehood [3].

---

[1]   Cf. Barker, *op. cit.*, chs. 3 and 4.

[2]   See Kyburg, 'Probability, rationality, and a rule of detachment' (*loc. cit.*), R. C. Sleigh, 'A note on some epistemic principles of Chisholm and Martin', *The Journal of Philosophy* **61**, 1964, pp. 216–218, Keith Lehrer, 'Knowledge and probability', *ibid.* pp. 368–372, and Herbert Heidelberger, 'Knowledge, certainty, and probability', *Inquiry* **6**, 1963, pp. 242–250. See also Salmon's and Kyburg's contributions to the present volume.

[3]   The ambiguity here is between allowing so many different possible states of affairs and allowing so many different possible kinds of individuals. I hope to be able to deal with it more fully on another occasion.

The situation is thus most unsatisfactory, and a good deal of further work will be needed in order for us to see our way through the thickets of hasty generalization. It seems to me possible to show, by means of sufficiently precise and well developed models, comparable to the systems of inductive logic which Carnap has developed, that in many cases the points of view of the different schools are by no means incompatible. In an earlier paper, I have made a few brief suggestions towards reconstructing some of Popper's ideas and concepts within a Carnap-style formalized inductive logic [1]. In a recent paper, it has been shown that at least in certain simple cases a very simple and intuitively plausible rule of acceptance may be set up on a probabilistic basis [2]. In this paper, it will be shown that certain kinds of inductive logic combine in an interesting way both eliminative and enumerative aspects, at least in the simple special cases that are so far amenable to systematic treatment.

These inductive logics include the system which I outlined in my paper 'Towards a theory of inductive generalization' and referred to in the sequel as TTIG [3]. I shall conform to the notation and terminology of that earlier paper, whose results will be relied on occasionally. Sometimes I shall also refer to another recent paper of mine, 'On a combined system of inductive logic' [4].

Although the system outlined in TTIG differs in certain respects from earlier treatments of inductive logic, it is nevertheless comparable with Carnap's well-known systems. It deals with the same kinds of languages as Carnap's classical work, *Logical Foundations of Probability* [5], and in the case of languages with a finite universe

---

[1] See 'Towards a theory of inductive generalization', *Proceedings of the 1964 International Congress for Logic, Methodology and Philosophy of Science*, Y. Bar–Hillel, ed., North-Holland Publishing Company, Amsterdam, 1965, pp. 274–288.

[2] Jaakko Hintikka and Risto Hilpinen, 'Knowledge, acceptance, and inductive logic', in *Aspects of Inductive Logic*, Jaakko Hintikka and Patrick Suppes, eds., North-Holland Publishing Company, Amsterdam, 1966.

[3] See footnote 1 on this page.

[4] In *Studia Logico-Mathematica et Philosophica in honorem Rolf Nevanlinna*, *Acta Philosophica Fennica* 18, 1965, pp. 21–30.

[5] Roughly speaking, with applied first-order languages. See Carnap, *op. cit.* ch. 3.

it may be obtained from Carnap's general approach by choosing
a suitable symmetric and regular measure function [1]. Even the
choice of this measure function is reminiscent of the measure
function m^* which Carnap at one time favoured. The distribution
of *a priori* probabilities to the different state-descriptions which
results from the use of m^* may be obtained by first giving an equal
probability to each structure-description and then dividing the
probability of each structure-description evenly among all the
state-descriptions that make it true [2]. In the system outlined in
TTIG certain closed sentences called constituents play essentially
the same role as structure-descriptions play in the system based
on m^*: each of them receives a finite *a priori* probability which
is then divided evenly among all the state-descriptions which make
it true [3]. These constituents may be characterized as the strongest
consistent closed sentences with a fixed number of layers of quantifiers [4]. One can also combine some of the features of the system
presented in TTIG and the system based on m^* in the obvious
way by making the assignment of *a priori* probabilities a three-
stage affair: first, finite probabilities are assigned to the constituents; then the probability of each constituent is divided evenly
among the structure-descriptions which make it true; and finally
the probability of each structure-description is divided evenly
among all the state-descriptions which make it true [5]. The result

---

[1]   Carnap, *op. cit.* secs. 55 and 90.

[2]   Carnap, *op. cit.* sec. 110.

[3]   As indicated in TTIG, this applies strictly speaking only to the monadic
case. As soon as relations are present, we need further explanations, which
will not be discussed in this paper.

[4]   Cf. Jaakko Hintikka, 'Distributive normal forms in first-order logic',
*Recursive Functions and Formal Systems, Proceedings of the Eighth Logic
Colloquium*, Oxford, July 1963, M. A. E. Dummett and J. N. Crossley, eds.,
North-Holland Publishing Company, Amsterdam, 1965.

[5]   This procedure is possible because each constituent is either made true
or made false by each given structure-description. The difference between
a constituent and a structure-description is in fact easily explained: a
constituent specifies which Q-predicates are instantiated and which ones
are not; a structure-description specifies how many individuals there are
exemplifying each Q-predicate.

is the system outlined in 'On a combined system of inductive logic' [1].

Since these new systems are thus very closely related to Carnapian methods, they appear to rely heavily on induction by enumeration, for Carnap's approach is generally considered as a typical case of a treatment of induction in enumerative terms [2]. The purpose of this paper is to show that in spite of the enumerative origins of my systems they nevertheless incorporate some of the characteristic features of an eliminative theory of induction and that they can therefore be used for the purpose of discussing the relation between these two approaches to induction. This possibility appears all the more interesting since these new systems were originally motivated by considerations ostensibly completely unrelated to eliminative induction. The main motive was in fact to find better ways of dealing with inductive generalizations in all universes, including very large and infinite ones.

In this paper, only the monadic case will be considered, for it is the only case that has so far been investigated in any detail. In this case, we are given k one-place predicates

(1) $$P_1(x), P_2(x), ..., P_k(x),$$

quantifiers, propositional connectives, and names for all of the N individuals in our universe. (This N is assumed to be finite; the denumerably infinite case is dealt with as a limit.) From (1) and from the propositional connectives we can build $2^k = K$ attributive constituents (Q-predicates) [3] of the form

(2) $$(\pm)P_1(x) \ \& \ (\pm)P_2(x) \ \& \ ... \ \& \ (\pm)P_k(x)$$

where the symbols $(\pm)$ may be replaced by a negation sign or by

_____

[1] See note 4 on p. 193. In that paper, only the case of an even distribution of _a priori_ probabilities to constituents was considered.

[2] Cf. Barker, _op. cit._, pp. 51–52: '. . . recent writers such as Reichenbach, Carnap, and Braithwaite assume just as blandly that induction must work by enumeration; and they do not even argue against the eliminative view, for they scarcely seem aware that it might be maintained.'

[3] Carnap, _op. cit._, sec. 31.

nothing at all in all the possible combinations. Let these attributive constituents be

(3) $Ct_1(x), Ct_2(x), ..., Ct_K(x).$

A constituent may now be characterized by saying that it specifies which attributive constituents are exemplified and which ones are not. Since attributive constituents (Q-predicates) in effect define the cells of the finest partition we can obtain by means of our predicates (1), it is easily seen that each constituent may be written in the form

(4) $(Ex)Ct_{i_1}(x)$ & $(Ex)Ct_{i_2}(x)$ & ... & $(Ex)Ct_{i_w}(x)$
                & $(x)[Ct_{i_1}(x) \lor Ct_{i_2}(x) \lor ... \lor Ct_{i_w}(x)],$

where

(5) $\{Ct_{i_1}(x), Ct_{i_2}(x), ..., Ct_{i_w}(x)\}$

is an arbitrary subset of the set of all our attributive constituents (3). This subset may even be empty ($w = 0$); then (4) will say that the universe is empty. It may also be an improper subset of the set of all attributive constituents ($w = K$); then (4) will say that all the possible kinds of individuals we can specify are exemplified in the world.

Constituents will also be called strong generalizations. There are obviously $2^K = 2^{2^k}$ of them. Each consistent closed statement in our language can be represented as a disjunction of some (or all) of the constituents. This representation will be called its normal form (more precisely, its disjunctive distributive normal form).

In the monadic case, each constituent receives a finite non-zero *a priori* probability, which is then divided (in the system outlined in TTIG) evenly among all the state-descriptions which make it true. Formally speaking, the simplest method would be to assign an equal *a priori* probability $1/2^K$ to each constituent. Because of its simplicity, we shall usually consider this case primarily or exclusively. It turns out that the qualitative results (concerning the direction of change, asymptotic behaviour, etc.) that one obtains on this assumption are in many important cases representative of what happens in other circumstances. They are not very realistic quantitatively; the inductive behaviour which corresponds to the assignment of equal *a priori* probabilities to the different constituents is wildly overoptimistic in that one jumps to generalizations on the slightest provocation.

One way of correcting this overoptimism is to try to assign to each constituent as its *a priori* probability the probability with which it would be true in a completely random finite universe with α individuals. It is easily seen that the *a priori* probability of (4) will then be

$$(6) \qquad \sum_{i=0}^{i=w} (-1)^i \binom{w}{i} \left(\frac{w-i}{K}\right)^{\alpha},$$

which for large values of α is approximately $((w)/K)^{\alpha}$. (Explanation: $((w-i)/K)^{\alpha}$ is the probability that each of the α individuals has one of $w-i$ specified attributive constituents. The number of such subsets of (5) for a given i is $\binom{w}{i}$.) In fact, it turns out that this approximation serves our purposes better than (6). The larger α one chooses, the more disorderly one expects the universe to be in the sense that generalizations are unlikely to be true in it. Thus α serves as a sort of index of caution as far as generalizations are concerned. Its precise meaning is seen from the fact that on the assignment (6) any one generalization is assumed to have the same *a priori* probability as there is of obtaining in a completely random finite universe a sample of α individuals compatible with (4).

On the basis of the *a priori* probabilities, probabilities on evidence (degrees of confirmation, *a posteriori* probabilities) can be calculated. Let us assume that our evidence consists of observations concerning n different individuals which exemplify c different attributive constituents. We may assume that these attributive constituents are

$$(7) \qquad Ct_{i_1}(x), Ct_{i_2}(x), ..., Ct_{i_c}(x).$$

Strong generalization (4) is then incompatible with the evidence unless $w \geqslant c$.

The degree of confirmation of (4) on this evidence may be calculated by means of the formula of Bayes:

$$(8) \qquad \frac{p(C_w)\ p(e/C_w)}{\sum_i p(C_i)\ p(e/C_i)}.$$

Here C_w is (4) and C_i is an arbitrary constituent, while the rest of the notation is self-explanatory. I shall not give a strict argument here but only a heuristic derivation whose results have elsewhere been shown to be accurate when $N \to \infty$. The simplest case is the one in which all the *a priori* probabilities $p(C_w)$ and $p(C_i)$ are assumed to be equal; then we can simply omit them from (8). What, then, about $p(e/C_w)$? The evidence says essentially that n observed individuals belong to exactly c of the w kinds which (4) allows to be instantiated. In a large universe, the conditional probability $p(e/C_w)$ might be expected to be $(1/w)^n$, for in the absence of any further assumptions the probability that a given individual belongs to one particular kind among the w ones might be expected to be $(1/w)$. By the same token, the conditional probability $p(e/C_j)$ might be expected to be $(1/(c+i))^n$ for a constituent C_j which says that exactly $c+i$ Q-predicates are exemplified in the universe, provided of course that the ones that have been observed are among them. Since there are exactly $\binom{K-c}{i}$ such constituents C_j, (8) reduces to the form

$$(8) \qquad \frac{\left(\dfrac{1}{w}\right)^n}{\displaystyle\sum_{i=0}^{K-c} \binom{K-c}{i}\left(\dfrac{1}{c+i}\right)^n}$$

or, simplified,

$$(9) \qquad \frac{1}{\displaystyle\sum_{i=0}^{K-c} \binom{K-c}{i}\left(\dfrac{w}{c+i}\right)^n}.$$

A fuller argument shows in fact that this is the degree of confirmation of (4) when $N \to \infty$ [1]. It is also seen that if we start from the unequal distribution of *a priori* probabilities mentioned above we obtain approximately for $N \to \infty$ and for large values of α the same expression (9) except that n has been replaced by $(n-\alpha)$.

In the combined system we have decided to stick as closely to

---

[1] See TTIG, pp. 283–284.

Carnap's measure function m^* as is compatible with our decision to give finite *a priori* probabilities to constituents. In assigning unequal *a priori* probabilities to the constituents in analogy to the unequal assignment explained above for the system of TTIG it is therefore advisable to use Carnapian probabilities instead of *a priori* ones. In Carnap's system based on m^* the probability that the first individual is compatible with (4) is (w/K), that the second one is also compatible with it $(w+1)/(K+1)$, and so on. Hence the probability that all of the α individuals are compatible with (4) is

$$(10) \qquad \frac{(w+\alpha-1)!\ (K-1)!}{(w-1)!\ (K+\alpha-1)!}.$$

For sufficiently large values of α this is also very nearly the probability that (4) is true in a universe with α individuals. It is therefore rather natural to assume that the *a priori* probability (weight) of (4) is proportional to (10). The parameter α is again of the nature of an index of caution.

In the same way, we might expect that the likelihood $p(e/C_w)$ may be calculated by treating the set (5) of the Q-predicates compatible with (4) as if it were the set of all the Q-predicates in a Carnapian system based on m^*. This easily leads us to guess that $p(e/C_w)$ becomes

$$(11) \qquad \frac{(w-1)!}{(w+n-1)!}\ \prod_{j=1}^{c} (n_j)!,$$

when $N \to \infty$, where n_j is the number of individuals in our evidence e satisfying the j-th Q-predicate $Ct_{i_j}(x)$ in (4). If we make the same guess for $p(e/C_i)$ and substitute the result into (8) we obtain (after obvious simplifications) the following guess for the degree of confirmation of (4):

$$(12) \qquad \frac{\dfrac{(w+\alpha-1)!}{(w+n-1)!}}{\displaystyle\sum_{i=0}^{K-c} \binom{K-c}{i} \frac{(c+i+\alpha-1)!}{(c+i+n-1)!}}$$

This guess turns out to be correct in the limiting case $N \to \infty$ and approximately correct for large values of N [1].

Simple though these results are, they enable us to make several interesting observations. Most of them are strictly true only in the limiting case $N \to \infty$, but they are approximately true in sufficiently large finite universes. In the sequel we shall normally consider the case $N \to \infty$ only.

Let us consider first the behaviour of (9), i.e. of the degree of confirmation of (4) in an infinite universe. The derivative of the expression under the line with respect to n is

$$(13) \qquad \sum_{i=0}^{K-c} \binom{K-c}{i} (\log w - \log (c+i)) \left(\frac{w}{c+i}\right)^n .$$

In this sum the absolute value of the positive terms increases without limit when n grows, while the absolute value of the negative terms decreases to zero. Assuming that $w > c$, there are in fact positive terms in (13). Then (13) increases and eventually becomes positive when n grows. When $w > c$, (9) may thus grow initially, but after a while it starts decreasing when n grows, and it is easily seen to approach zero as a limit when $n \to \infty$.

What this means is that if our strong generalization (4) postulates the existence of more kinds of individuals than are instantiated in experience, and if further experience does not provide the missing kinds of individuals, then the degree of confirmation of this strong generalization will ultimately decrease to zero, when more and more individuals are observed. In other words, the requirement of the variety of instances is enforced in our system in a very strong form. If we have not obtained as much qualitative variety among the observed individuals as is compatible with our strong generalization (4), its degree of confirmation will tend to zero. In spite of the enumerative character of our basic assumptions, in this case the degree of confirmation of a strong generalization is not increased by a mere addition of new instances if they are similar to the old

---

[1] For $\alpha = 0$, this was shown in 'On a combined system of inductive logic' (*loc. cit.*), and the general case may be dealt with in the same way.

ones. Instead, such instances will eventually have the effect of decreasing the degree of confirmation of (4). Thus the requirement of the variety of instances is in our inductive logic so strong that it overrules a form – albeit a somewhat unusual form – of a principle which has sometimes been put forward as being obviously correct and which says that the degree of confirmation of a generalization is never decreased by a positive instance of the generalization.

Similar results are obtained if n is replaced by $(n-\alpha)$ in (9), i.e. if we make the distribution of a priori probabilities to constituents an unequal one in the way explained above.

However, when $w=c$, there are no positive terms in (13). Then (9) grows with n and approaches 1 as a limit when $n \to \infty$. What this means is that after we have exhausted the qualitative variety of instances, induction becomes essentially enumerative.

So far, we have assumed that c remains constant when n grows, i.e. that each of the new observed individuals is like one of the old ones in the sense of satisfying the same attributive constituent. What happens if this assumption is not made?

There are two cases to be distinguished here. The new individual may falsify (4) altogether. However, if it does not do so and if the new individual is nevertheless unlike the old ones, it will have to satisfy an attributive constituent – e.g. $Ct_{i_{c+1}}(x)$ – which had not been instantiated before.

The new degree of confirmation of (4) is then obtained from (9) by replacing n by $n+1$ and c by $c+1$. The effect of these changes is seen by comparing the corresponding terms in the resulting new expression and in the old expression (9). The ratio of an old term to a new one is

$$(14) \quad \left\{ \frac{\binom{K-c}{i}\left(\frac{w}{c+i}\right)^n}{\binom{K-c-1}{i}\left(\frac{w}{c+i+1}\right)^{n+1}} = \right.$$
$$= \frac{K-c}{K-c-i}\,\frac{c+i+1}{w}\left(1+\frac{1}{c+i}\right)^n.$$

For sufficiently large values of n this is greater than 1, showing that (9) grows when simultaneously $n \to n+1$ and $c \to c+1$. In other words, for sufficiently large values of the number of observed individuals the observation of an individual unlike the ones previously observed and yet compatible with one's strong generalization increases its degree of confirmation.

The following survey shows all the different things that may happen when a new individual is observed (for sufficiently large values of n):

(A) $w > c$, i.e. elimination has not been completed.
(a) the new individual is like one of the old ones: (4) is mildly disconfirmed;
(b) the new individual is compatible with (4) but unlike any of the old ones: (4) is confirmed further;
(c) the new individual is incompatible with (4) and hence falsifies it.

(B) $w = c$, i.e. elimination has been completed.
(a) the new individual is compatible with (4) and hence like one of the old ones: (4) is confirmed further;
(b) the new individual is incompatible with (4) and hence falsifies it.

Reference to elimination here requires some further comments. If $w > c$ there are strong generalizations which are simpler than (4) (in the obvious sense of containing fewer attributive constituents) and which are nevertheless compatible with the evidence which we assumed that we have. They are obtained from (4) by omitting one or more of the attributive constituents

$$Ct_{i_{c+1}}(x), Ct_{i_{c+2}}(x), \ldots, Ct_{i_w}(x).$$

Now if the next observed individual is compatible with (4) but unlike any of the previously observed ones (case (A)(b)), it will be incompatible with at least one such simpler constituent (viz. with a constituent from which that particular attributive constituent is missing which is satisfied by the new individual). This simpler constituent is therefore ruled out by the new observation.

The two cases (A)(b) and (B)(a) in which a new individual can confirm (4) further thus admit of an alternative description. We may say that a new positive instance confirms (4) further if and only if it either eliminates at least one simpler strong generalization – case (A)(b) – or else if the earlier evidence had already ruled out all these competing simpler strong generalizations – case (B)(a).

This justifies our reierence to elimination in the formulation of the cases (A) and (B). In a way, we have distinguished from each other the eliminative and the enumerative aspects of induction: in the case (A)(b) induction proceeds by elimination and in the case (B)(a) it proceeds by enumeration. From this formulation it is also seen that in a sense the first and primary inductive task is elimination: mere enumeration begins to play a significant role only after elimination has been carried as far as it can possibly go.

It may be shown that the progress of the eliminative part of the confirmation of a strong generalization – say (4) – in our approach is closely connected with the main confirmation theorem of C. D. Broad and J. M. Keynes. It has been called by G. H. von Wright the 'Principal Theorem of Confirmation' [1]. It says that if the initial probability of a generalization is not zero, then its degree of confirmation is added to by each new observation which is implied by the generalization but which is not maximally probable relative to the previous observations.

In order to compare this theorem with our results, let us first note that each strong generalization has been assumed to have a non-zero *a priori* probability and that the first premise of the Principal Theorem of Confirmation is therefore satisfied in our approach. It is not possible, however, to formulate the whole force of the observation of a new individual as a statement which would be implied by a strong generalization. We can here consider only a part of the logical force of such a statement. Since we are primarily concerned with general (closed) statements, it lies close at hand to focus our attention on that part of each observation which can be expressed in the form of a closed sentence. This part is obviously constituted by the existential statement $(Ex)Ct_j(x)$ where $Ct_j(x)$ is the attributive constituent which the new individual is found to satisfy. The relevant part of the earlier observations may then be

---

[1] See G. H. von Wright, *The Logical Problem of Induction*, 2nd ed., Blackwell, Oxford, 1957, p. 119.

summed up in the form of a conjunction of such existential statements. If the observations are compatible with the strong generalization we are considering, this conjunction is implied by the strong generalization.

Construing observation-statements in this way as existential statements we can see what the Principal Theorem of Confirmation amounts to in our situation. It says that a strong generalization is confirmed by a new individual b which satisfies $Ct_j(x)$ provided that the following pair of conditions is satisfied: (a) $(Ex)Ct_j(x)$ is implied by the strong generalization; (b) $(Ex)Ct_j(x)$ is not maximally probable relative to the earlier observations, i.e. it is not entailed by the conjunction which represents the earlier observations. But this amounts to saying that the new individual is compatible with the strong generalization in question but unlike the individuals previously observed, in short, it amounts to a restatement of the case (A)(b). This fact brings out one aspect of the close relation of our results with eliminative induction as envisaged by Keynes and Broad.

So far we have mainly considered the system proposed in TTIG. Similar results may be obtained in the combined system mentioned above. The expression (12) for the degree of confirmation of (4) may be written in the following form:

$$(12)^* \qquad \frac{1}{\displaystyle\sum_{i=0}^{K-c} \binom{K-c}{i} \frac{(w+n-1)!\ (c+i+\alpha-1)!}{(w+\alpha-1)!\ (c+i+n-1)!}}.$$

If $w>c$, there are in the sum of $(12)^*$ terms in which $w>(c+i)$. For large values of n, such a term is by Stirling's formula approximately

$$(15) \qquad \binom{K-c}{i} \frac{(c+i+\alpha-1)!}{(w+\alpha-1)!} (c+i+n-1)^{w-c-i},$$

which grows without limit when $n \to \infty$. This shows that (12) diminishes towards zero when n grows. It is also easily seen that for sufficiently large values of n it diminishes monotonically. Thus we have the case (A)(a) as before.

When $w=c$, an arbitrary term with $i \geqslant 1$ is likewise approximately

$$(16) \qquad \binom{K-c}{i} \frac{(c+i+\alpha-1)!}{(c+\alpha-1)!} (c+n-1)^{-i},$$

which decreases to zero when $n \to \infty$. This shows that (12) grows and approaches one in this case when n grows without limit. For sufficiently large values of n it is seen to grow monotonically, verifying our case (B)(a).

What happens to (12)* when at the same time $n \to n+1$ and $c \to c+1$? The ratio of a new term in the sum of (12)* to the corresponding old term is now

$$(17) \qquad \frac{(K-c-i)}{(K-c)} \frac{(w+n)}{(c+i+n+1)} \frac{(c+i+\alpha)}{(c+i+n)}$$

which is <1 when n is sufficiently large. This means that for sufficiently large values of n (12)* increases, for when $c \to c+1$ the number of terms in the sum also decreases. This verifies the case (A)(b).

As far as the relation of elimination to enumeration is concerned, we thus obtain in the combined system qualitatively the same main results as in the system proposed in TTIG, as expressed by the five cases (A)(a)–(B)(b).

The separation we have effected between the eliminative and the enumerative aspects of induction enables us to compare the relative importance of the two aspects. Let us consider the share of elimination first. In the case of (4), our evidence is as good from an eliminative point of view as it can be if it shows that all of the w attributive constituents occurring in (4) are instantiated. In fact, this has to be the case if (4) is to be confirmed in the long run. This ideal state of affairs can be brought about by observing exactly w individuals provided that they are unlike one another. After having observed these individuals, the degree of confirmation of (4) is (when the even *a priori* distribution is presupposed)

$$(18) \qquad \frac{1}{\sum\limits_{i=0}^{K-w} \binom{K-w}{i} \left(\dfrac{w}{w+i}\right)^{w}} .$$

The difference between (18) and the *a priori* probability $1/2^K$ may be considered as the greatest potential share that elimination can have in the confirmation of (4). The share of enumeration is obtained by subtracting from 1 both (18) and the *a priori* confirmation $1/2^K$.

The value of (18) is easily seen to lie between 2^{w-K} and $(1 + 1/e)^{w-K}$. Normally, it is the larger the larger w we have.

Now in practice we do not know which constituent is true in the actual world. But if we have made a sufficient number of observations, which may be assumed to instantiate c attributive constituents, we know that the constituent which has the highest degree of confirmation is the one in which $c = w$. This number c may be therefore considered as a sort of approximation towards the true w. Now the higher c is, the more possible generalizations have our observations ruled out. In fact, the number of strong generalizations compatible with a number of observations among which c attributive constituents are instantiated is 2^{K-c}. Modifying slightly the terminology of G. H. von Wright and others [1], we may call this *the state of analogy* determined by the observed individuals. Its meaning should be clear from the definition: the lower the state of analogy, the fewer generalizations there are compatible with our observations and the further has the elimination progressed.

Our observation that (18) grows together with w may now be taken to give us the unsurprising result that the further elimination progresses, the higher becomes the relative share of elimination in the confirmation of the most probable strong generalization.

Similar results may be obtained by starting from an uneven *a priori* distribution or from the combined system considered earlier.

Although our result concerning the relative share of elimination in induction is not very surprising, we can obtain less obvious results by asking slightly different questions. The relative share of elimination in confirmation has been seen to grow when the

---

[1] Cf. G. H. von Wright, *Treatise on Induction and Probability*, Routledge and Kegan Paul, London, 1951, p. 91.

state of analogy decreases. But does the degree of confirmation of the most probable strong generalization also grow when the state of analogy becomes smaller and smaller?

This degree of confirmation is

$$(19) \qquad \frac{1}{\displaystyle\sum_{i=0}^{K-c} \binom{K-c}{i} \left(\frac{c}{c+i}\right)^{n}}.$$

In order to eliminate the effect of enumeration we must keep the number n of observed individuals constant and ask how (19) depends on c. A partial answer, which suffices for our present purposes, is obtained by means of the following heuristic argument: by considering the ratio of successive terms of the sum in (19), we can see that later terms are very small in comparison with earlier ones when n is large. Hence it may be expected that the behaviour of (19) is essentially determined by the first two terms when n is large, i.e. that (19) behaves in the same way as

$$(20) \qquad \frac{1}{1 + (K-c) \left(\dfrac{c}{c+1}\right)^{n}}$$

when n is large in comparison with K. Of (20) it is easily seen that for sufficiently large values of n it grows smaller when c becomes larger. It is not difficult to verify that this is in fact representative of what happens to (19).

What this shows is that although there is an eliminative element in induction, induction does not proceed by mere elimination. When a large number of individuals has been observed, the decrease of the state of analogy has an effect contrary to what it is typically taken by the eliminationists to be: instead of adding to the degree of confirmation of the most probable strong generalization, an increase in elimination has the effect of decreasing it, provided that the number of observed individuals is not changed. It is sometimes said that induction does not proceed by mere enumeration of instances. We have found a sense in which it may be said that induction does not proceed by mere elimination either.

In the combined system the corresponding results are less clear-cut. One can show, in any case, that an increase of c (while the other parameters, including n, remain constant) does not always yield higher degrees of confirmation. In brief, in the combined system induction does not always proceed by mere elimination, either.

Similar points can be made in the special situations to which the attention of the elimination theorists is often directed primarily or exclusively. These situations are the ones in which we are given a monadic predicate Q and are supposed to look for a necessary, sufficient, or necessary-and-sufficient condition for this Q among predicates definable in terms of certain monadic predicates $P_1, P_2, ..., P_k$ and propositional connectives. For our purposes, the simplest case is the search for a necessary-and-sufficient condition which we shall briefly discuss here. The main complication we have to heed here is the difference between those constituents and attributive constituents which contain only the predicates $P_1, P_2, ..., P_k$ and those which also contain the 'conditioned' predicate Q. Unless there is a statement to the contrary, we shall in the sequel mean the former and not the latter, and use for these constituents and attributive constituents the same notation as before.

It may be shown that there exists a necessary-and-sufficient condition of the desired kind for Q if and only if the following condition is satisfied:

For each attributive constituent (2), either all the individuals satisfying it also satisfy $Q(x)$ or else all of them satisfy $\sim Q(x)$.

In order to see that this condition suffices for the existence of a necessary-and-sufficient condition for Q, let us assume that those non-empty attributive constituents which are of the former kind are

$$Ct_{j_1}(x), Ct_{j_2}(x), ..., Ct_{j_u}(x),$$

and that those non-empty attributive constituents which are of the latter kind are

$$Ct_{j_{u+1}}(x), Ct_{j_{u+2}}(x), ..., Ct_{j_w}(x).$$

The empty attributive constituents may be taken to be

$$Ct_{j_{w+1}}(x), Ct_{j_{w+2}}(x), ..., Ct_K(x).$$

Then any statement of the following form will clearly express a valid necessary-and-sufficient condition of Q:

$$(21) \quad (x)[Q(x) \equiv (Ct_{j_1}(x) \lor Ct_{j_2}(x) \lor ... \lor Ct_{j_u}(x)$$
$$\lor Ct_{j_{w+1}}(x) \lor Ct_{j_{w+2}}(x) \lor ... \lor Ct_{j_{w+t}}(x))].$$

The new parameter t serves to bring out the fact that presence or absence of empty attributive constituents makes no difference in (21). This means that there are exactly 2^{K-w} logically non-equivalent necessary-and-sufficient conditions for Q in this case.

In order to show that our condition is necessary for the existence of a necessary-and-sufficient condition for Q, let us assume that the (possibly complex) predicate $\mathbf{Q}[x]$ expresses such a condition. Then this $\mathbf{Q}[x]$ is expressible as a disjunction of attributive constituents, i.e. a statement of the following form is true:

$$(22) \quad (x)[Q(x) = (Ct_{i_1}(x) \lor Ct_{i_2}(x) \lor ... \lor Ct_{i_s}(x))].$$

Taking now an arbitrary attributive constituent $Ct_0(x)$, it either occurs in (22) or else it does not. In the former case it is seen from (22) that $(x)(Ct_0(x) \supset Q(x))$ is true. In the latter case it is likewise seen that $(x)(Ct_0(x) \supset \sim Q(x))$ is true. For each attributive constituent implies the negation of every other attributive constituent, whence $(x)(Ct_0(x) \supset \sim (Ct_{i_1}(x) \lor Ct_{i_2}(x) \lor ... \lor Ct_{i_s}(x)))$ is true as soon as $Ct_0(x)$ does not occur in (22). This shows the required necessity.

Let us now assume that we have observed a total of n individuals which exemplify exactly c attributive constituents definable in terms of $P_1(x), P_2(x), ..., P_k(x)$. These observed individuals have to satisfy the condition which was just found to be necessary and sufficient for the existence of a necessary-and-sufficient condition: if one of them satisfies an attributive constituent $Ct_0(x)$ and has the predicate $Q(x)$, then every observed individual which satisfies $Ct_0(x)$ must also have the predicate $Q(x)$. If this condition is satisfied, there are by our earlier observation 2^{K-c} possible necessary-

and-sufficient conditions (22) compatible with the observations. The *a posteriori* probability that a necessary-and-sufficient condition exists for Q is the sum of the degrees of confirmation of all of these 2^{K-c} statements of the form (22) and compatible with evidence. If our universe is infinite and the number of observations n is very large, then by our earlier results this sum will consist almost entirely of the degree of confirmation of that strong generalization in which as few attributive constituents are said to be exemplified as is compatible with the evidence we have. Since we have to consider here attributive constituents which contain Q in addition to the P's, it is seen that this maximal degree of confirmation is (cf. (9))

$$(23) \qquad \frac{1}{\sum\limits_{i=0}^{2^{K-c}} \binom{2K-c}{i} \left(\dfrac{i}{c+i}\right)^{n}}.$$

This is like (19) except that K has been replaced by $2K$. It will therefore behave in the same way as (19). From our earlier results it thus follows that for large values of n (23) does not grow when c grows (while n remains constant) but rather becomes smaller. This is interesting because the number of possible necessary-and-sufficient conditions 2^{K-c} decreases when c increases. The number c is therefore a sort of index of the progress of elimination among the initially possible necessary-and-sufficient conditions. What we have found thus brings out one more limitation of a purely eliminative approach to induction: the probability that a necessary-and-sufficient condition exists is not determined by our index c of the progress of elimination, and after a sufficiently large number of observations this probability is actually smaller the greater c is. Once again it turns out that induction is a more complicated matter than the simple-minded eliminative (or enumerative) model presupposes.

The search for necessary conditions and for sufficient conditions may be analyzed in the same way.

The connection between confirmation and elimination has thus been found to be somewhat weaker than the eliminationists have sometimes supposed. The role of elimination in induction can be highlighted, however, by switching our attention to a concept different from confirmation.

So far, we have mainly considered constituents (strong generalizations) and their degrees of confirmation. Since all the other consistent generalizations (closed sentences) can be represented as disjunctions of constituents, we obtain in this way a degree of confirmation for each consistent generalization **G**. If the normal form of **G** is

$$(24) \qquad C_{g_1} \vee C_{g_2} \vee \ldots \vee C_{g_j},$$

the degree of confirmation of G is

$$(25) \qquad conf(\mathbf{G}) = \sum_{i=1}^{j} conf(C_{g_i}).$$

However, the notion of the degree of confirmation thus defined does not serve all the purposes one may have in mind in evaluating a generalization. We can make the degree of confirmation higher simply by choosing a generalization with a longer normal form, i.e. by choosing a weaker hypothesis. In most cases, this means trivializing our generalization. By considerations of this kind, and by others similar to the ones Sir Karl Popper has put forward with great vigour [1], we can show that the degree of confirmation is not really a good measure of the rational acceptability of a generalization. It misses entirely the effects of such factors as the information a generalization conveys, how well it has withstood attempted falsification, and so on. We shall try to define a better measure of the rational acceptability of a generalization and call it, taking our cue from Popper, the degree of *corroboration* rather than the degree of *confirmation*.

In TTIG I argued that in the case of constituents (strong generalizations) the degree of confirmation is in certain respects a very good measure of their respective claims to rational acceptance.

---

[1] Cf. e.g. Karl R. Popper, *The Logic of Scientific Discovery*, p. 270, note *3.

For strong generalizations we may therefore identify their degree
of confirmation and their degree of corroboration. What remains
open is then the extension of the notion of the degree of corroboration from constituents to arbitrary disjunctions of constituents.
One natural possibility here is to use as an index of the rational
acceptability of a generalization the degree of confirmation of the
least acceptable (least confirmed) strong generalization compatible
with it and with evidence:

$$(26) \qquad\qquad corr(\mathbf{G}) = \min_{i} \; [conf(C_{g_i})],$$

where the minimum is taken over those disjuncts C_{g_i} of (24) for
which $conf(C_{g_i}) \neq 0$. If there are no such disjuncts, $corr(\mathbf{G}) = 0$.

This notion has many features in common with what Popper
has said of his notion of corroboration. For instance, consider the
case in which $\vdash (\mathbf{F} \supset \mathbf{G})$. This is clearly possible only if all the
disjuncts occurring in the normal form of $\mathbf{F}$ also occur in the normal
form of $\mathbf{G}$. Then we have

$$(27) \qquad\qquad conf(\mathbf{F}) \leqslant conf(\mathbf{G})$$

and, conversely,

$$(28) \qquad\qquad corr(\mathbf{F}) \geqslant corr(\mathbf{G}),$$

provided that in (28) $\mathbf{F}$ is compatible with the evidence we have.
In other words, the stronger a statement is, the better corroborated
it is on given fixed evidence, provided it is compatible with this
evidence. In contrast to this, the weaker a statement is, the better
confirmed it is. This gives us one possible (partial) explication of
Popper's dictum that one should prefer improbable (and therefore
highly informative) hypotheses to probable (and therefore less
informative) ones. In one respect, we have gone further here than
Popper in that we are here considering not only probabilities *a
priori*, as Popper seems to be doing [1], but *a posteriori* probabilities
(degrees of confirmation) as well.

---

[1] Cf. e.g. Popper, *op. cit.*, p. 269, note *1.

A high degree of corroboration requires a variety of instances even more urgently than a high degree of confirmation. We have seen that when more and more evidence is obtained (in a large universe), one of the constituents becomes increasingly more probable (highly confirmed) while the *a posteriori* probability of all the other constituents approaches zero. From this it follows that we can in a large universe expect high degrees of corroboration only if the evidence we have rules out all but one of the disjuncts (constituents) in the normal form of the generalization we are considering. In this sense, elimination is a prerequisite of corroboration in an even stronger sense than the one in which it is a prerequisite to confirmation.

Consider, by way of example, a universal implication of the form

$$(29) \qquad (x)(\textbf{F}[x] \supset \textbf{G}[x]),$$

where $\textbf{F}[x]$ and $\textbf{G}[x]$ are complex predicates formed from our basic predicates $P_1, P_2, ..., P_k$. This implication may be transformed into the form

$$(30) \qquad (x)(Ct_{i_1}(x) \vee Ct_{i_2}(x) \vee ... \vee Ct_{i_w}(x)).$$

The number w here is often called the width of the complex predicate $(\textbf{F}[x] \supset \textbf{G}[x])$. Those constituents are compatible with (30) which say that some (or all) of the attributive constituents $Ct_{i_1}(x), Ct_{i_2}(x), ..., Ct_{i_w}(x)$ are exemplified but that no other attributive constituents are instantiated. As long as all these attributive constituents have not been exemplified in the evidence we have, there will be at least one constituent compatible with (29) and with our evidence which allows more attributive constituents to be instantiated than are instantiated in experience. For sufficiently large values of n, the degree of confirmation of such a constituent and hence the degree of corroboration of (29) will be arbitrarily small.

Thus it is seen that in order for our universal implication (29) to receive non-negligible degrees of corroboration in the long run, our evidence must exhibit as much variety as is compatible with (29): all the attributive constituents occurring in (30) must be exemplified before we can hope to obtain high degrees of corroboration for (29).

More specifically, the constituent which has the smallest degree of confirmation among all the ones occurring in the normal form of (29) is the one which says that all the attributive constituents $Ct_{i_1}(x)$, $Ct_{i_2}(x)$, ..., $Ct_{i_w}(x)$ are exemplified. (We are here assuming the even *a priori* distribution of probabilities to constituents.) This constituent may be written as (4). Its degree of confirmation thus equals the degree of corroboration of (29). This has earlier been found to be (9). Now the larger c is in (9) (while w remains constant), the larger is the value of (9). In other words, the more kinds of individuals have been observed, the higher is the degree of corroboration of (29), provided that n is large enough. There is thus a sense in which elimination (the growth of c) automatically increases the degree of corroboration of a universal implication.

These observations may be related to the recent discussion of the requirement of the variety of instances. Achinstein has set up certain formulations of the requirement and shown that no inductive logic that falls within the Carnapian λ-continuum of inductive methods satisfies these requirements [1]. Since our systems do not fall within Carnap's continuum it is of interest to ask whether, and if so in what sense, Achinstein's requirements are satisfied in our systems.

An example suffices to give the flavour of Achinstein's requirements. Consider two bodies of evidence, one consisting of

(31) $P(a)$ & $Q(a)$ and $P(b)$ & $Q(b)$

and the other of

(32) $P(a)$ & $Q(a)$ and $P(b)$ & $\sim Q(b)$.

According to Achinstein's requirements, (32) should give a higher degree of confirmation to the statement $P(c)$ where $c \neq a$ and $c \neq b$

---

[1]   Peter Achinstein, 'Variety and analogy in confirmation theory', *Philosophy of Science* **30**, 1963, pp. 207–221. Cf. Rudolf Carnap, 'Discussion: Variety, analogy and periodicity in inductive logic', *ibid.* pp. 222–227.

than (31). Since we are primarily concerned with generalizations, we may likewise ask whether (32) gives a higher degree of confirmation to the general statement

(33) $(x)P(x)$

than (31).

But why should (32) lend a higher degree of confirmation to either statement? Achinstein's examples are somewhat more complicated than ours, but even so his main appeal is simply to the alleged obvious fact that the requirement of the variety of instances implies this: since there is more variety in (32) than in (31), it ought to give higher degrees of confirmation to $P(c)$ and (by the same token, we may add) to $(x)P(x)$.

Our intuitions are notoriously ambiguous in this area, however, and I cannot therefore set a very great store on any one formulation before its alternatives have been examined. In the case at hand, there are two considerations which lead me to doubt whether Achinstein's formulation is acceptable.

First, (31) supports as strongly the generalization $(x)Q(x)$ (or, in a different form, $\sim (Ex) \sim Q(x)$) as it supports (33). Now if we should know that this statement is true, in addition to knowing (31), then it might very well be the case that the degree of confirmation of $(x)P(x)$ on this joint information is as high as its degree of confirmation on the sole evidence (32). In other words, in the type of case we (and Achinstein) are considering, the effects of the requirement of the variety of instances may be largely or totally drowned by other effects. It is not obvious how the former effect is to be separated from the latter ones.

Secondly, it is seen at once that the degree of corroboration of (33) on the evidence (32) is higher than on the evidence (31). It may be asked whether the intuitions on which Achinstein bases his formulation of the requirement of the variety of instances perhaps pertain to the degree of corroboration of (33) rather than to its degree of confirmation (or to the degree of confirmation of $P(c)$). It seems to me that we can perfectly well account for people's preference of (32) to (31) as a body of evidence in terms of corroboration, without having to set up any requirements which pertain to degrees of confirmation of the kind Achinstein considers.

In general, it seems to me that we have to keep in mind the possibility that some (perhaps many) of our inductive intuitions and preferences are based on our vague feeling for something like our degree of corroboration as distinguished from a degree of confirmation. If this is the case, these intuitions and preferences ought to be systematized and accounted for in terms of the former notion rather than the latter.

J. R. Lucas: *Does Hintikka's system represent our actual inductive procedures?*

I have two questions for Professor Hintikka. One is, to what extent it is possible within his system to represent one important feature of eliminative induction, namely the different importance given to the different kinds of variation. If you look at a textbook of chemotherapy, for instance, and you see what it says about the different sorts of clinical tests which may be applied to a new drug, you come across some such statement as that testing on a species of rodents and a species of non-rodents gives a more reliable result than testing simply on two species of rodents. So my first question is how far it is possible to represent this kind of different weighting in a system.

The second question is of a different nature. There is a curious feature about eliminative induction which is not possessed, or not to a marked degree, by enumerative induction, namely it is in a way self-overhauling. Take the case of thalidomide. It is quite clear that some variation of factors was eliminated from the standard set of tests through which drugs were put at their pre-medical stage, namely the variation of *pregnant* and non-pregnant experimental animals was not applied. Now when in practice it was found that this variation did make a difference, I would have thought that the intuitive reaction was to say that the previous weighting given to the other factors or the set of other tests, excluding the pregnancy variation, was wrong, was mistaken, was too high. So that in a way here what you need to be able to represent is that in your confirmation functor, if you are constructing a confirmation theory for eliminative induction, the argument's place must be capable of being filled, even if only in a higher-order theory, by confirmation functors, that is to say it is a characteristic of eliminative induction that it is self-overhauling in this respect. Now

I don't say that your own theory doesn't conform to this, doesn't lend itself to this. I wonder whether you could tell me whether it could be extended in some sort of way to do this.

R. CARNAP: *The concept of constituent-structure.*

It seems to me that Professor Hintikka's approach to inductive logic is very interesting. It seems to have certain advantages, for instance when compared with the old approach, based on the confirmation function c^* with which Hintikka compared it. This old approach was outlined in the appendix to my book *Logical Foundations of Probability* (1950) and preferred by me at the time to others.

We can say that Hintikka takes one step further from the Wittgenstein function $c^\dagger$ which was accepted by Keynes and others and which gives an equal *a priori* probability to each state-description. In contrast to $c^\dagger$, the confirmation function c^* gives an equal *a priori* probability to each structure-description, which is already a step away from the Wittgenstein function. This seems to me a positive step not only because it is easily seen that the other confirmation function $c^\dagger$ is unacceptable in that it does not fulfil the requirement that we should learn from experience. We can also say that the step from the function $c^\dagger$ to the function c^* was an improvement because structure-descriptions are more general, more abstract descriptions of the universe than state-descriptions.

This was expressed to me in a very lively way by Gödel many, many years ago. I told him that I had considered the problem of how to apply the general symmetry principle in inductive logic. This principle says that if there are possibilities of the same nature, in some sense, then they should be given equal *a priori* probabilities. What are these symmetrical 'possible cases' here? I told Gödel that there is no agreement as to what we should regard as these possible cases. Some believe that they are represented by state-descriptions; others think that they are represented by structure-descriptions. However, I had found that the former method would be unsuitable because with it we could not learn from experience.

Gödel said immediately that even before I had told him about this disadvantage he would have rejected the former method in favour of the latter. I asked him: Clearly there are two possible ways of proceeding here; as long as you do not study them and find out that one is unacceptable, how can you prefer one to the other? He said that according to his feeling there was virtually no choice at all. A state-description tells us of each individual to which predicate it belongs, that is to say, which properties it has, e.g. whether it is blue or not, etc. Now this is much too concrete, Gödel said, much too down-to-earth. However, if we consider structure-descriptions, we do not speak at all of each individual in the universe; we just say *how many* of them belong to the different predicates, for instance, how many of them are red and how many of them are blue, and so on. This is on a higher level; we are away from the particular individuals, whereas the other is so down-to-earth. I had a feeling that 'down-to-earth' here meant that we might so to speak get our hands dirty when dealing with particular individuals. In contrast, if we speak only of numbers, everything is clean and clear.

Hintikka concentrates his attention not on structure-descriptions but on constituents. They are still more general and abstract statements. This is therefore a step in the same direction as the step from state-descriptions to structure-descriptions which Gödel was talking about. A constituent does not tell us how many individuals belong to the different predicates, e.g. how many of them are white and green and yellow etc. A constituent only tells us of each predicate whether it is exemplified in the world or not. This is still more abstract than a structure-description.

Now I suggest that we might carry this approach one step further. We can go from the constituents to what might be called constituent-structures. Instead of saying of each predicate whether it is exemplified or not, we simply say *how many* of them are instantiated in the world and how many are empty. This is, so to speak, cleaner still in that it is still further from particular individuals. We might then see what happens if we give an equal *a priori* probability to each of these constituent-structures. If I understand Hintikka correctly, he said that giving an equal *a priori*

probability to each constituent is in some respects not quite satisfactory. I have not studied the question; but I wonder now what
the consequences of the use of constituent-structures might be in
this respect.

M. B. HESSE: *Enumeration, elimination, and analogy.*

In this paper and the others he refers to, Professor Hintikka is
making a very interesting and ingenious attempt to revise Carnap-
type confirmation theory to overcome some of the counter-intuitive
features of Carnap's early formulations. Success in such an enterprise must be judged primarily in terms of satisfaction of intuitive
criteria of what it is to be a good inductive inference, and second-
arily in terms of simplicity and economy of the postulates of the
confirmation theory. Hintikka's theory is still in process of development, and it is perhaps unfair to comment at this stage that
it is in danger of becoming unduly complex. I shall rather concentrate on the extent to which it satisfies the criteria of adequacy.

First, on a minor point of terminology. There is no doubt that
Hintikka is able to show that his 'combined system' does behave
in many of the ways we require of a confirmation theory. But some
of his claims for it may look more impressive than they in fact are,
because of his choice of the term 'strong generalization' for his
'constituents'. A constituent says of the world that exactly w of
the available Q-predicates are exemplified, but says nothing about
how many individuals exemplify each predicate unless it happens
that all or none do. Thus the theory cannot (or cannot yet) deal
with statistical generalizations in which a given proportion of individuals exemplify a predicate and the rest do not. Such generalizations are of course *stronger* than constituents, and to qualify
these latter as 'strong' is therefore somewhat misleading.

My main comments, however, have to do with the introduction
towards the end of the paper of the notion of 'degree of corroboration', and the discussion of Achinstein's example. Although
Hintikka shows that his 'degree of corroboration' satisfies some of
our requirements, it does have a slight air of being an *ad hoc*

device, and it is not clear from his brief description of it here what its general effects on the adequacy of the system will be. I want to contribute something towards elucidating these effects by further consideration of Achinstein's problems. First, if degree of *confirmation* (probability) is to be taken as the index of acceptability of hypotheses, then surely Achinstein is right in holding that his evidence (32) should confirm $(x)P(x)$ more highly than (31). This is because (32) eliminates the weaker (and therefore *a priori* more highly confirmed) rival hypothesis $(x)(P(x) \supset Q(x))$, whereas (31) does not. Thus Achinstein's appeal, like Hintikka's, is to elimination as well as enumeration, not 'simply to the alleged obvious fact' that variety of evidence implies higher confirmation. Since 'degree of corroboration' is introduced by Hintikka to deal with essentially eliminative arguments, it is not surprising that it can be shown to satisfy the variety criterion.

So far so good. But, in the paper referred to, Achinstein has another problem, namely, can confirmation theory satisfy our intuitive criteria with regard to *analogy* arguments? This problem can be expressed in terms of a simple example as follows: suppose our total evidence is $P(a)Q(a)R(a)S(a)P(b)Q(b)\bar{R}(b)$, then our intuitive requirements regarding analogy arguments would lead us to expect the posterior confirmation of $S(b)$ to be higher than that of $\bar{S}(b)$. And the greater the similarity of a and b as revealed in the evidence, the greater we should expect the difference to be between the two posterior confirmations. Achinstein shows that none of Carnap's λ-systems can satisfy this requirement; indeed it follows in all such systems that the posterior confirmation of $S(b)$ is equal to that of $\bar{S}(b)$. The reason for this (as I pointed out in my 'Analogy and Confirmation Theory', *Philosophy of Science* **31**, 1964, p. 323) is that the λ-systems satisfy Carnap's postulate $C8$, namely that c-functions are symmetrical with respect to Q-predicates (Hintikka's Ct's). This means that the prior probabilities are assigned in such a way that $c_0(Ct_1(a) \cdot Ct_2(b))$, where $Ct_1 \not\equiv Ct_2$, has the same value however similar or different a and b may be; that is, for example, if Ct_1 is $P_1P_2P_3, ..., P_k$, it has the same value whether Ct_2 is $P_1P_2P_3, ..., \bar{P}_k$, or $P_1\bar{P}_2\bar{P}_3, ..., \bar{P}_k$. Now although Hintikka's system is not formalized in this paper, it is clear that his *confirmation* functions, like Carnap's, are symmetrical with respect to Ct-predicates, and it therefore follows that these confirmation functions do not satisfy the analogy criterion.

Do his degrees of *corroboration* do so? The answer is no. Worse, on one of his assumptions about prior confirmation, it is not merely that $corr(S(b))$ is *equal to* $corr(\bar{S}(b))$, as is the case for confirmation in the λ-systems, but $corr(S(b))$ is actually *less than* $corr(\bar{S}(b))$. These highly counter-intuitive results are easily proved as follows: $corr(S(b))$ is equal to the confirmation of the least confirmed constituent compatible with the evidence and with $S(b)$. This is the confirmation of the most restricted world compatible with the truth of these statements. Similarly, $corr(\bar{S}(b))$ is equal to the confirmation of the most restricted world compatible with the evidence and $\bar{S}(b)$. The constituents of these two worlds differ only in terms containing S and $\bar{S}$; in the first the generalization $(x)S(x)$ is true, and in the second $(Ex)S(x)(Ex)\bar{S}(x)$ is true. On the assumption that all constituents have the same prior confirmation, the same evidence will clearly confirm the first constituent equally with the second, so that

$$corr(S(b)) = corr(\bar{S}(b)).$$

But on Hintikka's other assumption, that the prior probability of each constituent is the probability with which it would be true in a completely random finite world, the confirmation of the first is *less* than that of the second, because $(x)S(x)$ is true in fewer possible worlds than $(Ex)S(x)(Ex)\bar{S}(x)$. Hence in this case

$$corr(S(b)) < corr(\bar{S}(b)).$$

This result seems to reflect the fact that analogy arguments are essentially *enumerative*, whereas corroboration tends to explicate elimination.

Of course it may be possible to make some adjustment in Hintikka's system to deal with analogy arguments of this kind without adding undue complexity. But progress in this area demands that every suggested confirmation theory should be closely examined for counter-intuitive consequences, and it seems to me that our reliance upon analogy arguments throughout theoretical science makes satisfaction of the analogy criterion a *sine qua non* of adequacy for a confirmation theory. My own view is that in order to satisfy both the variety and analogy criteria in a natural way and without resorting to *ad hoc* devices it will prove necessary to depart even further from Carnap's original system by abandoning the postulate of symmetry of Q-predicates. I am at present developing a theory in which this is done.

J. HINTIKKA: *Reply.*

The comments which my paper has occasioned serve to call attention to several interesting ways in which the approach I sketch there can be carried further and in some cases has to be carried further.

One point on which further work is needed was indicated by Professor Carnap when he said that giving an equal *a priori* probability to each constituent is an unsatisfactory procedure. He suggests that the concept of a constituent-structure might help us in overcoming the difficulties here.

In terms of the notation I used, an equal distribution of *a priori* probabilities to constituents means that $\alpha = 0$. This is in fact the only case I considered in my earlier papers [1]. Although the confirmation functions one obtains in this way have some very natural qualitative (asymptotic) features, the quantitative results they give are seriously unrealistic. Carnap has consistently rejected the confirmation function $c^\dagger$ because it corresponds to inductive behaviour under which no learning from experience takes place. Well, the choice $\alpha = 0$ lands us in precisely the opposite sort of trouble. A man whose inductive behaviour is based on this choice is bound to exhibit a wild overoptimism in his inductive behaviour vis-à-vis

---

[1] 'Towards a theory of inductive generalization', *Proceedings of the 1964 International Congress for Logic, Methodology and Philosophy of Science*, Y. Bar–Hillel, ed., *Studies in Logic and the Foundations of Mathematics*, North-Holland Publishing Company, Amsterdam, 1965, pp. 274–288; 'On a combined system of inductive logic', *Studia Logico-Mathematica et Philosophica in honorem Rolf Nevanlinna, Acta Philosophica Fennica* **18**, 1965, pp. 21–30.

inductive generalizations. He 'learns too fast' in the sense of jumping to generalizations at a relatively slight provocation.

One has to compensate somehow for this overoptimism. What we need is an index of caution as far as inductive generalizations are concerned. The parameter α was introduced for this very purpose. The larger α is, the slower we are in putting our faith in inductive generalizations. When $\alpha \to \infty$, we become so timid that in an infinite universe we never dare to subscribe to any inductive generalization at all. It is rather interesting to see that in this case the system outlined in TTIG (and extended by taking in α) becomes the one based on $c^{\dagger}$ and the system ('combined system') outlined in my Nevanlinna *Festschrift* paper becomes the one based on Carnap's c^*.

Carnap's question was whether the concept of a constituent-structure helps us here. At first sight it may seem that it does not help us at all. The effects of assigning an equal *a priori* probability to each constituent-structure are in the right direction in one half of all the possible cases but in the wrong direction in the other half of all cases. The situation is this: an even distribution to con-stituent-structures favours those constituents in which either very few or almost all attributive constituents (Q-predicates) are instan-tiated. This is not what we want, for we want an index of caution, i.e. a measure of our reliance on *a priori* considerations alone, and a reliance on *a priori* considerations obviously leads us to prefer those constituents in which all or almost all attributive constituents are said to be exemplified. (The only thing we can expect *a priori* is that everything happens more or less at random, and in a large random world all the different kinds of individuals are likely to occur.) Thus we do not want a distribution which makes those constituents highly probable *a priori* (in relation to others) ac-cording to which few attributive constituents are instantiated, but rather one which makes them highly *im*probable.

Moreover, even in those cases in which the qualitative effects of assigning equal *a priori* probabilities to constituent-structures are in the right direction, they are much too small quantitatively to give us what we need.

What we should have here is not just one dimension, not just one flight of ladders towards those rarefied logician's heavenly spheres which Carnap so charmingly described to us. We should have two dimensions, one of which is just Carnap's old continuum of values of the parameter λ. As Carnap has carefully explained in his earlier works, the different values of λ represent different degrees of reliance on the *a priori* factor in making singular inductive predictions. What we need, and what α is calculated to give us, is a similar measure of the strength of the *a priori* factor in our inductive generalizations. With this difference, the two parameters λ and α are entirely parallel, and can in fact be combined into one and the same two-dimensional system of systems of inductive logic. What messes up things is simply the fact that the effects of *a priori* considerations may first look rather different in the two cases. In the case of singular inductive inference, *a priori* considerations suggest nice finite probabilities, determined by the widths of the predicates involved. In the case of inductive generalization, however, *a priori* considerations favour those constituents in which all (or almost all) Q-predicates are said to be exemplified. This is in fact what happens when a large value of α is chosen.

Thus what we have to do is not to try to get as close to a logician's heaven as possible, but rather to specify as closely as possible our position in the two-dimensional map of that inductivist's limbo in which we are all doomed to live. My parameters λ and α are intended to be co-ordinates of such a map.

Now our position in such a map depends in a sense on the structure of the real world. Carnap has shown how the choice of λ can be motivated in terms of the amount of order or disorder that there is in the world. By order, one here means essentially the regularity with which individuals are concentrated in relatively few attributive constituents among all those attributive constituents which are exemplified at all. Somewhat in the same way, the choice of α depends on the amount of regularity that there is in the world – regularity now in the sense that *all* individuals are concentrated into relatively few Q-predicates, leaving all the others empty.

It is precisely here that the concept of a constituent-structure becomes interesting and important after all. For what a constituent-structure specifies is just the number of different attributive constituents that are allowed to be instantiated (without telling us which these attributive constituents are, as a constituent would do). The smaller this number is, the smaller α we are in some sense justified in choosing. Thus the concept of a constituent-structure is connected with the basic idea which underlies the introduction of my new parameter α. Precisely how this connection is to be specified, remains to be investigated. The basic idea is clear enough: the more attributive constituents there are empty in the actual world, the more general laws hold as a matter of fact, and the better justified we are in some sense in assuming that the regularities that there are in our sample represent genuine regularities in the whole universe.

The concept to which Carnap calls our attention is thus an interesting and important one. It may even have something to do with the pure realm of general laws that Gödel was so impressed by: different constituent-structures go together with different speeds at which we are allowed to climb from the consideration of particular individuals to the Gödelian heaven of completely general truths.

The problems which Dr. Hesse and Mr. Lucas raise call for somewhat different considerations. I shall begin by considering the points Lucas raises, for they can serve as a background to my reply to Hesse also.

There probably are many ways of relating the kinds of observations which Lucas makes to detailed constructive work in inductive logic. The following seems to me the most straightforward, but I recognize that there may be others.

To Lucas' first question I can give a twofold answer. First, it is clear that in the particular systems of inductive logic which I outlined in my paper, the effect he seems to have in mind is *not* caught. The basic reason is the one indicated by Hesse. Like the members of Carnap's λ-continuum, all the systems I have been considering so far are symmetric with respect to the different Q-predicates (attributive constituents). All these predicates are on a par; evidence instantiating one of them is as good as evidence instantiating another. From this basic feature of my systems, various undesirable consequences follow. For instance, if the Q-predicates are to be identified, even roughly, with species of individuals, then the kind of difference between different species with respect to inductive evidence which Lucas mentions is not taken into account.

What I want to emphasize here is that this defect is only one among many difficulties and that this defect is shared by virtually all current approaches to inductive logic. The same asymmetry between different attributive constituents underlies the notorious paradox of confirmation: The generalization 'all ravens are black' is (according to many philosophers) confirmed by observed black ravens, but not e.g. by observed non-black non-ravens. The two Q-predicates 'black raven' and 'non-black non-raven', both of which are compatible with the generalization, are thus not on a par as far as evidence for it is concerned. It also seems to me that essentially the same problem underlies Goodman's difficulty about queer predicates like 'grue' (which means here green before 2000 AD and not green after 2000 AD). The difficulty is simply that the generalization 'all emerald-stages (prior to as well as posterior to 2000 AD) are green' derives more support from our observations (all of which are prior to 2000 AD) of emerald-stages than the symmetrical generalization 'all emerald-stages are grue'. Again we have a case of asymmetry between the different Q-predicates that can be formed from the basic predicates 'green' and 'before 2000 AD' and attributed to emerald-stages.

These difficulties may appear completely artificial, which they are not. It is a merit of Lucas' remarks that they bring out the fact that precisely the same asymmetry which these philosophers' examples highlight also underlies certain important features of actual scientific practice. The same fact is also brought out by Hesse's remark, based on her earlier work on the subject, that certain types of analogy inference turn on asymmetries between different Q-predicates.

It is not difficult, however, to modify the approach which I have outlined so as to allow formally for the required sort of asymmetry between Q-predicates. Work in this direction is still in progress, but certain points can easily be established. There is a very natural way of considering the basic atomic predicates in a given order, e.g. of thinking that our individuals are first divided into ravens and non-ravens according to the principles that underlie our inductive logic, and that the members of these two classes are then similarly divided into black and non-black objects. The details need not concern us here; suffice it to say that then we will find the generalization 'all ravens are black' confirmed by observed black ravens, and by them only. We can also consider several different orderings, and weight them in different ways.

Formally, there thus are no great problems in dealing with the difficulties that are due to asymmetries between different Q-predicates. The kind of variation which Lucas speaks of in his first question can be taken into account by slightly amplifying the approach I have sketched. Although I have not studied the question yet, I also expect that certain types of analogy inference can be accommodated in this way. Much work remains to be done here, however. For one thing, the intuitive basis of the kind of treatment that I have outlined is not fully understood yet. For instance, it is not clear what the concrete intuitive meaning is that is associated to my proposed ordering of the two predicates 'raven' and 'black' in the way I did above.

If all this is acceptable, then I can perhaps put Lucas' second question into a natural perspective. If we introduce parameters which indicate the strength of the various asymmetries that obtain between different Q-predicates, then we also need principles ('second-order' principles, if you want) governing the choice of these parameters and the changes in them that are occasioned by what experience shows us. I take that Lucas' second question pertains to precisely these matters. These second-order principles have not yet been worked out even in simple paradigm cases. However, it is fairly clear that they should in some sense embody (among other features) the 'self-overhauling' character of induction which Lucas describes.

Hence my answer to his second question is that there not only is room within my approach for the kind of questions he raises; if my approach is developed further along the lines just indicated, the considerations he is interested in will be among the questions we are inevitably led to consider by the problems that are due to asymmetries among Q-predicates. It seems to me that in this way we might obtain a useful framework for discussing many interesting features of our actual inductive practices.

My answers to the clear and pertinent questions that Hesse poses are largely implicit in what I have already said or in what I said in the original paper. Surely, what Hesse calls 'statistical gener-alizations', e.g. Carnap's structure-descriptions, are logically stronger than my 'strong generalizations'. Only, in the types of language I am considering (monadic first-order languages) they are not *generalizations*: they cannot be expressed without speaking of particular individuals, for we have no numerical concepts at our disposal.

As far as analogy inferences are concerned, I already conceded that those particular systems with which I dealt in my paper do not accommodate those types of analogy inference that turn on asymmetries between different Q-predicates. What ways there are of correcting this shortcoming was also indicated already. My notion of corroboration was not calculated to explicate analogy inferences, but rather to bring out that a high probability alone is not what a scientific generalization aims at. Moreover, this notion of corroboration was defined only for generalizations. (Perhaps this should have been spelled out more clearly.) Now in her remarks on the relation of this notion to analogy arguments Hesse clearly presupposes that it applies also to singular statements. Hence it is not surprising that what she finds is unsatisfactory, for the example is one to which the notion of corroboration was not intended to be applied in the first place.

The only substantial point on which I seem to disagree with Hesse is the evaluation of the intuitive foundation of Achinstein's requirement of the variety of instances. Hesse is right is saying that Achinstein's appeal is to some form of elimination, or at least can be motivated in such terms. My formulations in this matter may have been a little too concise. But I do not see any need for modifying what I intended to say in the original paper. There is an effect – not an eliminative but perhaps rather an enumerative one – which is simply overlooked by those who believe in the kind of requirement of the variety of instances which Achinstein sets up. Perhaps an extreme case illustrates what I have in mind. Suppose we have a universe describable in terms of two basic predicates, $P(x)$ and $Q(x)$. Suppose we take a random sample of a million individuals, and find all of them satisfying the Q-predicate $P(x)$ & $Q(x) = Ct_0(x)$. This constitutes very strong evidence for the constituent

(*) $(Ex)Ct_0(x)$ & $(x)Ct_0(x)$

and therefore also for the general implication

(**) $(x)(Q(x) \supset P(x))$

which is implied by (*). Now how would the situation change if one (and only one) of the observed individuals were to satisfy, not the Q-predicate $Ct_0(x)$ but rather the different Q-predicate $\sim P(x)$ & $\sim Q(x) = Ct_3(x)$? According to the simple-minded requirement of the variety of instances at issue, this modified evidence should support (**) better than the original evidence, because it exhibits a greater variety of instances. However, the new evidence supports (**) mainly by supporting the constituent

(***) $(Ex)Ct_0(x)$ & $(Ex)Ct_3(x)$ & $(x)[Ct_0(x) \lor Ct_3(x)]$

which again implies (**). But it was found in my paper that the support of the new evidence for (***) is much smaller than the support the old evidence gave to (*), given certain natural assumptions. Without denying that some sort of variety principle is in operation here, it thus seems that there is also another factor here whose effects have to be compensated against the effects of the variety requirement.

This other factor can also be illustrated intuitively. In the two situations which I considered, one might say the following: if the million observed individuals are completely uniform, then this supports very strongly (*) and therefore also (**). If there now is a single exception among the million observations, this actually diminishes our confidence in (**). For although the exception in itself does not contradict (**), it creates the suspicion that there might be other exceptional cases around, some of which would contradict (**).

At least, the consequences of this kind of argument should be weighed against those derived from the requirement of the variety of instances. This is the reason why it seems to me that the appeal by Achinstein and others to the requirement leaves an important feature of the situation out of the picture. This neglected factor is of course effective already in inferences from much smaller samples. Hence it seems to me that the whole issue deserves a much closer analysis than it has so far been given in the literature.

CONSILIENCE OF INDUCTIONS

MARY HESSE

Cambridge University

1. This paper is an exercise in what Goodman calls the 'new riddle of induction', which he takes to be, not the problem of *validation* of induction which Hume found to be insoluble, but rather the *explication* of the concept of 'valid induction' (*Fact, Fiction and Forecast*, p. 68). I shall assume here that the only serious attempts to solve this problem have been in terms of confirmation theories using inverse probability methods. I do not intend to go into the general question of how far and when use of such methods is justified, but rather to examine a particular kind of objection to the idea of confirmation theory as an explication of inductive methods, which is both philosophically interesting and also relevant to a post-positivist understanding of the structure of science. For it is ironic that the most cogent objections now come, not from the positivist statisticians of the thirties, but from non-positivist philosophers such as Kneale, Popper, and the contributors to the confirmation section of the recent Carnap volume in the Library of Living Philosophers. I shall discuss the claim that confirmation theory cannot deal with the theoretical structure of science as elaborated in deductive systems, and argue that the shortcomings of confirmation theory in this respect may be understood and to some extent overcome by a modification in the idea of hypothetico-deductive theories themselves.

I shall assume that the aim of an explication of 'valid induction' is to find a numerical or comparative function $c(h, e)$ – the 'confirmation of hypothesis h given evidence e' – which is a syntactic function of the statements h and e, and which has a high or comparatively high value in those cases where normally accepted or intuitive inductive methods would direct us to accept hypothesis h on evidence e, at least in comparison with other hypotheses having lower c-value. I shall further assume (though this is controversial, and I cannot argue it here) that $c(h, e)$ satisfies the usual axioms for a probability function, and that therefore, if the appropriate prior probabilities exist and are finite, $c(h, e)$ satisfies Bayes' theorem:

$$c(h, e) = c_0(h) \ c(e, h)/c_0(e).$$

A developed confirmation theory requires further axioms which essentially show how to assign the prior probabilities $c_0(h)$, $c_0(e)$ in a self-consistent and intuitively reasonable way, but in what follows I shall not assume any particular method of doing this, for indeed none of the methods so far suggested is satisfactory, and the arguments in favour of *some* probabilistic function are at present much stronger than those in favour of any particular choice of function.

2. *The validity of consilience of inductions.* In the Carnap volume in the Library of Living Philosophers [1], Hilary Putnam argues that in the particular case of Carnap's confirmation theory, no law can be given higher confirmation when it is deducible from a theory than when it is put forward on the basis of empirical data alone. And yet, assuming what Whewell called the 'consilience of inductions', scientists do regard laws as better confirmed when they are consequences of theories than when there is only non-theoretical evidence available; hence, Putnam concludes, Carnap's theory is inadequate as an account of scientific inference. As an example of this kind of inference in practice, Putnam gives the following. Prior to the first large nuclear explosion, suppose all the experimental evidence relevant to the nuclear theory T is summarized as L_1. Let L_2 be the predicted law, for which there is as yet no direct evidence, 'when two subcritical masses of uranium 235 are slammed together to produce a single supercritical mass there will be an explosion'. L_2 was believed with a high degree of confidence, solely because of L_1 and the theory T which explains L_1 and which

---

[1] P. A. Schilpp, ed., Library of Living Philosophers, *The Philosophy of Rudolf Carnap*, Open Court, La Salle, Illinois, 1963, p. 761.

also entails L_2. It is clear that any adequate confirmation theory ought to be able to explicate this inference to L_2.

I shall first give Putnam's own argument for the conclusion that Carnap's theory fails to explicate the inference, and then show that a much more general argument yields the same result, and applies to any probabilistic confirmation theory whatever. This result is of course a much more serious blow to the confirmation project than Putnam indicates. Putnam's argument is essentially as follows. An axiom of Carnap's system states that the value of $c(h, e)$ depends only on the predicates mentioned in h and e, and not upon any other predicates in the language. This is certainly a desirable condition for a confirmation theory, because it ought not to be the case that our assignment of c-values depends on the number of predicates currently in the whole scientific language, nor on our knowing what they all are. The confirmation of a hypothesis on given evidence ought to be independent of possible extensions of the scientific vocabulary in irrelevant respects. But if h is a predicted experimental law and e is an accepted experimental law, both these are expressed in the observation language, whereas a theory which links them is expressed in a theoretical language, or at least, if we do not like the terminology of two languages, it is likely to contain predicates which are essential to the deduction, and which are not among the predicates in e and h. It follows that the value of $c(h, e)$ cannot be affected by any theory mediating between evidence and prediction. All inference is therefore similar to what Mill described as direct induction from particulars to particulars. Theories are redundant.

There is however a much stronger theorem than Putnam's which shows not only that theories in a theoretical language cannot increase the confirmation of predictions, but also that no higher-level deductive system even in the same language can do so either. And this follows not only in Carnap's theory, but in any confirmation theory satisfying the probability axioms. Suppose the data consists of L_1, the prediction is L_2, and a theory T entails both L_1 and L_2. The theorem depends simply on the fact that $c(L_2, L_1)$ is a single-valued function of its arguments L_2, L_1, alone, and that therefore its value cannot depend on whether L_2 and L_1 are both deducible from some T or not. The confirmation of L_2 cannot be raised above its prior value by L_1 merely by virtue of the deducibility of L_2 and L_1 from T', but only if L_2 is dependent upon L_1 itself, in such a way that $c(L_2, L_1) > c_0(L_2)$. If L_2 and L_1 are independent, then under all circumstances $c(L_2, L_1) = c_0(L_2)$ [1].

There seem to be three main reasons why we might expect the contrary of this result. First, it might be argued that, since a theory can gain confirmation from the law L_1 which it entails, and this confirmation will be added to by all the variety of other confirmed data which it entails, such extra confirmation will be 'passed on' to predictions which it also entails. In other words we might hope to be able to show both that

$$(1) \qquad\qquad c(T_1 \, L_1) > c_0(L_2),$$

and also that

$$(2) \qquad\qquad c(L_2, L_1) \geqslant c(T_1, L_1),$$

so that, *merely by virtue of the deducibility of L_1 and L_2 from T*

$$c(L_2, L_1) > c_0(L_2).$$

That this argument is fallacious can easily be shown by transforming the c-values in (1) and (2) by Bayes' theorem; it then emerges that the condition for (1) is the contrary of the condition for (2), so that both cannot be satisfied together.

Secondly, the persuasive character of consilience may arise from the suggestion that when a theory is confirmed by data which it entails, it is then accepted, and thenceforth given confirmation-value 1. In that case, of course, all its further entailments would have confirmation 1. But this suggestion does not adequately

---

[1] Since completing this paper I have found that essentially the same point that is made in this paragraph is already made by Carnap in *Logical Foundations of Probability*, pp. 471–476 in discussing Hempel's suggested conditions of adequacy for a confirmation function. Carnap shows conclusively that in a probabilistic confirmation theory the condition 'If e confirms h, then e confirms every L-consequence of h' is in general not satisfied, but that the condition 'If h L-implies e, then e confirms h' is satisfied. The above theorem follows directly.

explicate situations where we wish to compare the c-values of incompatible theories which are confirmed by the same data, for two incompatible theories cannot both have c-value 1.

Thirdly, a satisfactory theory may be thought to do more to support predictions than do its data alone because of the systematic and explanatory character of the theory. But note that our problem cannot be solved by reflecting the systematic or explanatory characteristics of theories in their prior c-values. If we decided, for example, to give simple theories high c_0-values, or theories which conform to a general explanatory model such as mechanism, this would do nothing to raise the c-values of their predictions, since the above argument is quite independent of the assignment of c_0-values to the theories. Neither will it do to consider the consilience argument as resting on an *elimination* of alternative theories by the data, for the following reason. If T_1 and T_2 are the only alternatives, and $T_1 \supset L_1 \cdot L_2$, while $T_2 \supset \sim L_1$, then the truth of L_1 is sufficient to eliminate T_2 and hence establish T_1 and L_2. But again the intervention of T_1 is unnecessary, because here we know in advance that $L_1 \supset T_1$ and $T_1 \supset L_2$, and thus that $L_1 \supset L_2$, and L_1 and L_2 are not independent.

The theorem when applied to many cases of scientific inference by consilience is, however, highly counter-intuitive, and we seem to be faced with three alternatives:

(1)   Abandon the claim that probabilistic confirmation theories can explicate a generally accepted inductive method.

(2)   Abandon the claim that theories which are based on data (that is, are not *a priori*) do in fact give a greater contribution to the confirmation of the predictions they entail than do the data alone.

(3)   Reinterpret the notion of consilience, and of the relation of theory and law, so that consilience is not invalidated by the theorem.

We shall explore the third alternative.

3.   *Interpretation of laws.* Let us look at the problem in a different light. Suppose we accept the consequence that in confirmation theory a prediction only acquires confirmation directly from the

whole body of relevant data, and not *via* a theory. Does this entail that consilience is invalid or that theories are redundant?

Consider the case of the law of falling bodies deduced from Newton's theory. It has often been pointed out that not only do we regard Newton's theory as increasing our reliance upon the laws deduced from it, such as orbits of earth satellites before there was any experimental evidence about earth satellites, but also we actually allow it to *correct* laws previously generalized from data, as happened with Galileo's law of falling bodies and Kepler's third law of planetary orbits. And yet it seems very implausible to hold that the new form of Galileo's law is given a high c-value by Kepler's laws, the laws of the tides, comets, moons of Jupiter, etc., alone, without intervention of Newton's theory. Denote by L_1 the law (Kepler's second law)

'The radius vector from the sun to the earth sweeps out equal areas in equal times',

and by L_2 the law

'A body dropped from a tower falls a distance s in time t, where $s = f(t)$ (and f is a given function)'.

It is clear that, supposing L_1 and L_2 to be independent, as had been universally assumed before the sixteenth century, no confirmation theory can give a value to $c(L_2, L_1)$ which is greater than $c_0(L_2)$. Newton's theory, however, makes the following additional assertions:

T 'Any two masses in the universe attract with a force proportional to the product of the masses and the inverse square of the distance between them',

I_1 'The sun is a very large mass',

I_2 'The earth is a large mass, but smaller than the sun', and

I_3 'All bodies near the surface of the earth are relatively very small masses'.

Notice that T does not entail L_1 nor L_2 without the additional premiss I ($\equiv I_1 \cdot I_2 \cdot I_3$), for all we can deduce from T together with some rules of mechanics and of the calculus but without I is a pair of statements T_1 and T_2 as follows:

T_1 'The radius vector from one mass to another, where these are relatively far from other large masses, sweeps out equal areas in equal times',

T_2 'A very small mass starting from rest in the neighbourhood of a large mass, and relatively far from other large masses, moves towards the large mass so as to describe distance s in time t where $s = f(t)$'.

Alternatively, T_1 and T_2 may be regarded as L_1 and L_2 as *interpreted* by I_1 to I_3.

Now the question is, are T_1 and T_2 independent in the sense that $c(T_2, T_1) = c_0(T_2)$? The answer is no. In fact, in Newtonian gravitational theory, T_2 is a limiting case of some cases of T_1 when the transverse velocity is very small compared with the radial velocity. That is to say, we have here

$$c(T_2, T_1) > c_0(T_2).$$

Notice that this dependence does not even mention the theory T. But we could regard T_1 and T_2 as implicitly presupposing T in the definition of what a 'mass' is, and indeed in Newtonian theory, gravitational mass *is* understood as that which satisfies T.

Three important consequences follow from consideration of this example:

(1) L_1 can do nothing by itself to raise the confirmation of L_2, neither can it do so in virtue of the deductive system $T \cdot I$, which entails both L_1 and L_2.

(2) T_1 can however raise the confirmation of T_2, and T_1 and T_2 may be regarded as L_1 and L_2 respectively in the *interpretation I*.

(3)   But this confirmational relevance is not due to the fact that T_1 and T_2 are both deductions from T, for this has been shown to have no relevance; it is due rather to the fact that in the interpretation I, the events described by L_1 and L_2 are seen partially to *overlap*, because events satisfying L_1 are now interpreted as including those which satisfy L_2, and hence add to the previous extension of L_1.

In the light of (2) and (3) the conclusion that deducibility from a theory is not relevant to confirmation may seem much more palatable. For now consilience of inductions is saved, although for a reason different from that usually given, and the theory is shown to be necessary for consilience, although it is the theory *qua* reinterpretation of the language of the laws, not the theory *qua* deductive system.

4. *Analogy of laws.* This means that a confirmation theory can only explicate consilience of inductions if the language that is built into it is the language of the relevant scientific theory. Notice that it is not enough to build into it the theory plus the interpretation I, and then expect it to work upon the raw observation language of the laws, for this would again involve *deduction* of the laws, and what is required is not deduction but overlap. This may, however, seem like a *reductio ad absurdum* of the whole project, because surely it is the confirmation of theories and their predictions on the basis of laws that we require, not confirmation which presupposes particular theories in the language of the confirmation theory. There are two possible replies to this.

(1) $T \cdot I_1 \cdot I_2$ may indeed be given confirmation on the basis of L_1; it is only L_2 whose confirmation is unaffected. We might therefore adopt the expedient of moving to a confirmation theory in the language of T whenever $T \cdot I_1 \cdot I_2$ had a high confirmation on L_1. But this would be subject to several difficulties. First, we should still not be able to say anything about L_2, because in order to show that it, or rather its theoretical interpretation, is confirmed, we need I_3, and I_3 is logically independent of $T \cdot I_1 \cdot I_2$, and hence is given no confirmation by L_1. So consilience is still not explicated. Second, it is obviously quite unsatisfactory to have to contemplate a different linguistic basis for confirmation for every new theory which is suggested in science, and furthermore we should be unable to compare confirmations based on different theoretical languages.

(2) The second reply is more radical, and begins with the counter-question: how do we in fact know how to derive predictions such as L_2 from a theory T which is supported by L_1? This question boils down to asking how we choose I_3. And the answer is that to regard L_1 and T as relevant to L_2 is already to interpret L_2 as an instance of T, and therefore to presuppose I_3. But we do not do

this for all possible L_2's. For example, Newton would probably not have regarded a law about the flight of birds (L_3) as interpretable as an instance of T. There may be several kinds of reason for this, but at least one is the fact that the *analogy* between objects mentioned in L_1 and L_2 is closer than that between objects in L_1 and L_3. To depend upon this analogy is not of course to *presuppose* that the theory applies to L_2, and not to L_3, it is only to suggest that this prediction ought to be relied upon to a greater extent than L_3, that is that its confirmation ought to be raised by L_1 and T more than is the confirmation of L_3.

What I am suggesting is that the introduction of a genuinely new terminology is a comparatively rare event. Where it is introduced, no laws in the displaced observation language can be given a higher confirmation by introduction of the new theory than they had already in virtue of the other laws in their own language. But what more often happens is that a potential law is chosen for interpretation as a consequence of the new theory because it is already seen to have an analogy with known laws of the theory, and therefore does not require complete reinterpretation.

We must first consider what is meant by saying that there is an analogy between two laws. The sense of analogy required can be explained by considering how we could extend the notion of dependence between T_1 and T_2 in the Newtonian example to a dependence of the uninterpreted laws L_1 and L_2. The sets of objects satisfying L_1 and L_2 respectively, as described in the observation language, have no members in common, but there is an analogy between objects of the two sets, since in both cases we are concerned with the relative motions of solid bodies separated in space. The difference between Aristotelian and Newtonian physics was that the former did not and the latter did regard this analogy as sufficient to indicate an underlying causal identity.

As a first rather crude approximation we can represent the situation as follows. Law L_1 concerns certain bodies (sun and planets) which have certain observable properties we shall summarize as $F \cdot G$, and asserts that they have certain motions with observable properties which we shall summarize as $P \cdot Q$. (No attempt is made in this first approximation to deal with relational predicates.) L_2 concerns certain bodies (the earth and bodies falling towards it) having observable properties which are in some respects the same as those in L_1 and in some respects different. Let us denote these by $G \cdot H$. Similarly L_2 concerns motions which are in some respects the same as those in L_1 and in some respects different. Call them $Q \cdot R$. We can then represent L_1 as $(x)(F(x) \cdot \cdot G(x) : \supset P(x) \cdot Q(x))$, which we shall abbreviate as $(x)(F \cdot G : \supset P \cdot Q)$, and L_2 as $(x)(G \cdot H : \supset Q \cdot R)$.

Now we shall say that there is an analogy between L_1 and L_2, written $An(L_1, L_2)$. This relation is symmetrical, but not reflexive (because we shall not say there is an analogy unless the objects concerned are different in at least some respects), and not transitive. I shall not attempt here to specify sufficient conditions for the analogy relation [1], because all we need for present purposes is one necessary condition, namely that if $An(L_1, L_2)$, then there is a statement T of the form

$$(x)((F \supset P) \cdot (G \supset Q) \cdot (H \supset R))$$

such that $T \supset L_1 \cdot L_2$ but not conversely.

Informally, the statement $G \supset Q$ picks out from L_1 and L_2 their common features, and the statement T asserts that G and Q are the ingredients in L_1 and L_2 which make these laws substantially identical, while the features which are different in the antecedents account for those which are different in the consequents, and these features are irrelevant to the 'causal' law $G \supset Q$. We might say T 'abstracts the analogy' of L_1, L_2. T is therefore a theory about L_1 and L_2, and is not entailed by them.

To say that we should have $c(L_2, L_1) > c_0(L_2)$, and thus maintain consilience, is to suggest extending the notion of logical dependence from the case where the sets of objects referred to by L_1 and L_2 have members in common to the case where all the objects of L_1

---

[1] Sufficient conditions could be specified generally in, for example, Carnap's new theory (the η-theory, in R. Carnap and W. Stegmüller, *Induktive Logik und Wahrscheinlichkeit*, Vienna, 1959, Appendix B), by turning the problem round and defining the relation $An(L_1, L_2)$ to be that relation which holds when (i) no individual or set of individuals satisfies both L_1 and L_2 and (ii) $c(L_2, L_1) > c_0(L_2)$.

and L_2 respectively have *properties* in common, although the sets of objects have *no members* in common. (We are of course relying on an intensional interpretation of properties, for on an extensional interpretation *all* objects have properties in common, namely those sets that include the objects.)

Let us now try to reconstruct Putnam's example in terms of this schema. We have a number of laws about the atomic constituents of matter (for simplicity let us conflate them into one law L_1) which follow from nuclear theory T when the objects mentioned in the laws are interpreted as objects of that theory. We have a further predicted (putative) law L_2 about the explosion of uranium 235, which also follows from T in a suitable interpretation, but of which there are as yet no known instances. We make this interpretation of uranium 235 because there are already known, independently of the theory, to be analogies between the objects of L_1 and those of L_2 (including analogies between chemical elements, and so on). Let L_1, L_2, T be represented as above. Then L_2 follows from T, but we have already seen that this in itself does not give L_2 extra confirmation. L_2 does not follow from L_1, nor is there even an overlap of the sets of objects satisfying L_1 and L_2 respectively, since we may suppose that the set predicated by $F \cdot G \cdot H$ is empty. Hence unless further steps are taken, L_1 and L_2 are independent, and L_2 can gain no confirmation from either T or L_1.

This result is an example of a characteristic of Carnap's first theory of confirmation, in which arguments by analogy are given no confirmatory value. But it is not a necessary characteristic of all probabilistic confirmation theories, and it is indeed sufficiently counter-intuitive to render any theory in which it appears quite inadequate as a general explication of inductive methods. It has indeed been corrected in Carnap's η-theory, in which it can be shown that, if L_1 and L_2 are as specified above, then

$$c(L_2, L_1) > c_0(L_2),$$

in virtue of the occurrence of the predicate G in both laws, that is, in virtue of the relation $An(L_1, L_2)$. If we accept that a consistent confirmation theory incorporating this desirable feature is thereby shown to be possible (although there are unsatisfactory features about this particular one), then consilience is rescued at least to this extent – that L_2 is given confirmation by its analogy with L_1, though not by its deducibility from T.

5. *Theories as sets of analogical laws.* Is this a sufficient explication of consilience? Does it not still leave the theory in the air, as irrelevant to the prediction of new laws? In the example of the nuclear explosion it appears so, but perhaps this is an illusion derived from thinking in conventional terms of *levels* of theory and law. Might we not derive a new law L_2 by analogy with a *theoretical* statement T_1 rather than a known law L_1? We should then have the following: $T_1 \supset L_1$, hence $c(T_1, L_1) > c_0(T_1)$. Also L_2 is analogous to T_1 (for example, regard L_1 in the previous example as T_1 in this). Then $c(L_2, T_1) > c_0(L_2)$. So it looks as though the c-value of T_1 is raised by L_1, and then raises that of L_2, which now does not *follow* from T_1 but is analogous to it. Unfortunately, however, if $An(L_2, T_1)$, then there must be a T' such that $T' \supset T_1$, $T_1 \supset L_1$ and $T' \supset L_2$. But we know that in that case we cannot have $c(L_2, T') > c(L_2, L_1)$ by the previous argument. It therefore follows that $c(L_2, T_1) = c(L_2, L_1)$, and hence L_2 is not given confirmation by the analogy with T_1 unless there is also an analogy of equal effectiveness with L_1.

We have to conclude from this argument that we never rely upon a predicted law by consilience in virtue of its deducibility from a theory, nor even its analogy with a theory, unless it also has a logical dependence on or an analogy with known laws. I have been unable to think of a counter-example in scientific practice to this result, although there may well be one. But until one is produced it is worth exploring the consequences of the result. It is very difficult to rid oneself of the idea of a theory as a *deductive* system with *levels* of consequences, in spite of many indications that this is a highly artificial reconstruction, of which the fate of consilience is only one example. What might very tentatively be suggested is that the function of the theory is the indication and systematic extraction (or abstraction) of *analogies* between a number of empirical systems, the best theory being the one which embodies the strongest and most extensive analogy. A theory would therefore be established not so much when its deductive consequences are large in number, but when the number of analogous systems realizing it in the empirical world is large. (This would incidentally have the effect, given the above definition of analogous laws, that the number of its empirically realized deductive consequences is also large.) The function of the theory in relation to prediction of laws would then be to indicate what are the respects in which a new system has the strongest analogy with other systems, for those will be the respects which will yield the best confirmed laws in the new system (the confirmation being, of course, analogical and not by deduction). The whole process would be something like Mill's induction from particulars to particulars (which incidentally, if we are realistic, also takes place by analogy and not identity of instances). Mill's inference does not presuppose a general law, except in deciding what is an instance. At the level of laws, induction takes place by analogy, not presupposing a higher level theory, except in the sense that the theory indicates which analogies to use in the inference.

At this point a possible objection should be considered. It has been suggested that the relation of analogy between laws is *sufficient* for the existence of some theory which abstracts the analogy and is such that it entails the laws without being entailed by them. It has further been implicitly claimed that only a theory of this character will support consilience, and that therefore not all theories which satisfy the hypothetico-deductive conditions of merely entailing laws do support consilience. But might it not be possible to show that *all* hypothetico-deductive theories can be formulated in such a way that they express an analogy between their entailed laws in the sense defined? If this were the case the condition of analogy would of course be trivial. To show that this trivialisation is not possible it is sufficient to show that not all pairs of laws deducible from some deductive system T have an analogy in the sense defined. And to show *this* in the case of a general definition of analogy suggested in the footnote above, it is sufficient to show that not all pairs of laws L_1, L_2 deducible from some T satisfy

$$c(L_2, L_1) > c_0(L_2).$$

This is indeed the case, for instances of pairs of laws which fail to satisfy this condition in Carnap's η-theory can easily be given, for example

$$L_1: (x)(E \cdot F : \supset P)$$
$$L_2: (x)(G \cdot H : \supset R)$$

which are entailed by

$$T: \quad (x)((F \supset P) \cdot (H \supset R)).$$

The account of theories suggested here helps to elucidate one problem in the logic of the use of *models* as interpretations of theories. A realistic view of models would hold that successful use of a model (such as the billiard ball model of gases) indicates that gases are 'really' composed of systems of particles having a high analogy with Newtonian billiard balls, and that this interpretation of kinetic theory can be *refuted* when the model is found to depart too far from experimental data on gases. The problem then arises that there is a sense in which *every* such model that has been proposed has been refuted as soon as proposed, because though there may be analogies between the system being explained and the model (between, for instance, gases and clouds of billiard balls) there are also always differences, distortions and deliberate falsifications or simplifications introduced in thinking about the theory in terms of the model. If this is always the case, what is it that happens when a model is dropped as being too different from the theory to be further useful? In order to answer this question it seems to be necessary to divide the properties of the model into 'essential' and 'inessential' properties. If inessential properties are not consistent with the theory, the model need not be discarded, but if essential properties are inconsistent, then the model is refuted. Our analysis of theories suggests a way of distinguishing essential from inessential properties of a model. According to the view presented here, theories consist just in the abstraction of analogical laws from a large number of empirical systems. Properties of a model which are essential, therefore, are those (such as mechanical properties) which are related by laws already known to be analogous to the laws of a great many other systems, whereas those which are inessential (for example, the colour, size, and two-dimensional motions of billiard balls) are those which are not so related, and which are therefore irrelevant to the theory.

Finally, it should be said that no claim is being made here that all cases of theoretical inference are covered by this analysis. There will no doubt be some theories which use a radically different language from the observation language, and which are dependent on no analogies already recognized in the observation language. What is being claimed here is

(1) that these cases are rarer than the hypothetico-deductive account of theories suggests, and

(2) that where they do occur there is no inductive inference, but only hypothetico-deductive 'conjecture', and *a fortiori*, that they are explicated by no confirmation theory, and no consilience of inductions can be assumed.

L. J. COHEN: *An argument that confirmation functors for consilience are empirical hypotheses.*

Dr. Hesse's very interesting paper falls into two parts. She argue-first that if confirmation functors are to satisfy the usual probability axioms one cannot use the familiar notion of a hypotheticos deductive system in order to explicate increase of confirmation by what Whewell called consilience. She then argues, secondly, that this explication may still be achieved if one replaces the familiar notion of a hypothetico-deductive system by the notion of a theory which picks out the analogy between laws instead of entailing them.

In the interests of brevity I shall confine my own remarks to the first of these two propositions. For reasons set forth elsewhere [1] I myself believe that in a quantitative confirmation theory for eliminative induction, or confirmation by consilience, degree of confirmation is best not taken as any function at all of any relevant probabilities. But even on Hesse's assumption that confirmation functors here should satisfy the usual probability axioms I cannot see that she has established any kind of incongruence between hypothetico-deductive systems, on the one hand, and confirmation by consilience, on the other.

If we are to apply the twentieth-century terminology of confirmation functors, etc., to describe Whewell's very important insight [2], we must say – at the simplest – something like this. We have two sets of sensory 'impressions', reported in E_1 and E_2, respectively, which are 'colligated' by induction, as Whewell put it, into two 'facts' of very different kinds, described in L_1 and L_2, respectively. A 'conception of the mind' is then 'superinduced' upon these two facts, whereby they are both seen to exemplify, despite their great difference from one another, a single general

---

[1] Cf. 'A logic for evidential support', *British Journal for the Philosophy of Science* **17**, 1966.

[2] Cf. W. Whewell, ed., *The Philosophy of the Inductive Sciences*, vol. I, pp. 42 ff. and vol. II, 1840, pp. 210 ff.

theory – call it T. This latter development is called by Whewell a 'consilience of inductions', and is said to provide a very high degree of support for the theory so achieved. In other words we have an earlier stage of scientific investigation at which E_2 is thought irrelevant to L_1, given E_1, i.e.

(1) $$c(L_1, E_1 \ \& \ E_2) = c(L_1, E_1),$$

and a later stage of investigation at which E_2 is thought positively relevant to L_1, i.e.

(2) $$c(L_1, E_1 \ \& \ E_2) > c(L_1, E_1),$$

and this is just because E_2 is positively relevant to T, i.e.

(3) $$c(T, E_1 \ \& \ E_2) > c(T, E_1).$$

Dr. Hesse's argument, transposed into these terms, is that no probabilistic confirmation theory can explicate the dependence of (2) on (3), since $c(L_1, E_1 \ \& \ E_2)$ is a single-valued function of its arguments and cannot depend on whether L_1 is deducible from T or not. But I should have thought that one way at least to explicate the dependence of (2) on (3) would be to construct two confirmation systems, S_L and S_T, such that T is not well-formed in S_L, and (1), but not (2) or (3), is provable in S_L, while both (2) and (3), but not (1), are provable in S_T. S_L would explicate the pattern of our reasoning about confirmation before we have thought up the 'conception' expressed in T, while S_T explicates the pattern afterwards. In this way we should do justice to Whewell's insistence that 'in every inductive inference an act of invention is requisite', by which a new conception is superinduced on old facts, and at the same time we could retain the notion of a hypothetico-deductive system which seems so close to Whewell's own ideas about the hierarchical structure of scientific theory. If one sets out with the object of explicating the way in which degree of confirmation is increased by what *Whewell* called consilience, this procedure seems to me to be preferable to Hesse's.

Perhaps Hesse will object that, as she remarks in her paper on a somewhat different issue, 'it is obviously quite unsatisfactory to have to contemplate a different linguistic basis for confirmation for every new theory which is suggested in science, and furthermore we should be unable to compare confirmations based on different theoretical languages'. Presumably she herself would therefore not wish to pay any attention here to Whewell's insistence on the inventive element in inductive generalisation. But, if one may disregard that point of Whewell's, then it is perfectly easy to represent the consilience situation in a higher-order confirmation theory that can take statements about first-order confirmation systems as arguments of its confirmation functors. For what is at issue, when we discuss how valuable a case of consilience we have, is just the extent to which our collateral information supports the view that S_T is a more adequate explication for the language of science than S_L. We want to know at least whether

$$c(S_T \text{ is fully adequate, } I) > c(S_L \text{ is fully adequate, } I)$$

should be derivable in our second-order confirmation theory, where I reports all the collateral information available.

Of course, to put the question this way is to treat (1), (2) and (3) as empirical hypotheses, not as L-truths. But by raising earlier the question of the choice between S_L and S_T I was by implication arguing that this is just how (1), (2) and (3) should be treated. For if we suppose that $c(L_1, E_1 \& E_2)$ has a higher value in S_T than in S_L, then to that extent the choice between S_L and S_T depends on how good a case of consilience is afforded by the deducibility of both L_1 and L_2 from T; and how good a case this is depends in turn on the nature of the difference between L_1 and L_2. If our collateral knowledge tells us that this variation of circumstance – from the circumstances of L_1 to the circumstances of L_2 – is a valuable one for the testing and confirmation of hypotheses like T, we shall conclude from that empirical premiss to the superiority of S_T over S_L. But, if it is like finding that a law of mechanics which works for blue marbles also works for red ones, we shall conclude from our knowledge of such matters as the independence of marbles' colour and velocity that there is very little reason for choosing a system in which (2) is derivable. If we want to deal realistically with induction by variation of circumstance, as distinct from enumerative induction, we cannot afford to ignore the empirical evidence that exists for differences between the degrees of support obtainable by different kinds of variation. It was an *empirical* discovery that there was something radically deficient in the battery of tests that registered thalidomide as non-toxic.

In short, it seems to me that when the full complexity of the consilience (minus concept-invention) situation is appreciated it ought in principle to be possible to explicate it without abandoning either the notion of a hypothetico-deductive system or the requirement of a single linguistic basis. But of course we are as yet still far from actually having any satisfactory first-order confirmation system for scientific theories, let alone a second-order system of the kind desiderated above.

J. L. MACKIE: *A simple model of consilience.*

I should like to consider a simple model of consilience which is closely related to that offered by Dr. Hesse in the section on Interpretation of Laws. L_1 is the law 'All M are N'; L_2 is the law 'All P are Q'; L_3 is the law 'All R are S'; I_1 is the statement 'All M are RA and all RA are M and all N are SA and all SA are N'; I_2 is the statement 'All P are RB and all RB are P and all Q are SB and all SB are Q'; L'_1 is the law 'All RA are SA'; L'_2 is the law 'All RB are SB'; I is the conjunction of I_1 and I_2; and T is the conjunction of I and L_3. That is to say, L_1 and L_2 are logically independent laws about subjects which are *prima facie* different and non-overlapping, but I_1 and I_2 interpret L_1 and L_2 as asserting L'_1 and L'_2 respectively, and L'_1 and L'_2 are applications of, and are entailed by, L_3. We may call L_3 the theoretical law, but the theory, T, includes both this and the interpretation statements summed up as I.

The deductive relations in this model are as follows. T entails L'_1 and L'_2, and also L_1 and L_2; L_3 entails L'_1 and L'_2 but does not entail L_1 or L_2; L_1 & I entails L'_1, and L'_1 & I entails L_1, but L_1 does not by itself entail L'_1, or *vice versa* – and corresponding relations hold for L_2 and L'_2.

It seems plausible to say that L'_1 confirms L_3, that is, that 'All RA are SA' confirms 'All R are S'. Now since L_3 entails L'_2, we want to say that L'_1 confirms L'_2 by way of L_3. Hesse's theorem shows that this can be the case only if L'_1 confirms L'_2 directly, that is, only if 'All RA are SA' confirms 'All RB are SB'. But, as Hesse points out, we can well admit such confirmation by analogy. Thus we can agree both that the theoretical law L_3 is confirmed by its applications L'_1 and L'_2, and also that each of these confirms the other, that there is consilience between them. On the other hand, we admit that L_1 does not confirm L_2 (or *vice versa*), although both are deducible from T; this fits in with Hesse's theorem.

The implications of this model agree fairly closely with what Hesse says at the end of the section on Interpretation of Laws. However, the model shows that it is not essential that 'the events described by L_1 and L_2 are seen partially to *overlap*': the classes RA and RB might well exclude one another. Also, Hesse's statement that 'the fact that T_1 and T_2 are both deductions from T' (i.e., in my formulation, that L'_1 and L'_2 are both deductions from L_3) 'has been shown to have no relevance' seems too strong. It is true that *mere* deducibility is not enough, but it is highly relevant that L'_1 and L'_2 are deducible from L_3 *in a particular way*, namely as applications of the law 'All R are S' to the more specific subjects RA and RB. This, and the point that there is an *analogy* between L'_1 and L'_2, are surely only different ways of looking at the important connection between them. Again, any evidence that disconfirmed L_3 would also tell against the analogical confirmation of L'_2 by L'_1, at least unless it could be shown that there was a closer analogy between L'_1 and L'_2 than between L'_2 and the disconfirming evidence, and the latter would be equivalent to finding a law, say L_4, which was not disconfirmed by this evidence but of which L'_1 and L'_2 could still be regarded as applications.

At the same time this model does some justice to what Dr. Cohen calls 'Whewell's very important insight'. The 'conception of the mind' which brings L_1 and L_2 together is the interpretation I which transforms them into L'_1 and L'_2, which do confirm both one another and the theoretical law L_3 which they each '*exemplify*'.

It seems to me that what Hesse has shown is not that the hypo-thetico-deductive model is incompatible with, or even irrelevant to, confirmation by consilience, but rather that we get confirmation by consilience only where the consilient inductions *exemplify* a single principle or theoretical law; it is not sufficient that they should merely be co-deducible from what we lump together as a single 'theory'.

All of this is independent of the question where the terms symbol-ised by 'R', 'S', 'A', and 'B' come from, whether they are additions to the scientific language or are already present in it when L_1 and L_2, which do not use these terms, are first formulated. Even if these terms are available, it may be quite an achievement either to see the truth of the interpretation statements I_1 and I_2, or to frame them as hypotheses for testing. In the gravitational example, the term 'mass' (which would correspond roughly to my 'R') as used in Newton's law (my L_3) is in some way a refinement of a term available to Galileo and Kepler. But some terms in nuclear theory may be completely new in relation to the language of chemistry, Again, in some cases, such as the gravitational example, L_3 may be confirmed only by L'_1, L'_2, and similar laws, or indirectly by L_1, L_2, and so on, so that L_3 is itself up for consideration when the consilience is suggested, and is the main beneficiary of this consilience; in other cases, e.g. the molecular theory of gases, L_3 (here the laws of the mechanics of elastic bodies) may be well confirmed already by L_1 and I_1 (e.g. the behaviour of billiard balls and the observation that they are, approximately, elastic bodies) and then the important part of the theory is I_2, the molecular interpretation of gases. But these differences do not affect the central fact of consilience, the confirmation relations which link L'_1, L'_2, and L_3 together, and give point to the interpretation statements which connect them with L_1 and L_2.

This account is very far from 'leaving the theory in the air'. It remains true, at the end as at the beginning, that L_1 does not confirm L_2: there is no way of going from one *uninterpreted* empirical law to the other without bringing in the theory at all. What is true is that we can go from L'_1 to L'_2 without bringing in L_3: the analogical confirmation of L'_2 by L'_1, and its indirect confirmation by way of L_3, are *alternative* reconstructions. But L_3 alone is not the theory: the theory, T, includes the interpretation statements, and these are in general synthetic statements, not mere linguistic transformations. The theory, including these statements, is vital both for consilience and for the prediction of new laws; and this is not just the theory '*qua* reinterpretation of the *language* of the laws' (the italics are mine), but rather the theory as including new, synthetic, assertions about features which are common to the things or situations that are the subjects of the laws, but which are not mentioned in the initial observational formulations of those laws, L_1 and L_2.

W. C. KNEALE: *Requirements for consilience.*

I have found Dr. Hesse's paper very interesting, but I must confess that I have misgivings about her account of consilience, partly because I do not share her hope that it may be found possible to explain consilience of inductions within a probabilistic theory of confirmation, but mainly because I do not think it plausible to suppose that all cases of consilience can be analysed in the way she suggests.

If I understand her right, she holds that a theory may be related to a set of empirical laws in the way John Stuart Mill thought that a law was related to a set of pairs of events, namely as a summary of analogies each of which would be equally respectable by itself. And according to her explanations it is apparently a necessary condition for the holding of an analogy between two laws L_1 and L_2 that L_1 should be replaceable by a conjunction CS_1 and L_2 by a conjunction CS_2 where C is a non-trivial common part and S_1 and S_2 are special hypotheses each independent of the other and both alike independent of C. It is true she does not talk about replaceability, but the phraseology she uses when introducing the expression $An(L_1, L_2)$ seems to me to imply what I have just said. Now if this condition is fulfilled, it does indeed follow that

$$c(L_2, L_1) > c_0(L_2)$$

in a probabilistic theory of confirmation. For

$$c(L_2, L_1) = c(CS_2, CS_1)$$
$$= c(S_2, S_1)$$
$$= c_0(S_2),$$

and

$$c_0(S_2) > c_0(L_2),$$

simply because S_2 without C is less restrictive than L_2. But it does not seem correct to say that consilience occurs only between hypotheses of law for which it is possible in principle to distinguish C, S_1, and S_2. Often, as in Putnam's example, consilient hypotheses appear to be related rather as the determinates red and green, both of which involve colour, though neither is to be defined as a conjunction of colour with something else.

M. B. Hesse: *Reply.*

I have little to quarrel with in Dr. Cohen's helpful remarks. It is true that if what Whewell means by consilience is the inductive support of a theory which has involved a new 'conception', 'super-induced' upon the facts, then no single confirmation system will explicate the dependence of Cohen's expression (2) on his (3). I have said as much at several points of the paper, and I do not deny that this may be a correct description of certain aspects of theoretical inference. However, *if* this is what Whewell means by consilience (and his modes of expression are not precise enough to enable one to be confident about this), then I think Whewell is wrong to claim that 'in every inductive inference' such a new conception is involved. Some inferences take place by means of analogies which do not involve a new basic language or a second confirmation system, and it is these which I attempted to explore. I am, however, inclined to agree with Cohen that something like the second-order confirmation system he describes will be needed for complete explication of the inference-relations between different theories, and that the first-order c-functions may then be in a sense empirical. Since the difficulties of such a system are, as he admits, formidable, it seems wise to see first how far a single-order system can be made to go.

Professor Mackie has provided a further useful example to show that it is analogy rather than mere deducibility which justifies inductive inference. In response to his remarks and those of Cohen, I should like to try to spell out more clearly what the upshot of this thesis seems to me to be for the hypothetico-deductive account of theories. For the reasons given in section 4 of my paper, I do not believe there is any *inconsistency* between the hypothetico-deductive account and the account in terms of analogy. It does, however, seem clear that deducibility of laws from theory is not a *sufficient* account of accepted patterns of inductive inference. The further question arises as to whether it is *necessary*. I now incline to the view that it is not necessary, for the following reason. In section 4 I informally described the function of the theory as that of picking out from L_1 and L_2 their common features, which are asserted by the theory to be the essential causal factors which 'explain' both L_1 and L_2. In terms of the example there given, this means that the theory might be just the statement $(x)(G \supset Q)$. This theory does not attempt also to 'explain' those features in which the objects described by the laws differ, although in the original statement of the laws these features might have played an equally prominent part. For example, when a law regarding falling bodies is first stated, it is stated to hold between lumps of matter with all their commonly-assumed spatio-temporal and material characteristics, and a particular body, the earth, with all its commonly-assumed characteristics. In the statement of the law no distinction can initially be made between features later regarded as 'essential' to the motions and those which are accidental. A satisfactory theory is not required to 'explain' features other than those which it itself regards as essential; in other words, the law as originally stated is unlikely to be deducible *in toto* from an acceptable theory, but only those features of the law in respect of which the law is analogous to other laws. No doubt we tacitly modify our expression of the law accordingly, and regard Galileo's law, for example, as referring to bodies only in their dynamical aspects, but in its original form, when it might be expressed

$(x)(F \cdot G : \supset P \cdot Q)$, it is clearly not deducible from a theory expressed as $(x)(G \supset Q)$ [1]. I conclude that while the hypothetico-deductive account is compatible with the account of theories as statements of analogies between laws, it is neither a necessary nor a sufficient condition for the relation of theory and law developed in this paper.

On Professor Kneale's interesting remarks I have two points to make. First, he suggests that for an analogy to hold between two laws L_1 and L_2, it is necessary that L_1 be *replaceable* by $C \cdot S_1$, and L_2 by $C \cdot S_2$, where by replaceable he seems to mean that there is logical equivalence between these mutually replaceable expressions. This is certainly not the case in general, and it is not even the case in the highly simplified example I give, for if L_1 is $(x)(F \cdot G : \supset P \cdot Q)$ this is not *equivalent to* $(x)((F \supset P) \cdot (G \supset Q))$, but only *entailed by* the latter expression. What is necessary for the relation $An(L_1, L_2)$ to hold is that there should be some theory which explains the two laws as arising from common properties or relations among the objects described by the laws, and in more complex cases there may well be more than one such theory. Kneale's proof of the condition $c(L_2, L_1) > c_0(L_2)$ in fact holds only in the most trivial case of analogy of laws.

Secondly, I find very interesting his suggestion that consilience may depend on a relation between hypotheses which is like that between determinates of one determinable. An adequate comment on this would be too long for inclusion here, but I will briefly indicate the way it would go. Broadly speaking, our intuitive criteria for a relation of inductive analogy between two objects are the same as our criteria for classifying them in the same or neighbouring species or kinds [2]. This may not be true of all methods of classification, but it is true of those which aim to reveal objective

---

[1] This aspect of the non-deducibility of laws from theories which explain them is additional to the points made by Feyerabend, Sellars, and others, regarding the possibility that law statements are *corrected* by theories which explain them.

[2] I have begun to explore the relation between analogy and classification in my 'On defining analogy', *Proc. Aris. Soc.* **60**, 1959–1960, p. 79, and in 'Aristotle's logic of analogy', *Philosophical Quarterly* **15**, 1965, p. 328.

relations between the objects classified, for these relations will be
of the kind: members of a species share such-and-such properties
in common [1], therefore it is likely that other properties possessed
by some of them will also be possessed by others; that is to say,
the relations between members of a species are those of inductive
analogy. Now a classification may be based on possession of properties in common, as in the suits of a pack of playing cards, or it
may be based on relations which are more like those of determinables
to determinates, as for instance the properties 'having petals', and
'having red petals'. 'Having red petals' predicated of a certain
object would certainly be regarded as a better analogical ground
for predicting 'having yellow petals' of another otherwise similar
object, than for predicting of it 'having no petals'. How to express
and how to weight properties at different levels, such as 'having
petals', 'having no petals', and 'having red petals', is currently a
matter of debate in classification theory, but there is no reason
to suppose it in principle insoluble, and any acceptable solution
will also be a potential solution of the problem of defining analogy-
relations in the language of a confirmation theory. In other words,
Kneale's conception of what kinds of relation between laws and
hypotheses can be expressed in confirmation theory seems to me
too narrow. We can already see how to proceed beyond his very
simple example, and there is no compelling reason why we should
not deal satisfactorily with still more complex cases.

---

[1] This does not imply that there is a set of necessary and sufficient
defining characteristics of a species, for the relation between the objects
of one species may be that of 'family resemblance'.

INDUCTIVE LOGIC AND INDUCTIVE INTUITION [1]

RUDOLF CARNAP

University of California, Los Angeles

I should like to discuss here some questions about the nature of inductive logic, the role of rationality in the foundation of inductive logic, and finally the epistemological question of the source of our insights about validity in inductive logic: a source I propose to call 'inductive intuition'. In earlier years, the whole question of the legitimacy and the very existence of inductive logic was still under debate. When I talked then to philosophers about logical probability and inductive logic, I had to spend most of my time in an attempt to convince them that such things existed. In recent years, I think, the situation has changed considerably; the radical doubt is less frequently expressed. Therefore I will not talk about it today. I will rather presuppose that there is such a thing as inductive logic and clarify some aspects of it. I shall not try here to solve problems *within* inductive logic, because this is, to a great extent, mathematical work. Among philosophers it seems more fruitful to discuss more general problems which we have still to solve and clarify [2]. There are especially two problems to which I want to address myself here. The first is usually known as the problem of justification, and the second is the epistemological problem of inductive logic.

When I speak here about justification, I do not have in mind the grand old problem of justification discussed so much since Hume's time. I think it has become clear in recent years that the old problem is not the right way of asking the question. But still

---

[1] This paper was written in a period of research on inductive logic supported by the National Science Foundation (Grant G 22315).

[2] Carnap, R., 'The aim of inductive logic', in E. Nagel, P. Suppes, A. Tarski, eds., *Logic, methodology, and philosophy of science*, Proc. of the 1960 Intern. Congress, Stanford, California, 1962.

some question of justification must be raised; that is the task of the philosopher. But I would like to give the question a form different from the customary one. If we search for a justification, the first thing we have to make clear to ourselves is this: to which particular point or points in the system of inductive procedure should we direct our scrutiny? Where should we probe for justification or, as I prefer to put it, for reasons? Many believe that the essence of inductive reasoning is to make inferences of a special kind. From this point of view, the demand for justification would naturally be directed at any alleged principles of inductive inference. I would not say that it is wrong to regard inference making as the aim. But from my point of view it seems preferable to take as the essential point in inductive reasoning the determination of probability values. I need hardly add that by 'probability' I mean here, not the frequency concept of probability, which is used in statistics and in physics, but another concept, which is sometimes called 'the logical concept of probability'; I call it also 'the inductive concept of probability'. In my view inductive logic is the theory of this particular concept of probability. I believe the distinction between the two concepts is clear enough today, so I need not say more about it. Inductive probability is related to degree of belief, as Ramsey explained it decades ago [1]. But I would like to distinguish two kinds of questions of degree of belief, or two theories about degree of belief. The one is a factual, empirical theory which belongs to psychology. It investigates under what conditions people have beliefs of such and such degree. (The degree of belief of a person X in a proposition H is measured in the customary way by the highest betting quotient with which X is willing to bet on H.) This psychological investigation is in itself very interesting. But in inductive logic we are not concerned with the actual degrees of belief that people have and the causal connections between these degrees and other factors, but rather with the *rational* degree of belief. Thus inductive logic has the task of telling us how to arrive at values for our degree of belief which

---

[1] Ramsey, F. P., *The foundations of mathematics and other logical essays*, London and New York, 1931.

we can defend as rational. I share the view, going back to Bayes, that it is useful to investigate degrees of belief in connection with decision making. From this point of view we have to distinguish between empirical decision theory which investigates decisions based on actual degrees of belief, and normative decision theory which determines rational degrees of belief as those which lead to reasonable decisions. Later I shall explain the relation between inductive logic and this theory of rational degrees of belief; they are not identical.

Thus we have to consider the question: how can we find principles which guide us to reasonable degrees of belief? I call a system of degrees of belief for a given field of propositions a *credence function*. We wish to distinguish between reasonable and non-reasonable credence functions. Therefore we search for principles of rationality for credence functions. As the first example of a principle or requirement of rationality I will mention the requirement of coherence proposed by Ramsey and de Finetti [1]. Their argument is as follows. Suppose a person has a certain credence function for certain propositions indicating his willingness to accept offered bets on each of these propositions. (It may be a real person whose credence function we determine by a psychological investigation, or merely a fictitious person we assume hypothetically.) Suppose that this credence function is of such a kind that we can find a finite system of bets which fulfills the following two conditions. First, in each of the bets, the betting quotient is equal to the value of the credence function for the proposition in question: therefore the person will accept all these bets; and further, the system is such that in each possible outcome, that is to say, for each logically possible assignment of truth values to the propositions involved in these bets, the total balance of the gains and losses in the various bets of the system is negative: in other words, the person suffers a net loss in each possible case. Since this disastrous character of the given betting system can be determined

---

[1] De Finetti, B., 'La prévision: ses lois logiques, ses sources subjectives', *Annales de l'Institut Henri Poincaré*, 7, 1937, pp. 1–68. English translation in H. E. Kyburg and H. E. Smokler, eds.: *Studies in subjective probability*, New York, 1964.

by a purely logical analysis before any of the predictions on which bets are made in this system is found to be true or false, it would obviously be unreasonable for the person to accept such a betting system. Therefore his credence function, which makes him accept this betting system, is unreasonable. De Finetti calls a credence function, or, as he says, a system of beliefs, 'coherent' if and only if it excludes any system of bets of this unfortunate kind.

So this is our *first requirement of rationality*: the credence function must be *coherent*. Now there is an interesting theorem asserted by Ramsey and later proved by de Finetti. It says that a credence function is coherent if and only if it satisfies the ordinary basic axioms of the calculus of probability. Thus, in particular, a credence function must fulfill the addition principle: for incompatible propositions A and B, the credence value (degree of belief) for the conjunction A *and* B must be the sum of the values for A and for B.

The first requirement of rationality seems quite plausible. Our second example of a required property is similar. I use for it the term 'strict coherence' because it implies coherence but is some-what stronger. It excludes not only those very bad betting systems which I described earlier, but also betting systems of the following kind which are not quite as bad, but still, I think, unacceptable. A betting system of this kind is such that among the possible cases there is at least one in which the bettor will lose, but none in which he will make a net gain. Loss and gain are meant here for the total balance over all the bets of the system. Why should a betting system of this kind be regarded as unreasonable? The bettor incurs here a risk since in one possible case he would suffer a loss. Now is it not clear that it would be unreasonable for any-body to agree voluntarily to a contract involving a risk for him which is not balanced by a possible gain? So therefore any betting system of this kind, where loss is possible but gain is impossible, is unreasonable. Now *the second requirement of rationality* says that a credence function must be *strictly coherent*: that is to say, it must also exclude betting systems of the kind just described. Here we have another theorem which was proved by Shimony [1]. It says

---

[1]   Shimony, A., 'Coherence and the axioms of confirmation', *Journal of Symbolic Logic*, **20**, 1955, pp. 1–28.

that a credence function is strictly coherent if and only if it fulfills, in addition to the basic axioms of probability, the condition which I call *regularity*. Any probability function and, in particular, any credence function, is called 'regular' if and only if for any molecular proposition H (that is, roughly, a proposition expressible by a sentence without variables) its value is zero only if H is logically impossible.

The next example of a rationality requirement refers, not to the credence function, but to what I call the *credibility function*. This is defined as follows. The credibility of a proposition H, with respect to another proposition A, for a person X means the degree of belief that X would have in H if and when his total observational knowledge of the world was A. For judging whether a person is intellectually rational or not, it is better to look at his credibility function than at his credence functions. While the credence functions merely reflect his momentary beliefs at various times, his credibility function expresses his underlying permanent disposition for forming and changing his beliefs under the influence of his observations.

We can easily see that, if we apply the test of reasonableness to a man's credibility function rather than to his credence functions, then we obtain more requirements of rationality. As one example I will give the *principle of symmetry* with respect to individuals. It says that a credibility function should be invariant with respect to any exchange of individuals. For example, let H and A be two propositions. We choose arbitrarily two individuals a and b; we change H into H' by taking b instead of a, wherever a is referred to in H, and likewise a instead of b; and we transform A into A' in the same way. Then the principle says that the credibility of H given A should be equal to the credibility of H' given A'.

This principle is obviously not valid for credence. A man may have good reasons for believing strongly that a is clever without believing that b is clever. But the principle must be required for credibility. If a man has exactly the same information about two persons a and b, it would be unreasonable for him to believe strongly in a's cleverness but not in b's.

For credibility, in contrast to credence, there are quite a number of requirements. This is of great importance for inductive logic because these rationality requirements for credibility form the basis for the axioms in inductive logic. By inductive logic I mean the theory of logical probability. I use the symbol 'C' for conditional logical probability (in my book I used for it the term 'degree of confirmation'). Each particular C-function in inductive logic is supposed to be defined in logico-mathematical terms. And also the axioms for C-functions are in these terms. This is the justification for using the term 'logic' for the theory of C-functions. But there is a close relationship between the C-functions and credibility functions. Functions of both kinds are functions from pairs of propositions to real numbers of the interval from 0 to 1. Let us say that a particular credibility function (no matter whether of an actual person or just imagined) and a C-function correspond to each other if, for any pair of propositions, both have the same value. Our aim in inductive logic is to exclude by axioms those C-functions whose corresponding credibility functions have been recognized as being unreasonable. Therefore we choose the axioms in inductive logic in such a way that they correspond to the known rationality requirements for credibility functions. Thus we accept in inductive logic the customary basic axioms of the probability calculus, because this assures that the corresponding credibility functions satisfy the requirement of coherence. Similarly, we accept the axiom of regularity in order to assure strict coherence. And we lay down an axiom of symmetry with respect to individuals and other invariance axioms in view of the corresponding rationality requirements for credibility functions. The axioms themselves, and likewise the theorems based upon the axioms, deal only with mathematical properties of the C-functions. But if you ask for my reasons for choosing just these axioms, then I go over to the theory of rational decisions and point out the corresponding rationality requirements. Thus in the justification of the axioms I have to talk about credibility functions, the decisions to which they would lead, gains and losses, and the like, while inductive logic itself is free of these subject matters.

Let us consider now the *epistemological question* with respect to inductive reasoning. For this question it does not matter much whether we look at inductive reasoning in the customary way, as a form of inference, or in the way I prefer, as a procedure of finding probability values. In either form, the question of the validity of inductive reasoning goes back to – or, at least, can usefully be based upon – considerations about the rationality of decisions. I have made earlier some considerations of this kind; and they are often made for giving reasons for, or justifying some kind or other of inductive reasoning. Now let us think about the question of the kind of factors we may legitimately appeal to in such arguments about rationality. As a matter of fact, in the history of the subject the following factors have often been used by one or the other philosopher:

(a) deductive logic or deductive reasoning;
(b) inductive reasoning;
(c) past experience;
(d) general synthetic principles (as for instance the principle of the uniformity of the world).

To save time, I will not speak about the last point, because I believe that today the majority of philosophers reject this, though some, for instance, Russell, still appeal to such a principle. I used myself in the monograph *The Continuum of Inductive Methods*, in 1952 [1], the factor of past experience; I said that a C-function used for making decisions is a kind of tool. If we are not satisfied with the working of a tool, we change it. If our experiences seem to indicate that our tool, the C-function, does not work well, we might change it on the basis of those experiences. Today I would not say that it is wrong to proceed in this way. If you want to, you may use past experience as a guide in choosing and changing your C-function. But in principle it is never necessary to refer to experiences in order to judge the rationality of a C-function. Think of the situation in arithmetic. You can show to a child that three times five is fifteen by counting five apples in each of three baskets and then counting the total. But I believe most of us would agree that this is not necessary; we can find out what three

---

[1] Carnap, R., *The continuum of inductive methods*, Chicago, 1952.

times five is without counting actual objects. We regard arithmetic as a field of *a priori* knowledge. And I believe that the same holds for inductive logic.

The first of the four factors is obviously legitimate and necessary: without deductive reasoning we can hardly make any argumentation.

Thus there remains the big question of the second factor. I think that it is not only legitimate to appeal to inductive reasoning in defending inductive reasoning, but that it is indispensable. This is a rather audacious statement to make, because it looks like defending a vicious circle. But I believe all procedures of self-clarification, of making clear to ourselves what it is we have in mind, are in a way circular. We clarify B through A, and then we turn around and explain A with the help of B. I think we cannot do without it. If a person were unable to distinguish valid from invalid steps in inductive reasoning, even in the simplest cases, in other words, if he were inductively blind, then it would be hopeless to try to convince him of anything in inductive logic. In order to learn inductive reasoning, we must have what I call the ability of *inductive intuition*. My friends warned me against the use of the word 'intuition'. So I hasten to add that I do not mean by 'intuition', here 'inductive intuition', a source of knowledge that is infallible. I don't think there is anything infallible in human knowledge or activity. Certainly inductive intuition may on occasion lead us astray; the same holds for all other kinds of intuition, for example, spatial intuition, which we use in geometry. Maybe you have the feeling that this mysterious inductive intuition is a rather dubious basis for such a serious enterprise as the construction of a system of inductive logic. If so, I would like to call your attention to the fact that the situation in deductive logic is exactly the same. If you had before you a person who were deductively blind, that is to say, unable to distinguish between valid and invalid deductive inferences, or between deductively valid and invalid statements, even in the simplest cases, then you could not do anything with him. You could not convince him of the validity of the *modus ponens* inference. You tell him, 'You just told me that it is raining now.' 'Yes,' he says. 'You told me before that if

it is raining then the lawn is wet.' 'Yes.' 'So then you believe now
that the lawn is wet.' 'Why should I?' he replies. Then you go
through the whole procedure again in a different order, and with
different words. If all efforts were in vain, you would have to
conclude that he is deductively blind, and you would give up.
Of course, no normal person is deductively blind, although there
are great differences in the speed of learning. There are some
situations where a child might not go along. But you find enough
cases where, after lengthy explanations, he agrees with you in the
distinction between what is valid and what is not; and then you
base the whole system of deductive logic which you want to teach
him, on these simple steps. Basically, the whole teaching of deductive logic consists in cutting up the long chains which lead to
complicated results like the theorems in *Principia Mathematica*,
into very small steps where each step is simple enough to be
accepted, after some deliberation, by a normal person. But the
essential point is this: you have to appeal to his deductive intuition,
in order to teach him deduction. Thus we see that the epistemological
situation in inductive logic, as I described it earlier, is not worse
than that in deductive logic, but quite analogous to it.

Although in choosing axioms for inductive logic we have to rely
on our inductive intuition, the intuitive plausibility of an axiom
may be more or less strong; and in the course of the development
of a system, there may be progress by an increase in plausibility.
Sometimes an axiom is replaced by one or several more plausible
axioms; or for a given axiom more plausible reasons are found.
The latter was the case with the axiom of regularity. In my book
of 1950 [1], I could only give some weak reasons (§ 53, C 53-3).
Later, Shimony discovered that regularity corresponds to strict
coherence, which is clearly a property to be required or at least
strongly desirable.

The remarks I have made here about inductive intuition should
not be taken as anything more than a few rough, preliminary hints.
For fruitful work in a new field is is not necessary to be in possession

---

[1] Carnap, R., *Logical foundations of probability*, Chicago, 1950, 2nd ed.
1962.

of a well-founded epistemological theory about the sources of knowledge in the field. Both arithmetic and geometry were successfully developed for more than two thousand years before the first detailed epistemological theories for both were offered by Kant; and although some important insights have since been gained, there is even today no complete agreement. On the other hand, it is certainly helpful, also for work on substantive problems within a new field, if we can achieve even a little, more explicit awareness of what we are doing and how new knowledge in the field is gained. When we face a difficult problem, this insight may help us to see in which way and in which direction we should look for a possible solution. Thus our working procedure, which in the beginning is inevitably more or less instinctive, may slowly become more consciously directed.

M. Bunge: *Induction, a motley assembly.*

One of the main troubles with 'the' problem of induction seems to be that it is an incredibly heterogeneous set of questions. Here is a sample of this motley collection.

1. *Probability theory.* In the last fifty years this has become a branch of pure mathematics, totally unconcerned with the methodological or even the logical relation between a hypothesis and its evidence: probability theory is a calculus that can be interpreted in a number of ways. The setting up of a particular interpretation of the specific symbols of this framework is not always a mathematical problem and in any case only some models of probability theory are relevant to the problems of induction – namely those in which the domain of individuals is taken to be a set of statements. The physical interpretations of probability (e.g., Popper's propensity interpretation) have nothing to do with induction, for they regard probability as an objective property of a physical system (eventually coupled with an experimental set-up). The belief that probability theory deals with problems of inductive inference seems to originate in a purely linguistic muddle, namely the ancient equivocations:

$$\text{'plausible'} = \text{'verisimilar'} = \text{'probable'} =$$
$$= \text{'nondemonstrative'} = \text{'inductive'}.$$

2. *Theory of scientific inference* (in particular, theory of errors of observation). This application of mathematical statistics is used in the purification and evaluation of both data and hypotheses. It could be used in 'inductive logic' but as a matter of fact it is not so employed and in any case it is not a chapter thereof.

3. *Psychology of belief* and in particular, decision theory applied to actual and ideal acts of acceptance and rejection of hypotheses, methods, rules of procedure, courses of action, etc. It has only been claimed but never proved that degrees of belief actually combine in accordance with the axioms of probability theory: this is an open problem for psychologists to investigate. In any case, decision theory is closer to psychology and technology (in particular operations research) than to philosophy.

4. *Seductive logic.* This, usually called 'inductive logic', is the study of inconclusive but plausible (if preferred, reasonable but nondemonstrative) inference. The various kinds of inductive reasonings (chiefly generalization from observed cases and generalization from low level inductions) constitute just a subset of the class of nondeductive inference patterns. Just as important and challenging are analogies of various kinds (chiefly substantial and structural) and a number of celebrated fallacies without which hardly a step could be made in scientific research – e.g., strong and weak assertion of the consequent. The study of these various kinds of nondeductive (and mostly noninductive) kinds of reasoning is necessary in order to understand them and avoid being overrun by them. But it seems impossible to have an *a priori* science of useful fallacies, because all such inferences depend on the nature of the case: they are non-formal. Yet there is no question that they must be studied, and indeed in a fresh way, which avoids the traditional oversimplifications that have rendered 'inductive logic' totally alien to real science. Prominent among these oversimplifications are the tenets: (a) that every hypothesis is just a package of data, as illustrated by 'All dogs bark'; and (b) that every hypothesis entails (without conjoining it with auxiliary hypotheses and data) its own evidence – a case met nowhere in science.

5. *Theory of partial truth*: the study of approximate truth and approximate falsity as they occur in applied mathematics (e.g., numerical integration) and in empirical science. The very notion that this concept is used daily in science seems foreign to most philosophers and logicians, this being why we still lack an accepted theory of partial truth. (See however Popper's theory in *Conjectures*

and Refutations, and my own in *The Myth of Simplicity*.) We need theories of partial truth consistent with two-valued logic – no paradox intended, because two sets of truth values can be handled at the same time: those assigned to statements for the sake of their logical processing, and those allotted to them on the basis of their coherence with previously accepted statements (e.g., data and other theoretical statements). Such a theory should make contact with the theories of errors and of plausible reasoning, and it should not insist on identifying degree of truth with probability, or with degree of rational belief, or with degree of confirmation. The concept of truth is a much more fundamental one and in scientific research one goes after (partial) truth, in particular after (partially) true probability statements. Besides, save in a few simple cases, one does not know how to assign probabilities to statements.

6. *Methodology*, in particular the introduction of comparative and even quantitative concepts of theory coverage, explanatory power, originality, and predictive performance. These concepts are handled intuitively in the practice of scientific research and they are linked, also informally, to the basic concept of partial truth. Yet no fully fledged theories about those concepts are available that could be applied to an analysis of scientific theories.

Only one half of the fields listed above are strictly philosophical: seductive logic, the theory of partial truth, and methodology. None of them deals exclusively or even mainly with induction. Moreover they are not in good shape, and this for the following reasons. First, they have been lumped together under the heading *Induction* and have therefore suffered from too close an association with an inductivist and anti-theoretical philosophy. Second, some of them – notably the theory of partial truth – have been either neglected or entirely misunderstood through the conviction that probability theory would supply all the answers.

The upshot is this. First, there are genuine problems about induction. Unfortunately these problems have hardly been faced, due to an oversimplified view of both theory (as mere information systematization) and experiment (as sheer observation). Second, the problems about induction cover only a fraction of what is labelled 'induction' in modern philosophy. Third, other problems in the philosophy of science are more urgent than the problems of induction because they are more basic; chief among them is the problem of partial truth. Fourth, we cannot ask a special mathematical theory, such as the probability calculus, to serve as an all-purpose tool.

To put it bluntly: (a) although Popper did write the obituary to inductivism, he has not killed induction; (b) although Carnap did keep the interest in induction alive, his inductive logic does not concern science; (c) meanwhile the chief problems about induction – among them the evaluation of scientific theories in the light of other theories and of empirical data – are still there waiting to be tackled.

J. W. N. WATKINS: *Hume, Carnap and Popper.*

I wish to outline the Hume–Carnap–Popper situation as I see it.

1. We may surely regard scientific theories, along with everyday beliefs, as belonging to the subject matter of Hume's epistemological enquiries. (He extolled Newton's great achievement [1], predicting that Newtonian theory 'will probably go down triumphant to the latest posterity' [2].) Imagine some important body of scientific knowledge – eighteenth century astronomy, say – laid out as a well-articulated, hierarchical system of statements. For Hume, the statements at the lowest level of the system would be reports about sense-impressions, lively memory-images, etc. The statements at the highest level would be the sweeping and exact laws of Newtonian physics. Somewhat below these would be empirical generalizations about natural regularities (the apparent movements of the planets, etc.). And somewhat above the lowest level would be observational records concerning physical things (Mars, Jupiter,

---

[1]   See D. Hume, *History of England*, Edinburgh, 1792, vol. VIII, p. 334.

[2]   D. Hume, *The Philosophical Works*, T. H. Green and T. H. Grose, eds., vol. III, p. 183.

the moon, the tides, etc.). So understood, the main levels of the hierarchy are:

level-0: sensory reports;

level-1: observational reports about things;

level-2: empirical generalizations about things;

level-3: exact and universal laws of mathematical physics.

Hume's dogmatic-slumber-disturbing thesis results from the conjunction of a logical point and a psychological claim. His well known logical point might be re-stated thus: no level-1 statement can be logically derived from any conjunction, however large, of level-0 premises, and no level-2 statement can be logically derived from any conjunction of level-1 premises. Hume did not say much specifically about level-3 statements [1]. But we may add, in line with his general position, that no precise level-3 statement can be logically derived from any conjunction of imprecise level-2 statements [2]. Hume's psychological claim is that we *have* to make inferences from level-0 to level-1 beliefs and from level-1 to level-2 beliefs: a logical purist who tried to abstain from such inferences would be condemning himself to a state of solipsism and paralysis against which his animal instincts would soon rebel.

The conjunction of Hume's psychological claim with his logical point means that *sanity and science demand a robust and systematic illogicality.*

There are philosophers who consider Hume's problem a pseudo-problem to be disposed of by roundly declaring that induction just *is* rational. But I consider this a pseudo-solution of a real problem. Imagine such a philosopher transposed to a setting where

---

[1] He interpreted them in what would now be called a positivist or instrumentalist way. See, for example, the last paragraph and associated footnote of sec. VII, Part I, of *An Enquiry Concerning Human Understanding.*

[2] 'An opinion that something is *universally* true clearly goes further than experience can warrant ... I may add that whatever is held to be precisely true goes further than experience can possibly warrant' (C. S. Peirce, *Collected Papers*, § 5. 382 n. 1, vol. v, pp. 239–240 n). Popper also emphasises this point (*Conjectures and Refutations*, p. 186).

a magical rather than a scientific outlook prevails: to *show* that he and his fellows are rational in holding magical beliefs turns out to be rather difficult; so he roundly declares that magic just *is* rational. But we should not take him seriously.

Carnap's and Popper's very different methodologies of science can both be viewed as serious responses to Hume's challenge: both men have tried to show, though in very different ways, that scientific knowledge (understood as an extension – a very remarkable extension – of everyday, pre-scientific knowledge) does not, after all, have an inherently illogical structure. Both men may be said to have tried to re-rationalize what Hume had de-rationalized. The question is, has either succeeded?

2. Carnap tried to rationalize the inductive ascent of science with the help of confirmation functions constructed around the concept of logical probability. Had his original programme been completed we should have had a confirmation function which permits us, as rational men with an understanding of the *a priori* theorems of probability and a horror of illogical inferences, to work up from suitable level-1 evidence statements to the capture (as 'well confirmed') of desirable level-2 and level-3 theories, without capturing unwanted items.

Carnap is the first to admit that such a powerful and effective confirmation function does not yet exist. The confirmation functions that *are* available lead us away to very different destinations, to the capture of what are, from the standpoint of theoretical science, quite miserable kinds of statements: tautologies[1], ad hoc hypotheses[2], and purely existential statements (since these are negations of statements with zero probability, namely law statements)[3].

---

[1] *Logical Foundations of Probability*, p. 286.

[2] *Ibid.*, p. 298.

[3] *Logical Foundations of Probability*, p. 571. Law statements can get a positive degree of *qualified-instance confirmation*, but this concept brings in other difficulties. Carnap himself mentions that a law which has been *refuted* (by a *small* number of negative instances) may nevertheless get a C_{qi}^*-value *close to* 1 (*ibid.*, p. 573). The shift to qualified-instance confirmation is severely criticised in Popper, *Conjectures and Refutations*, pp. 282 f. Also see E. Nagel in *The Philosophy of Rudolf Carnap*, P. A. Schilpp, ed., pp. 799 f.

In the old days (for instance, at the time of *Testability and Meaning*) Carnap regarded the degree to which a hypothesis has been confirmed by accepted observation reports as something like an index of its empirical or scientific acceptability. He emphasized that we have to decide, conventionally, how highly confirmed a hypothesis should be for it to be accepted: one might very well decline to accept a hypothesis only somewhat better confirmed than its negation, preferring to suspend judgment until further evidence tips the scales more markedly. But I do not think that at that time Carnap would have countenanced a counter-confirmation acceptance-policy. He would surely have regarded it as a transgression of empiricist methodology for someone who regards the hypothesis h_1 as better confirmed than the incompatible hypothesis h_2 nevertheless to accept h_2 and reject h_1. Degrees of confirmation were not supposed to dictate but they surely were supposed to constrain the accepting and rejecting of hypotheses [1].

His pupils sometimes suggest that for them now to recall those far-off days when empirical acceptability was so naively associated with degree of confirmation requires a mighty effort of memory [2]. And Carnap himself is now very guarded about the relation between confirmation and acceptance. Thus he says (in his remarks – in this volume – on Kyburg, Bar–Hillel and Salmon) that degrees

---

[1] See *Testability and Meaning*, § 2.

[2] Yet not so very long ago J. G. Kemeny was saying that 'it is the last step [the determination of whether we are scientifically justified to accept the hypothesis on the given evidence] that Carnap is interested in. Just how does the expert decide that the given evidence makes the hypothesis sufficiently probable for acceptance?' (*The Philosophy of Rudolf Carnap*, P. A. Schilpp, ed., p. 712). In his reply Carnap said that Kemeny had 'been very successful in presenting in non-technical terms the aims and methods of inductive logic' (*ibid.*, p. 979).

True, Carnap had said earlier that he does not agree with the 'widely held view' that 'it is the proper aim of inductive logic to supply *rules of acceptance*' (*ibid.*, his italics). He went on to say, however, that it is in fields of *practical* application that rules of acceptance are insufficient, and that 'there is no compelling objection against' their use 'in purely *theoretical* fields, and especially if the reconstruction is applied only to the acceptance of universal laws' (*ibid.*, p. 973, his italics).

of confirmation are relevant 'for determining estimates, betting quotients, and many other things, *maybe even acceptance* [1]'.

For my part, I regard this dissociation, or at least this loosening of the association, between confirmation and acceptability as a confession of failure. If qualified-instance confirmation is excluded (as I believe it has to be – see footnote 3, p. 273), then we have no confirmation function which allows us to proceed from level-1 statements to a level-2 statement. The best we can do is to move sideways (say, from meteorological records to the prediction that it will rain in London in July 1970). We can also proceed, as we now know all too well, right out of our empirical system to tautologies and purely existential statements.

I believe that Carnap's answer to those of us who harp on these unwanted results is that inductive logic is still in its infancy and can hardly be expected to cope as yet with high-powered scientific reasoning: after all, deductive logic at the time of Aristotle could cope only with very limited and rather trivial sorts of inference (simple arithmetical inferences were beyond it); when inductive logic shall have undergone a development comparable to that which deductive logic has undergone since Aristotle, then it may handle interesting scientific hypotheses satisfactorily.

But perhaps there is something *inherently* wrong with inductive logic. In his present paper Carnap says that radical doubts about logical probability and inductive logic are less frequently expressed now than in earlier years. Well, where I work no one impugns probability logic; but there continues to be some doubt about the possibility of constructing an inductive logic with its help. For logical probability, as Popper has very often said [2], is a measure of *paucity* of content. The absolute logical probability of a statement (its probability relative to tautological 'evidence') is at a maximum when the statement has *no* content (is itself a tautology). The logical probability of a statement relative to non-tautological evidence is at a maximum when the statement has no content

---

[1]   *This volume*, p. 148; my italics. He adds that for acceptance we should *also* employ a measure of content. But this would vary *inversely* with a probabilistic measure of confirmation.

[2]   For example, in *Conjectures and Refutations*, p. 219.

which goes beyond the evidence [1]. The value of r in the formula

$$p(h,\ e) = r$$

can rise above $\frac{1}{2}$ only if h does not, as it were, go beyond e by more than a rather modest amount.

Hume's point about the invalidity of induction could now be re-stated, by saying that the content of, say, a level-2 statement goes *far beyond* ('infinitely' far, presumably) any consistent set of statements at lower levels. As we ascend a hierarchically organized body of scientific knowledge, such as eighteenth century astronomy, we typically find greater generality, more precision, and what may be called ontological novelty, at each higher level. Such a structure is, so to speak, *immensely top-heavy*. It seems to me almost as obvious that statements at the top of such a system cannot be probabilified as that they cannot be verified by statements at the bottom. Unfortunately, the inductive logician, realizing that his probabilistic logic can manage only relatively puny hypotheses and not the giant systems of modern science, may tend to feel that the latter have grown *too big* and need cutting down to a less unmanageable size [2].

3.   To meet Hume's challenge concerning the inherent irrationality of our empirical thinking, Popper had to do (at least) these two

---

[1]   See *Logical Foundations of Probability*, 1950, p. 297.

[2]   This tendency crops out in Russell's famous paper of 1912 'On the Notion of Cause': 'The assumption that *all* laws of nature are permanent has, of course, less probability than the assumption that this or that particular law is permanent; and the assumption that a particular law is permanent for all time has less probability than the assumption that it will be valid up to such and such a date. Science, in any given case, will assume what the case requires, but no more. In constructing the *Nautical Almanac* for 1915 it will assume that the law of gravitation will remain true up to the end of that year; but it will make no assumption as to 1916 until it comes to the next volume of the almanac' (*Mysticism and Logic*, pp. 196–197). I think that Carnap's rather sniffy attitude, at the end of his book (*Logical Foundations of Probability*, p. 575), to scientific laws ('... not indispensable ... serve as efficient instruments ...') is a manifestation of the same tendency.

things: (1) refute Hume's psychological claim that our thinking about the world just *does* proceed in an inductive, and therefore in an illogical, way; (2) develop a purely deductivist methodology which shows how rational choices between competing theories (especially at level-3 but also at level-2) *are* possible despite the absence of any inductive inferences, whether of a verifying or of a merely probabilifying nature, from level-1 statements to higher level statements.

I shall take his logical-cum-empirical refutation of Hume's psychological claim as read [1]. Nor shall I discuss whether Popper's methodology really is free of all inductivist ingredients, since I have replied elsewhere to Salmon on this point [2]. And I shall take the existence of provisionally accepted basic statements (level-1 statements) to be unproblematic [3]. What I shall discuss is the

---

[1] See *Conjectures and Refutations*, 1963, pp. 42–46. It is well known (a) that Hume himself allowed, as an important exception to his 'drip-drip' theory whereby beliefs are formed by repetitious experiences, that we sometimes form a general belief after a single experiment; and (b) that to account for this he claimed that, in forming more and more (first-order) habits of belief, we continually strengthen our (second-order) habit of forming beliefs, and hence come to form these more and more easily. (On this view, grand-parents should be reckless generalizers by comparison with their cagey grand-children.) What is, perhaps, not so well known is that Hume, warming to his *ad hoc* explanation, goes on to say that we come to form universal hypotheses *upon the slightest provocation*; 'What we have found once to follow from any object, we conclude will for ever follow from it'. Our proliferating hypotheses are kept in check 'because we frequently meet with *instances to the contrary*' (*Treatise*, ed. Selby–Bigge, p. 131; my italics). Except that he never gave up the residual dogma that observation of at least *one* instance must precede formation of a general hypothesis (a dogma enjoined by his psychological maxim: no idea without antecedent impressions), Hume was nudged by awkward psychological facts into something very like a trial-and-error theory of belief-formation.

[2] In my note on 'Non-Inductive Corroboration', *this volume*, pp. 61–66.

[3] In his interesting paper, 'Sensationalism' (*Mind*, N.S. **75**, 1966), J. Agassi claims to have rendered 'Popper's theory of the empirical basis of science superfluous' (p. 18). He feels that Popper's idea of provisionally accepted basic statements still concedes too much to the traditional idea of empirical *data*: instead of *accepting* observation reports and seeking explanations for *what* they report, we should merely try to account for the fact

suspicion (seldom far below the surface in critical discussions of Popper's epistemology) that, far from solving the problem of rational choice between competing hypotheses, his methodology really leads to thorough-going scepticism.

Many philosophers who have given up the hope that any of our empirical statements about the external world are certain, cling all the more tenaciously to the hope that some of them are at least less uncertain than others. Such philosophers tend to characterize as *scepticism* the thesis that *all empirical statements about the external world are equally uncertain.* I will use ST_1 as an abbreviation for this (first) 'sceptical' thesis.

Now Popper's philosophy *is* 'sceptical' in the sense of ST_1; but then 'scepticism' in this sense seems to me to be unavoidable. Presumably, a statement can be near-certain, logically speaking (we are not interested in mere psychological certainty here), only if it is highly probable relative to a certainty. A certainty scale is like a greasy pole: *if* the man furthest up could cling to the top, the next man could cling to his ankles, and so on down. But if the top man has nothing to cling to, they all slide down into uncertainty. Now even though some level-0 statements (which are not about the external world) might be taken as in some sense certain, there seems to be no possibility of explaining how a level-1 statement could be 'highly probable', in any clear and non-

---

that certain people have made certain reports; we *may* treat a report as true, but equally we may treat it as false and explain it as a product of crude measurement, sense illusion, or even as a lie (p. 19).

But first, on Popper's methodology, explanatory hypotheses which boldly correct the alleged facts they were to explain are (other things being equal) preferable, because less *ad hoc*, then those which leave the explicandum intact. And second, Agassi's approach does not, after all, dispense with an empirical basis: he still needs (provisionally) accepted observation reports, not about things, but about *people's reports* about things. After all, for there to be an explanatory task, *something* must be currently accepted as calling for explanation.

Popper had mentioned that we may occasionally prefer to explain, not the things reported, but rather the reports—not flying saucers, for example, but reports of flying saucers (*Ratio*, 1, 1957, p. 24). I do not see that any philosophical advantage is to be gained, from Agassi's or from any other standpoint, by elevating such exceptions into a general rule.

psychologistic sense, relative to level-0 statements. And even if, for the sake of argument, we make the unPopperian supposition that some level-1 statements can be taken as 'certain', then although we could now rule out various level-2 and level-3 statements as false, we would still be confronted by a plethora of unfalsified and mutually incompatible universal hypotheses, all having zero probability and all, therefore, equally uncertain from a logical point of view.

But philosophers who place their hopes, not on certainties, whether absolute or relative, but on rational argument and criticism, will prefer to characterize as *scepticism* the thesis that *we never have any good reason for preferring one empirical statement about the external world to another*. I will use ST_2 as an abbreviation for this second sceptical thesis. ST_1 and ST_2 are by no means equivalent. ST_2 implies ST_1 (on the assumption that, if one hypothesis *were* less uncertain than another, that *would*, other things being equal, be a reason for preferring it). But ST_1 does not imply ST_2: there may be reasons having nothing to do with relative certainty for preferring one hypothesis to another.

Empirical scientists cannot expect to have good reasons for preferring a particular explanatory hypothesis to all the (infinitely many) *possible* alternatives to it. But they often do have good reasons for preferring one out of several competing hypotheses which have actually been proposed. How one hypothesis may be rationally appraised as better than the other hypotheses under discussion, and what a future hypothesis would need to do for it to be even better than this one – this is what Popper's methodology is about. Having said something elsewhere about his idea of corroboration appraisals [1], an idea which depends on the assumption that science aims at progressively better explanations, I wish in conclusion to say a word about his idea of verisimilitude appraisals, an idea which depends on the assumption that science aims at getting progressively closer to the truth. The notions of corroborability and of verisimilitude are closely related, but the second is richer.

---

[1]   In my 'Non-Inductive Corroboration', *this volume*, pp. 61–66.

Popper's theory of verisimilitude [1] involves these two theses. (1) *A clear meaning* can be given to such claims as: 'the hypothesis h_2 is closer to the truth than the hypothesis h_1' (or, 'h_2 has greater verisimilitude than h_1' or, 'h_2 corresponds to the facts better than h_1' or even, 'h_2 is truer than h_1'). (2) We may have *good reasons for claiming* that a particular hypothesis h_2 is closer to the truth than a rival hypothesis h_1.

As to (1): h_2 would have greater verisimilitude than h_1 if, for example, the truth content of h_2 exceeds that of h_1 while the falsity content of h_1 exceeds that of h_2. (The content of a statement is the class of its non-tautologous consequences; its truth content, the class of its true consequences. Its falsity content is its content minus its truth content.) Notice that a false theory may nevertheless have a high verisimilitude. Also, verisimilitude, unlike probability, can *increase* with content. Both the verisimilitude and the probability of an inconsistent statement are zero; but whereas the probability of a tautology is one, its verisimilitude is zero, since it has no content.

As to (2): let us consider a clear-cut case. Suppose that the following pre-experimental conditions are satisfied.

(i) h_1 and h_2 are internally consistent and mutually inconsistent theories.

(ii) The domain d_1 of h_1 is a proper subdomain of the domain d_2 of h_2.

(iii) For any prediction derivable from h_1 about any element i in d_1 there is a more precise prediction about i derivable from h_2.

(iv) Some of the predictions derivable from h_1 diverge to an empirically discernible extent from those of h_2.

(v) h_2 yields testable predictions outside d_1.

Now suppose that the following post-experimental conditions are satisfied. (I am still taking provisionally accepted basic or level-1 statements as philosophically unproblematic.)

---

[1]   See his *Conjectures and Refutations*, 1963, pp. 231 f.

(vi) Many and varied tests have been made on h_1 and h_2 within d_1; h_2 has survived all these tests but h_1 has not. (All crucial experiments between h_1 and h_2 have gone against h_1.)

(vii) Many and varied tests have been made on h_2 outside d_1, and h_2 has survived all these tests.

In other words, h_2 not only says more (is more comprehensive and precise) than h_1, but has stood up to tests, whereas h_1 has broken down under test. This does not *verify* the claim that h_2 is closer to the truth than h_1: that claim remains conjectural and may even get undermined later, if subsequent tests start telling heavily against h_2. But in the meanwhile, in default of such adverse evidence, there are good reasons for preferring this claim both to the (perverse) claim that h_1 has more verisimilitude than h_2, and to the (implausible) claim that h_1 and h_2 have an exactly equal verisimilitude.

If we 'accept' a scientific hypothesis, as better corroborated and as seeming closer to the truth than its existing competitors, we should obviously do so in a very unsolemn sense of 'accept'; for the critical context in which our hypothesis got to the top may be transformed tomorrow by the introduction of new evidence or a rival hypothesis into the discussion, or by a re-examination of logical relations between propositions already under discussion. A good Popperian sense of the word is this: to accept one out of a number of competing scientific hypotheses is to select it as the one most worth superseding by a better one. In this unverificationist sense of acceptance, Popper has provided a rationale for the acceptance and rejection of level-2 and, more importantly, of level-3 hypotheses.

As I see it, then, the Hume–Carnap–Popper situation is this. The three men have answered the questions, 'Does science have an inductive structure?' and 'Is science inherently illogical?' as follows.

	'Inductive?'	'Illogical?'
Hume	'Yes'	'Yes'
Carnap	'Yes'	'No'
Popper	'No'	'No'

But Carnap's attempt to rationalize the alleged inductive ascent of science with the help of probability logic fails, because probability varies inversely with content. On the other hand, corroborability and verisimilitude can *increase* with increasing content. With these deductivist notions, Popper has re-rationalized what Hume had de-rationalized. The glory of science is no longer the scandal of philosophy.

Y. BAR–HILLEL: *Bunge and Watkins on inductive logic.*

1. I agree entirely with the first sentence and the last sentence of Bunge's discussion of Carnap's talk but with hardly anything else he said in between. I agree that there is no such thing as 'the' problem of induction – if one excepts what Carnap calls 'the grand old problem of justification' originating with Hume and agrees with him, as I do, that this 'is not the right way of asking the question' – but that there exists instead an incredibly heterogenous motley of problems having something to do with 'induction'. Carnap, in his talk, addressed himself to two of these problems but certainly had no intention of implying that these were the *only* two such problems.

I also agree – and say so myself that 'the evaluation of scientific theories in the light of other theories and of empirical data'[1], as well as in the light of many other factors, creates one of the major problems of methodology of science.

But I regard Bunge's statement that 'the belief that probability theory deals with problems of inductive inference seems to originate in a purely linguistic muddle' as based on muddled thinking, in particular since Bunge himself had said a few lines before that 'only some models of probability theory are relevant to the problems of induction'. Carnap claims that his theory of logical (or inductive) probability deals with inductive inference (though only with an important and rather peculiar interpretation of this phrase). Bunge did not even attempt to present a single argument against this view.

---

[1] *This volume*, p. 271.

Even if Bunge is right in claiming that 'decision theory is closer to psychology and technology (in particular operations research) than to philosophy' – and I find it extremely hard to evaluate such an indefinite and vague statement – what is the purpose of this statement? Does it make decision theory an inferior science? Does it show that inductive logic is irrelevant to decision theory? Does it prove that Carnap's recent attempt to introduce his conception of inductive logic on a decision-theoretic basis is unsound?

It can hardly be doubted that science has progressed, among other ways, also with the help of 'useful fallacies'. A study of how this happened, in general and in specific case histories, is bound to be as enlightening as studies of the impact of metaphysical and other non-rational or even irrational beliefs on the progress of science. Which modern inductive logician has claimed that all this can be handled through inductive logic alone? Who are the anonymous inductive logicians who held the oversimplified tenet 'that every hypothesis entails its own evidence' (by which Bunge must surely mean 'all of its own evidence' and not just 'some of its own evidence')?

Whether one really needs an independent theory of partial truth, or of verisimilitude, remains to be seen. I do not think one has to insist on identifying degree of truth with probability, but a methodological Occam's razor should certainly encourage one to try this identification out. Bunge presents no real reasons against this attempt. Surely, neither Popper nor Bunge has so far given any reason to believe that it will be simpler to assign verisimilitudes to statements rather than probabilities.

Bunge's statement that the 'concepts of theory coverage, explanatory power, originality and predictive performance' are 'linked to the concept of partial truth' is again so utterly indefinite that it is even hard to reject it outright. After all, what is meant by 'linked'? If Bunge means that they are definable in a theory of partial truth, then he is doubtless utterly mistaken. If he means that a full-fledged theory of these concepts will somehow, somewhere, refer to partial truth, this remains to be seen. Assuming that this *must* be the case is surely just begging the question.

Let me finally voice another protest against the ritualistic and

irresponsible phrase referring to 'an inductivist and antitheoretical
philosophy'. Few philosophers have contributed more to an understanding of the function of theories in science than Carnap and
Hempel. Call their philosophy 'inductivist', if you like, but to call
it 'antitheoretical' is an intolerable affront.

2. Carnap, like so many other methodologists, had for a long
time underestimated the need for explication of the term 'acceptance'. He had also for a long time thought that acceptability
of theories is uniquely determined by their (posterior) degree of
confirmation. Later on, he changed his mind in both respects. I
regard this as a great achievement. Watkins regards Carnap's
'loosening of the connection between confirmation and acceptability
as a confession of failure'. We could leave it at that. But I am
afraid that Watkins' different evaluation of Carnap's change of
mind makes him also miss its point.

For Popper and his friends, like Watkins, logical probability
is 'in' and inductive logic is 'out' because it contains the 'out'
term 'inductive'. But in Carnap's usage, inductive logic *is* the
theory of logical probability. And since Carnap, when he writes
on these subjects, has the strange habit of using these terms in
accordance with his own usage (unless he quotes other people, of
course), the fact that in the Popper circle 'no one impugns logical
probability' is a (partial) justification for his statement 'that
radical doubts about logical probability and inductive logic are
less frequently expressed now than in earlier years'. Popper may
not like some of Carnap's axioms and regard Carnap's conception
of logical probability as faulty and only his own one as correct,
but surely a defense of his own axioms as based on Inductive
Intuition was one of the major topics of Carnap's talk.

I think that Watkins' misgivings against Carnap's overly instrumentalistic attitude, in 1950, to scientific laws ('. . . not indispensable . . . serve as efficient instruments . . .') are justified, but
I am quite sure that Carnap would be glad to make another
'confession of failure' in this respect, today; as a matter of fact,
this change of mind is quite evident in his publications from 1956
onwards.

I have some doubts as to whether the interpretation given to some of Popper's views by his colleague, Watkins, is correct. I do not think, contrary to Watkins' first claim, that Popper is especially interested in 'our thinking about the world', in particular in showing that it does not 'proceed in an inductive, and therefore in an illogical, way'. I am sure that Popper and Carnap – and Watkins – will agree that many of us are very often quite "illogical" in our thinking about the world and even commit the sin of thinking in an inductive way, whatever this may mean. I take it that both are out to show that science can be *reconstructed* as a rational undertaking, with Popper continuing to believe that his reconstruction is radically opposed to that of Carnap's, in spite of the insistence of Carnap and myself that this is not the case.

On the other hand, if Watkins is right in his second claim that Popper intended to 'develop a purely deductivist methodology which shows how rational choices between competing theories . . . *are* possible despite the absence of any inductive inferences', then one can also say that Popper has failed in this endeavour, though he never confessed to it. His failure would be twofold: first, the degree of (posterior) confirmation (if it were definable) *is* a factor in the comparison of theories and, secondly there are many other factors involved besides degree of confirmation and content measure (if it were definable – and these two measures being interdefinable, the difficulties in defining them adequately are the same).

K. R. POPPER: *Theories, experience, and probabilistic intuitions.*

1.   According to Professor Bar–Hillel's account, 'For Popper and his friends like Watkins, logical probability is "in" and inductive logic is "out", because it contains the "out" term "inductive". But [Bar–Hillel continues] in Carnap's usage, inductive logic *is* the theory of logical probability.' Of course we all know that Professor Carnap uses these two terms, 'logical probability' and 'inductive logic', as synonyms. But this does not commit *us* to using them as synonyms. Moreover, I should not dream of quarrelling about terms and their usages: I have no objection to Carnap's or anybody's *terminology*, though I prefer another.

'Logical probability', in my terminology, is a shorthand term for 'the logical interpretation of the formal calculus of relative probability' (as axiomatized in my *Logic of Scientific Discovery*, new appendices *iii to *v). It seems very nearly to coincide with Carnap's earlier term 'regular *c*-function' and his present term 'credence function'; omitting, however, any reference to '*degrees of belief*'. It is one of the interpretations which assumes that the arguments '*a*', '*b*', '*c*', . . . of the function '$p(a, b)$' are names of statements. Thus one of the main differences between Carnap's usage of 'logical probability' and mine is that I do *not* interpret logical probability as a *theory of belief*, or as a theory applicable to 'degrees of belief'.

My usage of the term 'logical probability' commits me, like Carnap, to ascribing to certain statements the *numerical* probabilities 1 and 0. But any other specific *numerical* values, such as $\frac{1}{2}$ or $\frac{2}{3}$, transcend, in my usage of the term, both pure logic and 'logical probability'. Thus the ascription of a certain 'width' to certain predicates does not fall within the province of what *I* call 'logic' or 'logical probability'.

Referring to Carnap's present paper, I should accept the *term* 'strictly coherent credence function' (as long as it is *not linked with* '*degrees of belief*') as falling into the field of 'logical probability'; but I should not call every instance of a 'strictly coherent credence function' a 'logical probability', because *according to my terminology*, the ascription of a numerical probability value such as $\frac{1}{2}$ to a statement carries us beyond logic.

What I call the theory of logical probability may be compared with metrical geometry such as, say, Euclidean geometry. In Euclidean geometry, the only distance (or area or volume) whose numerical measure is defined by the theory itself is the zero distance (or area or volume). Other ascriptions of specific numerical values are extra-theoretical: they are not introduced by the theory, but by arbitrarily defining a yardstick. (If the theory is the geometry of the real world these ascriptions may be part of physical theory, provided it contains a fundamental constant of length; but the choice of the Paris metre is not like this.) In the theory of logical probability we have not only 0 but also 1; all other ascriptions of specific numerical values are, in my terminology, extra-logical applications; although there may be, in the objective or physical interpretations of probability, ascriptions which are part of physical theory.

Incidentally, I am not very interested in logical probability as such; I am, however, very interested in logical *im*probability, that is in $1-p(a)$ or $1-p(a, b)$. The reason is that logical improbability may be used as a *measure of* (absolute or relative) *content*; and indeed I am very interested in the *content of theories*, and in the problem of comparing the contents of theories, because I think it important for pure logic *and* for methodology. For example, I say of two theories, such as Einstein's and Newton's, that the first has a greater content than the second if and only if they are so related that (a) the first can answer (to at least the same degree of precision) every problem the second can answer; and (b) the first has an answer to problems which the second cannot answer. (I should therefore, in particular, say that the first has a greater content than the second if it entails it unilaterally.) Thus for me, it is not logical probability which is 'in', but rather the *problem of comparing contents*. (I stated already in 1934 in my *Logik der Forschung* that a statement or a theory has a greater content than another if it forbids or excludes more possibilities. J. G. Kemeny in 1953 proposed putting this model-theoretically: he proposed to define the absolute content of a theory a as the class of models which do not satisfy a. Yet it does not seem that there is a simple analogous definition of the relative content of a given b, though I have found a simple *measure* of the relative content of a given b, viz. $1-p(a, b)$ [1]).

Incidentally Bar–Hillel later expresses 'doubts as to whether the interpretation given to some of Popper's views by his colleague

---

[1]   See K. R. Popper, *The Logic of Scientific Discovery*, 1934, 1959, sect. 6: 'Not for nothing do we call the laws of nature "laws": the more they forbid, the more they say'; and, for example, sects. 31 to 35, and especially pp. 112–113, and 119; furthermore, R. Carnap, *Logical Foundations of Probability*, 1950, p. 406, 'Remarks for readers of [Semantics]'. Kemeny's model-theoretic definition of content is on p. 297 of his 'A Logical Measure Function', *Journal of Symbolic Logic* 18, 1953, pp. 289–308.

Watkins is correct'. Indeed Professor Watkins has interpreted me correctly, as can easily be found out by everybody who looks up the references Watkins gives on p. 277 to my *Conjectures and Refutations* [1].

Bar–Hillel might have looked at these five pages before ascribing to Watkins the preposterous view that people 'are never illogical', a view which of course neither Watkins nor I ever held. That this 'interpretation given to some of' Watkins' views by Bar–Hillel is incorrect is obvious: what Watkins alluded to was the fact that the rationalist Hume turned into an irrationalist because despite his great logical discovery that induction is irrational, Hume failed to reconsider his (psychological and methodological) view that we must, and do, depend on induction.

There are lots of other places where Watkins and I are misinterpreted by Bar–Hillel. To mention another example, Bar–Hillel says: 'Surely neither Popper nor Bunge' (whom Bar–Hillel characteristically accuses of 'muddled thinking') 'have so far given any reason to believe that it will be simpler to assign verisimilitudes to statements rather than probabilities'. But what I call 'verisimilitude' was not introduced because it is 'simpler' to assign verisimilitudes rather than probabilities to statements, but it was introduced by me (on the basis of Tarski's two concepts, of truth and of deductive system) with the aim of showing that scientists or philosophers (such as Peirce) do not talk nonsense when they say of a theory – say Einstein's – that it is 'a better approximation to the truth' than another – say Newton's.

2. I have briefly explained that what I call 'logical probability' is both somewhat similar to and somewhat different from Carnap's concept of 'logical probability'. But I have not yet said why I do not adopt Carnap's terminological identification of 'logical probability' with 'inductive logic'. The reason is very simple. I do think that there is such a thing as 'logical probability' *in my sense* (though I do not think it very important compared, say, with

---

[1] K. R. Popper, *Conjectures and Refutations*, 1963, pp. 42–46.

physical probability or propensity, or with logical content). But I do not think that there is such a thing as an 'inductive logic', in Carnap's or *in any sense*.

(a) While most people will admit the existence of 'logical probability' in my sense (that is, of a logical interpretation of the calculus of probability [1]) Carnap himself says in his present lecture of his 'inductive logic' that it is still a project.

(b) Inductive logic has been a project since Aristotle, and a probabilistic inductive logic has been a project for almost 400 years – since Francis Bacon, and, according to Carnap himself [2], since Bernoulli and Laplace. That it has made very little progress is clear: while Bacon and Laplace sketched a project hoping to apply it to our acceptance of strictly universal theories, this project has, at least for a time, been abandoned by Carnap, although he now indicates that he may perhaps take it up again.

Consider in this context Carnap's (apparently abandoned) 'instance confirmation' of a universal theory or hypothesis or law which was defined in his *Logical Foundations* by the degree of confirmation of the next instance of the law. This is a function which I have shown, about fifteen years before it was proposed by Carnap, not to satisfy the calculus of probability. For in this calculus the following holds *universally*.

If a and b are inconsistent, though each of them is consistent in itself, then

$$p(a, b) = 0.$$

But Carnap's instance confirmation of a hypothesis a 'would

---

[1] In fact, a calculus of relative (and absolute) probability that can be *proved* to be a generalization of the logic of derivation was, to my knowledge, first constructed by myself. See K. R. Popper, *The Logic of Scientific Discovery*, new appendices *iii to *v. It is essential for such a calculus that b in $p(a, b)$ may have zero absolute probability (and even that b may be inconsistent, which is a still stronger demand). However, no notice of the existence of this calculus seems to have been taken by most Bayesians, as shown, for example, by I. J. Good in his comments on Miller's Paradox of Information, Appendix II to his 'How to estimate probabilities', *Journal of the Institute of Mathematics and its Applications* 2, 1966, pp. 364–383.

[2] Cp. R. Carnap, *Logical Foundations of Probability*, 1950, pp. 47 f.

give the hypothesis a probability of $\frac{1}{2}$ if, on the average, it is refuted by every second singular statement of this sequence' [1] – that is, the sequence of its instances. I called this conclusion 'devastating' [*'niederschmetternd'*] and I still think it is. But I have not seen an admission that it is so – though I am glad to note that 'instance confirmation' does not seem to have been mentioned for some years.

(c)   Richard C. Jeffrey has recently developed a very interesting theory of the probability of universal laws [2]. But this is a theory of purely subjective belief rather than a theory of 'logical probability'. Admittedly, being based upon the formal calculus of probability, it satisfies Ramsey's, de Finetti's, and Shimony's so-called rationality criteria; yet the attribution of what I call absolute probabilities is purely subjective. It can therefore hardly be described as a logical theory, or an 'inductive logic'.

(d)   I have given a considerable number of reasons why such a logical theory – a theory which is both inductive *and* probabilistic – not only does not exist, but cannot exist.

(e)   Some of these reasons, although they do not formally refute Jeffrey's new theory, show that it is inadequate from the point of view of scientific method. Example: assume that the theory h is the hypothesis: 'During the next (not yet observed) 24 hours, the sun will rise and set at Rome.' And assume that an overwhelming amount of observations and historical evidence has given this hypothesis a probability very close to 1. Then even a small consecutive number of falsifications (the sun's not setting within 120 hours, say) will hardly diminish this probability; just as the probability of throwing heads with a die which has in one million throws produced 'heads' half a million times will change very little if we obtain a succession of seven 'tails' [3].

---

[1]   Quoted from K. R. Popper, *The Logic of Scientific Discovery*, p. 257 (First German ed. 1934, p. 191; 2nd ed. p. 203.), *Conjectures and Refutations*, 1963, p. 283, note 70, and P. A. Schilpp, ed., *The Philosophy of Rudolf Carnap*, 1963, pp. 216 f., note 70.

[2]   R. C. Jeffrey, *The Logic of Decision*, 1965, pp. 171–194.

[3]   Cp. K. R. Popper, 'Probability magic or knowledge out of ignorance', *Dialectica* 11, 1957, pp. 354–374; see especially sects. 5 and 6.

But the really fundamental difference between Jeffrey and myself is that he is interested in beliefs, and subjective degrees of belief, while I am interested in theories and their contents, or in what Bolzano called statements-in-themselves (see (4) below).

(f) For all these and other reasons [1], I do not think that the term 'probability' which is intuitively used in speaking about the 'probability of a hypothesis' is a probability *in the sense of the calculus of probability*.

(g) I agree with Hume that neither the classical idea of induction (the inductive appraisal of *universal* theories or hypotheses) nor Carnap's idea of induction (the appraisal of predictions) is logically defensible.

(h) I think, contrary to Hume, that *induction by repetition* plays no role in science, and that science does not go beyond the *testing* of theories; a procedure which does not involve induction either in the classical or in the Carnapian sense.

(i) These are a few of the reasons why I do not think that there is such a thing as an 'inductive logic', in Carnap's or in any other sense. And this may explain why we prefer not to use Carnap's terminological identification of 'logical probability' and 'inductive logic', which seems to us to beg a question of central importance. But of course I am not interested in words. Indeed, if anybody should propose to call the method of testing theories by the name 'induction', I should have no disagreement with him; nor if he said that he believed in the existence of induction in this (and *only* in this) sense.

But let me turn to questions which I find more important.

3. Watkins, Lakatos and I share the conviction that theories are all-important, not only in science, but in prescientific inquiries (where they take the shape of myths), and in ordinary life, and *in every language*. Ordinary language, scientific language, an interpreted artificial language and even a *'purely observational' language*, are all *theory-impregnated*. As Charles Darwin wrote long ago, 'How odd . . . that anyone should not see that all observation

---

[1]   See my remarks on G. L. S. Shackle and C. L. Hamblin, below under 13.

must be for or against some view . . .' [1]. This remark of Darwin's contains part of our approach; for a 'view' in Darwin's sense is, of course, a *theory*.

The way in which all ordinary and all scientific languages are theory-impregnated was briefly sketched (incidentally by way of a criticism of Carnap) in my old *Logik der Forschung* where I wrote, discussing the statement 'Here is a glass of water' [2]:

'By the word "glass", for example, we denote physical bodies which exhibit a certain *law-like behaviour* [*Körper von bestimmten gesetzmässigen Verhalten*] and the same holds for the word "water".' Later I elaborated this and extended it quite generally to *all universal terms*: I pointed out that all universals are dispositional terms, even such apparently observational terms as 'red'. A body is red if its surface is dispositioned to reflect red light, that is, light of certain frequencies. And I pointed out that in this sense, 'the customary distinction between *'observational terms'* (or *non-theoretical terms*) and *theoretical terms* is mistaken, since all terms are theoretical to some degree, though some are more theoretical than others . . .' [3].

Incidentally, even 'looking red' is a dispositional term: 'It describes the disposition of a thing to make onlookers agree that it looks red' [4].

Now one of the consequences of the fact that there cannot be a 'pure' observational language, free from the contamination of theories, is that all observational evidence statements, and especially all records of 'observational knowledge', are contaminated by theories. Thus they must not be accepted uncritically. But the application of a critical method to them obviously leads to the systematic criticism of theories and thus to the critical (non-inductive) method which I advocate.

---

[1] Francis Darwin (ed.), *More Letters of Charles Darwin*, vol. I, 1903, p. 195. Darwin's passage ends with the words (which I admit slightly weaken it as a support of my thesis) 'if it is to be of any service!'.

[2] K. R. Popper, *The Logic of Scientific Discovery*, p. 95, end of sec. 25.

[3] K. R. Popper, *Conjectures and Refutations*, 1963, pp. 118 f.

[4] *Loc. cit.* The passage was first published in 1956.

More especially, since the *unavoidably selective* recording of observational knowledge will depend on the theories held, Carnap's concept of 'total evidence' or of a person's *'total observational knowledge'* which marks the transition from Carnap's 'credence function' to his 'credibility function' will be necessarily contaminated by theories held by the person in question: his 'knowledge' will thus be quite unreliable (and, indeed, *in*credible) [2].

4. My emphasis upon theories is connected with my thesis that 'scientific knowledge' may be regarded as *subjectless*: it may be treated as a system of *theories-in-themselves* (in Bolzano's sense) on which we work like workers on a cathedral, though we should try to do so in a critical spirit: the belief or faith of a scientist, though it may inspire him, poses no problem for the theory of 'scientific knowledge' (that is, for the theory of theories-in-themselves); though of course this faith may cause as much trouble as most inspirations do. (Like E. M. Forster, I do not believe in belief; and I certainly do not believe that the problem of belief is a problem of the theory of scientific knowledge.)

All this will show that I have some reasons to doubt the possibility of an 'inductive logic', whether it is an interpretation of the probability calculus, or a theory of degrees of (rational or irrational) belief, or of 'credence', or of 'credibility'.

5. *But no theory of inductive belief is needed.* As Watkins said, we can 'develop a . . . methodology [of science] . . . which shows how rational choices between competing theories *are* possible despite the absence of any inductive inferences'. Bar–Hillel comments that 'Popper has failed in this endeavour, though he never confessed to it'. [Yet Bar–Hillel does not give any indication that he knows what my 'endeavour' is: what role, for example, my formula for 'degree of corroboration' plays in my methodology. All that he says indicates, rather, that he has no idea what I am trying to do.]

I certainly have no sense of failure, even though I am quite used to 'confessing' to any mistakes I have made (as for example

---

[1]   *Added in proof.* Cp. my remarks in this volume, pp. 137 f.

in section 77 of my *Logic of Scientific Discovery*). In fact, I have the very opposite of a feeling of failure: the fruitfulness of the basic ideas of my *Logic of Scientific Discovery* in all fields of knowledge in which they have been tried has far exceeded my boldest hopes. I do not only have in mind the physical, biological, and social sciences (fields in which many of my results and those of my collaborators are still unpublished); I have in mind not only the history of science and of philosophy, but also such unexpected fields as the history of mathematics, the history of art, and even that of music, and religion; to say nothing about the explanation of theory formation at prescientific levels.

Of course I have corrected some of my earlier views (and 'confessed' to their being mistaken whenever appropriate). The most important of these corrections was the change from the frequency interpretation to the propensity interpretation of probability [1]. In the main, however, the more fundamental ideas of my early book have turned out to be, somewhat unexpectedly, so very nearly correct in so many fields, that I can only say that I feel that I was very lucky in having struck so rich a mine of results.

Of course, I am very far from asserting that my *Logic of Scientific Discovery* was anything like the last word in carrying out its programme. I am glad that my co-workers and I have made much progress since. Yet most of the fundamental problems of a non-inductivist methodology were indeed solved before, or in, 1934; and especially its main points:

(a)   That science starts from problems (*P*).

(b)   That we never start from a *tabula rasa* – not even the lower animals do – but from a horizon of expectations; that is to say, we always have some 'background knowledge' (*B*), which is theoretical and open to improvement.

---

[1]   See K. R. Popper, 'The propensity interpretation of the calculus of probability, and the quantum theory', S. Körner, ed., *Observation and Interpretation in the Philosophy of Science*, 1957, pp. 65–70 and 88 f.; 'The propensity interpretation of probability', *British Journal for the Philosophy of Science* 10, 1959, pp. 25–42; and 'Quantum Mechanics without the "Observer" ', in M. Bunge (ed.): *Quantum Theory and Reality*, 1967, pp. 7–44 (esp. pp. 28–41).

(c)   That we try to solve our problems by proposing many, and more often than not untenable, tentative solutions, that is, competing tentative theories (*TT*).

(d)   That these theories are subjected to a *selective process* of error elimination (*EE*) which on the prescientific level is usually unconscious, while on the scientific level it consists in consciously hunting down our mistakes by criticizing our various competing theories; that is to say, by way of critical and comparative discussions in which crucial experimental tests play an important part whenever we can design such tests.

(e)   That the result of this is, as a rule, a *new problem situation* (P_2); so that we can describe the procedure (taking B, the background knowledge, for granted) by the schema

$$P_1 \to TT \to EE \to P_2.$$

(f)   Scientific progress can be gauged by the difference in depth between P_1 (the old problem situation) and P_2 (the new problem situation).

To sum up, my theory is a theory of *the growth of scientific knowledge*. Its main instrument is logic which I regard as the *organon of critical discussion*, based upon the retransmission of falsity from the conclusion to the premises.

While my theory of science is a theory of *selection* (Darwin), the theory of induction by repetition is one of *instruction* (Lamarck) or of the inculcation of knowledge.

6.   The main progress I made more recently is connected with the realization that theories (and their appraisal) can only be *understood* by going back to the problems – to the problems the theory solves (P_1) and to those which it opens up (P_2).

7.   The whole progress is an adventure into the unknown – into *open possibilities*. This openness prevents the application of *probability*. But the discussion of competing theories involves that of *content*, and of verisimilitude which is, in practice, truth content [1].

---

[1]   For verisimilitude, see K. R. Popper, *Conjectures and Refutations*, 1963, Ch. 10 and addenda. Also K. R. Popper, 'A theorem on truth content', in

8. The growth of knowledge does involve a growth of our language. The theories which impregnate our language are constantly criticized and replaced. In this way we solve Bacon's main problem: how can we eliminate our prejudices (*idola*) which may interfere with, and invalidate our observations. Bacon thought we could do so by purging our minds of all preconceived theories. I hold that we need preconceived theories; accordingly, what is needed to solve Bacon's problem is an *attitude of criticism* towards our theories: we must *try* to refute them, not to verify or confirm them.

9. In Carnap's lecture, the main point which needs criticism is his appeal to *intuition as a source of knowledge*.

This is a topic I treated fairly extensively in 1960 in a lecture 'On the Sources of Knowledge and of Ignorance' [1]. In this lecture I criticized the doctrine of the 'sources of knowledge' as well as the doctrine that 'intuition' is a 'source of knowledge'.

We might say that the main *intuitive* difference between Carnap and myself is as follows. He maintains that intuitions are not only important, but to some extent reliable: and I maintain that intuitions, like all other beliefs, are, *qua* beliefs, irrelevant for science, and only of interest to psychology; to the theory of scientific knowledge they become interesting only after having led to the production of criticizable statements-in-themselves in the sense of Bolzano.

10. Carnap says that deductive logic is based on deductive intuition. I contest this claim. Any rule of inference can be criticized by trying to find a *counter example* – that is to say, an instance of the rule with *true* premises and a *false* conclusion.

The main argument against the parallelism, defended by Carnap, between deductive and the so-called inductive logic, is that while deductive logic can be rationally criticized by the search for

---

P. K. Feyerabend and G. Maxwell, eds., *Mind, Matter, and Method, Essays in Philosophy and Science in Honor of Herbert Feigl*, 1966, pp. 343–353. David Miller has since given a simplified proof and an extension of this theorem.

[1] Now in K. R. Popper, *Conjectures and Refutations*, 1963, pp. 3–30.

counter examples, there is no such criterion for the invalidity of any alleged rule of inductive logic.

(a)   It is interesting that Carnap gives an example of a deductive inference (whose validity, he holds, must be accepted intuitively) but no corresponding example of an inductive inference.

The reason is, I suppose, that no convincing example of any similar inductive rule of inference exists.

(b)   I have had students who thought that 'All men are mortal; Socrates is mortal; thus Socrates is a man' was a valid inference. Yet they realized the invalidity of this rule when I discussed with them a counter example (arising from calling my cat 'Socrates').

My point is that there is no similar rule of inductive logic which is either intuitively valid or which stands up to criticism in the light of the history of science.

11.   Some rules (or definitions) which were once regarded as intuitively convincing by Carnap (such as his instance confirmation [1]) are clearly untenable and, I suppose, no longer defended by him. Rules suggested by others as intuitively convincing have also had to be abandoned under the fire of criticism. Consider for example the rule discussed by me in (2)(e) (the 'Diminishing returns of learning by induction') and the probabilistic straight rule, refuted by Miller [2]. This shows how right Carnap is when he says 'I hasten to add that I do not mean here by "inductive intuition" a source of knowledge that is infallible'. Quite so. But then Carnap should not *appeal* to intuition, but to critical argument; as to Carnap's term 'inductively blind' I am quite ready to confess that 'inductive blindness' correctly describes the condition in which I find myself, since I am not blessed with 'inductive intuition'. But I think that

---

[1]   Cp. R. Carnap, *Logical Foundations of Probability*, 1950, pp. 571 f., where intuitive reasons are given; and p. xvii of the second edition, 1962.

[2]   'A paradox of information', *British Journal for the Philosophy of Science* 17, 1966, pp. 59–61. The published "replies" to this paradox seem to me either to support Miller's position (see, for example, formula 5 on p. 144 of J. L. Mackie, 'Miller's so-called paradox of information', *ibid.*, pp. 144–147: this formula, which Mackie regards as validly derived from the straight rule, is actually the same as Miller's paradox), or to miss his point, or both.

there are many people, and good scientists among them, who are not only inductively but also physically blind (and one of the greatest of musicians became deaf). These scientists can, nevertheless, follow critical arguments. Though we are inductively blind, we *can* argue *pace* Carnap, both about induction, and about the critical appraisal of scientific theories.

12. It seems to me clear that the intuitive basis of Carnap's induction consists in something like this: if we toss a fair coin, we shall after sufficiently many tosses have an observational frequency of heads close to what I should call the *objective probability* or *propensity* of heads turning up and $p(h, b) = \frac{1}{2}$, where h is 'heads turning up' and b describes the experimental conditions. According to the inductive intuition thus analysed, we can learn something about the objective probability from the observation of frequencies.

These intuitive [1] considerations suggest the following *simple inductive rule* (a very weak form of the so-called 'straight rule'): If in a very large number of repetitions of an experiment we find that the result a occurs with the frequency m/n, then the best estimate of the probability of a, with respect to this experimental evidence, is equal – or at least approximately equal – to m/n.

I have consciously given this rule a form which is not very definite, and therefore not very strong. In the form given, it applies only to 'large' numbers of repetitions; and it does not claim that m/n is the best estimate: it only claims that the best estimate will be 'approximately equal' to, or 'near' to, m/n.

Since the rule, in this form, is weak, all its stronger variants will be destroyed with it, if we can refute it; as indeed we can [2].

For the simple inductive rule is false . . . A simple example

---

[1] What follows from here down to and excluding footnote 1 on p. 300, is quoted almost *verbatim* from pp. 359 f. of my paper, "Probability magic, or knowledge out of ignorance", *Dialectica* 11, 1957, pp. 354–374. The next two footnotes here numbered 22 and 23 are there printed on p. 359 and p. 360.

[2] The variants refuted include an innumerable number of theories of induction (among them the whole of Carnap's so-called *Continuum of Inductive Methods*, 1952).

may ... show that this rule leads to utterly absurd results in cases where the condition of *independence* (in the sense of the objective theory) is not satisfied.

A striking example by which we may refute the simple inductive rule is the game 'Red or Blue'.

A gambler plays heads or tails on credit terms with his banker: a book is kept in which he is credited 1 shilling every time he wins, and debited 1 shilling every time he loses. If, after any toss, he owes money to the bank, we say that we have observed the event 'Red'. If he does not owe any money, the observed event is 'Blue'. The game 'Red or Blue' consists in betting upon the occurrence of one of the events, Red or Blue.

Now from the point of the *objective theory*, it is quite clear that

(i)   The probability of Red = the probability of Blue = $\frac{1}{2}$, or very nearly so. (There is a slight but completely negligible asymmetry in the conditions, in so far as 'Red' means 'debit', while 'Blue' means 'credit or *zero balance*'. [This asymmetry may easily be avoided by describing zero balance as 'no game' from the point of view of the people who bet on the events 'Red' or 'Blue'.]) Thus we may say, from the objective point of view, that

$$p(a, b) = p(-a, b) = \tfrac{1}{2},$$

where a is red, $-a$ is blue, and b are the conditions of the game (the experimental set-up).

(ii)   The sequence of a and $-a$ is not independent. The calculations [1] show that this fact leads to very unexpected results. If we arrange for a colossal experiment, tossing the coin every second for a whole year, then the following holds: there will be a probability of 0.9 that the *difference* between the two observed frequencies (that of a and that of $-a$) will exceed 1/6; that is 2 months. There will be a probability of more than 0.5 that the difference between the two observed frequencies will exceed 2/3 (that is 8 months). And there will be a probability of more than 0.4 that the difference will exceed 0.8 (that is almost 10 months).

---

[1]   All the results are taken from W. Feller, *An Introduction to Probability Theory and its Applications*, vol. 1, 1950, pp. 250 ff. The original papers are there quoted in footnotes on p. 252.

In other words, it is in this game *objectively improbable in the extreme* that estimates according to the simple inductive rule will succeed [that is, in coming near to the objective probability of $\frac{1}{2}$]; and it is extremely probable that the deviations between the inductive estimate and the value 1/2 will be very great indeed; and this will be so even if we take tremendous numbers of observations – more than could possibly be observed in many a lifetime [1].

To say the very least, this result is surprising, and shows that the intuitive idea underlying simple induction is mistaken; or that it depends on what we call in the objective theory of probability 'the mutual independence of the single experiments' [2].

Feller comments characteristically, and this should warn us against inductive intuitions: 'Few people will believe that a perfect coin will produce preposterous sequences in which no change of lead [his name for what I have called a change from 'Red' to 'Blue' or *vice versa*] occurs for millions of trials in succession, and yet this is what a good coin will do rather regularly' [3].

13. In order to show further the discrepancy between various inductive intuitions, I may point out that Professor C. L. Hamblin has argued intuitively, and in my opinion successfully, in favour of an *axiom system for 'probable'* in which 'probable' is interpreted as 'more probable than not' and in which the following is universally valid:

If p is probable and q is probable, then *p and q* is also probable [4].

---

[1] This is the end of the quotation from my paper in *Dialectica*. I may say that the problem of what I call the game of 'Red or Blue' has since been very fully and interestingly developed by Feller in the 2nd ed. of his *An Introduction to Probability Theory and its Applications*, 1957, pp. 71–85, 280–310. See especially table 2 on p. 81, and the comments following it.

[2] If on the other hand we assume mutual independence of the single instances (that is, for the one case in which the intuitive idea does not break down) then all universal laws have zero absolute logical probability; a value which cannot be raised by any evidence. See K. R. Popper, *The Logic of Scientific Discovery*, 1959, appendix *vii, especially pp. 367 f.

[3] W. Feller, *op. cit.*, 2nd ed., 1957, p. 81.

[4] C. L. Hamblin, 'The Modal "Probably" ', *Mind* 68, 1959, pp. 234–240. The system referred to is there described on p. 240.

Of course, this rule is invalid in any calculus of probability. But it seems to me intuitively valid if 'probable' is interpreted by 'believed in'; which speaks *either* against the interpretation of the calculus of probability as a calculus of (rational or other) degrees of belief, or else against reliance on intuition. There are some more such examples in the writings of Professor G. L. S. Shackle and of Hamblin. I may repeat one passage (quoted by Shackle) in which Hamblin criticizes the theory of games: 'We might say that the economic-political sphere is more like a special sort of poker-game in which at each stage each player can without prior warning *invent* a new sort of move for himself – in effect, invent new rules for the game' [1].

I believe (like Hamblin) that this also holds for the growth of scientific knowledge. Hamblin continues:

'The circumstances in which we *can* fall back on . . . probability [in the sense of the probability calculus] are in fact severely limited. We must *first* have a clearly delimited field of possibilities . . . logically exhaustive and mutually exclusive . . .' [2].

Hamblin writes later

'. . . what has been said applies equally to *any* application of reasoning based on the orthodox concept of probability [including] any of the probabilistic accounts of induction, from Keynes to Popper' [3].

---

[1]   G. L. S. Shackle, *Decision, Order and Time*, 1961, Cambridge University Press, p. 99.

[2]   *Loc. cit.*

[3]   Shackle, *op. cit.*, p. 100. I do not think that Hamblin means that I have a probabilistic account of induction like Keynes or Jeffreys or Carnap, but I think that he objects to my 'degree of corroboration' $C(a, b, c)$ of a hypothesis a in the presence of empirical tests b and the 'background knowledge' c:

$$C(a, b, c) = (p(b, ac) - p(b, c))/(p(b, ac) - p(ab, c) + p(b, c)).$$

It looks to me as if Hamblin may not be aware of the fact that I regard this formula merely as a means of showing that certain 'desiderata' can be consistently combined, and as applicable to the *discussion* of certain competing theories, but *not as of any numerical significance* (except perhaps in those statistical cases in which Hamblin's conditions for the application of the probability calculus are satisfied). In other words, I completely agree with Hamblin, though he does not seem to be aware of this fact.

Hamblin's arguments are all highly intuitive (though at the same time based on critical reasoning).

14. As a last argument against relying on inductive or probabilistic intuition I may mention the following.

We have transitivity for deductive inference:

$$\text{If } a \vdash b \text{ and } b \vdash c \text{ then } a \vdash c,$$

(where '$a \vdash b$' means 'a logically implies b'); but we have no transitivity for 'a almost logically implies b', (in Carnap's sense [1]), where '$a \to b$', that is 'a almost logically implies b', is defined by:

$$a \to b \equiv p(b, a) = 1.$$

(In the context of a Carnapian finitist object language, or of Jeffrey's *Logic of Decision*, we may perhaps replace, in our present discussion, '$= 1$' by, say, '$\geqslant 0.99999$'.)

Now we may not only have

(1) $a \to b$ and $b \to c$ but not $a \to c$

but we may even have:

(2) $a \to b$ and $b \to c$ and $p(c, a) = 0$

and what is still stronger

(3) $a \to b$ and $b \to c$ and a contradicts c.

(For a proof, let a be $(x)Ax$; let b be $(Ex)Ax$; and let c be non-a. Then for a sufficiently large universe, the result will approximately follow from Carnap's theory; for an infinite universe it follows either from Carnap's theory or from mine.)

Now let us translate this into the belief-language (rational or otherwise). '$x \to y$' can be read 'if x is to be believed in, y is almost certainly to be believed in', or perhaps 'given x, we must believe that y is almost certainly true'. Yet this or a similar reading, which seems adequate if we interpret (for example, in Jeffrey's sense) the

---

[1] R. Carnap, *Logical Foundations of Probability*, 1950, p. 314.

probability calculus as a calculus of degrees of beliefs, makes (2) and (3) in the presence of (1) for me clearly counter intuitive. This may just be due to my inductive blindness. But it may also be due to the fact that (2) and (3) show the inadequacy of interpreting the probability calculus as a calculus of beliefs.

15. None of these problems (or puzzles) seems to me to have the slightest bearing on either scientific method or the critical appraisal of scientific theories. Though they are in my opinion fatal to the project of an inductive logic in Carnap's sense, they do not affect in the least my non-inductive theory of the critical appraisal of scientific theories, and of the growth of scientific knowledge through the elimination of error.

J. HINTIKKA: *Conditionalization and information.*

I should like to make only two marginal remarks on Professor Carnap's interesting and lucid survey of some of the problems one encounters in constructing inductive logic. My remarks are of the nature of queries and suggestions rather than criticisms or supporting arguments.

The first is related to Carnap's concept of a credibility function. It is supposed to be related to one's credence functions in such a way that whatever credence function one has is obtained from one's credibility function by conditionalization with respect to the total evidence one has. In short, credence is credibility with respect to total evidence.

For many purposes, the proposition whose credence we are examining must be thought of as being expressed by a sentence in some well-defined language. In the terms Carnap employed, it must belong to some well-defined field of propositions. We can try to study also the credence that could be thought of as being given to infinite sets of sentences, but it is doubtful that this is a realistic model of our actual beliefs. In any case, for many purposes it is advisable to operate with individual sentences in some well-defined language and not with infinite sets of sentences.

But if so, then it becomes questionable whether the total information one has can be expressed by a single sentence or even by a denumerably infinite set of sentences which belongs to the language in question. And if it does not belong to the language, we cannot conditionalize with respect to it without going beyond the language in question.

Thus there are more problems about the conditionalization involved in the transition from credibility to credence than one first realizes. This point is related to certain other issues that come up in connection with Carnap's program, e.g. with the evaluation of Carnap's work on the λ-continuum of inductive methods (and on its unpublished refinements).

Somebody might argue as follows against the significance of Carnap's λ-continuum: the choice of one particular value of λ rather than another in any one application of inductive logic can only be justified in terms of one's observational knowledge of the universe of discourse we are speaking about. In fact, Carnap has himself indicated some of the features of the universe that are relevant in this respect. (The more uniform the world is, in a certain sense, the smaller λ should one select.) But certainly this kind of background knowledge should be formulated by an explicit proposition A' which is a part of the total evidence A relative to which one's credence is determined. Hence no free parameter λ is needed.

I am not sure how Professor Carnap would respond to this line of argument. Sometimes he seems to view λ and similar parameters as auxiliary concepts which we would in the last analysis like to replace by definite numerical constants. I am not quite sure myself, either, how the situation is to be viewed. One reasonably clear thing here is, in any case, that the kind of information concerning the uniformity of one's universe, on which one's choice of λ turns, cannot be expressed by a finite sentence in an applied first-order logic if one's universe is infinite. The great theoretical interest of Carnap's parameter λ depends in my view partly on this very fact. It gives us a method of changing our probability distribution on propositions by a procedure other than conditionalization with respect to a given proposition.

Generalizing a little, one can perhaps say that the scheme Carnap is putting forward presupposes that conditionalization is in the last analysis the only rational method of changing one's probability distribution. On the other hand, it seems to me that a considerable part of the interest of the work Carnap has actually done is due to the fact that he has been discussing in a very interesting way some entirely different methods of making such changes, viz. those resulting from changes in λ. The question I want to pose, not just to Carnap but to everybody interested in these matters, is precisely this: Is conditionalization in principle the only rational method of rearranging our credence values? Are there kinds of information, or differences between different kinds of information, that cannot be formulated in terms of explicit premises and which therefore cause other types of changes? Richard Jeffrey has argued for the latter alternative, referring e.g. to observational knowledge so vague that it cannot be explicitly formulated. It has also been pointed out that conditionalization is likely to be a very poor model of how people in fact rearrange their beliefs, even when they behave as rationally as anyone can hope. However, the problems that arise here are not all empirical but are also conceptually quite deep, and largely unexamined. Even 'the mathematical theory of general conditional probabilities is not yet in a very good state' (Dana Scott). Of course, these difficulties are as much a problem e.g. for a Bayesian as for Carnap, for there is not so very much that has been said by Bayesians either, about types of changes of one's credences other than conditionalization.

This is one group of problems to which I would like to call your attention. It seems to me that part of the energy that is being expended on the current controversies between Popperians and Carnapians could be much more profitably devoted to these concrete problems which are not unrelated to the controversy.

The second point I want to touch on, is the concept of 'inductive intuition' which is compared by Carnap to 'deductive intuition' in an illuminating manner. It seems to me, however, that it is not the only court of appeal here, but that the best way of achieving philosophical clarity in either field (inductive logic or deductive logic) is to learn to develop and to systematize (I am almost tempted to say to educate) our intuitions. One way of doing so is to connect

them with other, related intuitions. It is not the case that a
'deductively blind person' is as immune to persuasion as Carnap
suggests, at least not if he is willing to make other sorts of con-
cessions. These are related essentially to the connection between
our deductive concepts and other concepts about which we also
have clear and even clearer intuitions. In the case of a deductive
logic one such concept might be the notion of a 'consistent description of a possible state of affairs' – a concept Carnap himself
essentially relied on in his concept of a state-description. It might
be agreed e.g. that a person who refuses to admit a deductive
consequence thereby assumes the possibility of producing a consistent description of a possible state of affairs under which the
premises are true but the conclusion false. (Of course this is
precisely what the 'deductively blind' person *cannot* do in Carnap's
example.) This is a line of thought that can be pushed pretty far,
as I have tried to show elsewhere.

In the case of inductive logic, there is a group of concepts related
to the notion of inductive probability which have not always been
brought to bear on this notion. In terms of any notion of inductive
probability we can define a concept of (semantic) information in
certain simple ways which have in fact been studied at some length
by Carnap and Bar–Hillel. Now the concept of information is one
about which we also have fairly clear-cut intuitions – intuitions
which in my view are often sharper than those that pertain to the
rationality of inductive behaviour. It seems to me that one of the
best ways of educating one's inductive intuitions is to connect
them with whatever ideas we have about the information that
different statements convey. Some interesting light may be shed
on the rationality of the different choices of credibility function
in this way, it seems to me. In general, a useful approach to the
philosophy of induction seems to open here. It has been used by
Carnap and others occasionally, but it seems to be capable of being
pushed much farther. My own tentative results in this direction
seem to suggest that the choice of parameters like λ can scarcely
be restricted at all *a priori*, at least not as long as we restrict ourselves to the kind of languages Carnap has so far considered in
print.

R. Carnap: *Reply to M. Bunge*

Here, I think, I need not say much. Some points have been cleared up by Bar–Hillel. Bunge is certainly right in asserting that the problems which are commonly discussed under the title 'induction' form a very heterogeneous set. But it is not clear to me whether and how this remark is meant as an objection against my theory, which I call 'inductive logic'. Certainly my theory has nothing to do with most of the problems of the problem complexes listed by Bunge. This holds also for his theory (4), to which he gives the name 'seductive logic'; since my theory does not deal with inferences. Bunge mentions my name only in the last paragraph. There he says that my inductive logic 'does not concern science'. Now it is true that the elementary theory constructed up to now refers only to a form of language corresponding roughly to the observational language but not to the theoretical language. To construct a system of inductive logic for the theoretical language is considerably more difficult because of the much more complicated logical structure of this language. I have made some preliminary studies of these problems, and I am convinced that the construction of such a system is possible. But this is a task for the future.

Reply to J. W. N. Watkins

In section II of his discussion, Watkins seems to assume as beyond doubt that rules of acceptance are needed. If we interpret the statement '*X* decides to accept the hypothesis *h* (for example, an empirical or theoretical universal statement)' as meaning '*X* decides to proceed as if he knew with certainty that *h* is true', then it seems to me that the arguments against rules of acceptance, which I have given elsewhere, show that, by an acceptance in this sense, *X* would often be led to unreasonable practical decisions. These undesirable consequences could be avoided if exact rules were to specify in which particular respects *X* should proceed as if he knew that the hypothesis *h* were true. But talking of 'inference' from level 0 to 1 and from 1 to 2 and similar formulations suggest the unrestricted procedure.

In his last paragraph Watkins describes the Hume–Carnap–Popper situation. But I cannot agree with his description of my position. As I see it, the essential point in the inductivist doctrine which was taught by Hume and John Stuart Mill and by many other philosophers, and which is rejected by Popper, seems to me the following assertion: science makes an inductive ascent starting from level 0 and leading to statements of level 1 and then level 2, and finally level 3, by proceeding according to rules of inductive inference. If I understand Watkins correctly, he asserts that I try to rationalize this 'alleged inductive ascent of science'. I am surprised by Watkins's assertion, since I have made clear my opposition to this main thesis of traditional inductivism in my book *Logical Foundations of Probability*, 1950, pp. 192f.

I do not deny that there are differences between Popper's and my conceptions in the methodology of science. But Popper and Watkins, by overlooking important points of agreement like the one just mentioned, give a wrong picture of the situation.

Reply to Y. Bar–Hillel

On most of the important points of the discussion I am in agreement with Bar–Hillel. I was amazed by Watkins's characterization of my conception as 'anti-theoretical'. Therefore I am gratified to see that Bar–Hillel comes to my defence, pointing out that in recent years I have given some attention to theoretical laws and theoretical concepts.

On the other hand, I am not sure that Bar–Hillel is right – this time in agreement with Watkins – that I, though not today, still in 1950 had an 'overly instrumentalistic' view of scientific laws. First I should like to call your attention to the context in which I used the phrases quoted by Bar–Hillel. His first quotation is from the title of subsection 110H of my *Logical Foundations of Probability*; the title is 'Are Laws Needed *for Making Predictions?*'. In the last paragraph I say: 'We see that the use of laws is not indispensable *for making predictions* (both italics are added here) and similarly in the last sentence of this paragraph. I would regard a philosopher's conception of scientific laws as 'instrumentalistic' only if he regards laws as *merely* instruments or tools, to be judged only as useful or not; in contrast to genuine factual statements, which assert something about the world, and therefore are to be judged as either true or false. I have always regarded laws as represented by assertive sentences. In the Vienna Circle I defended this view against Schlick who, following Wittgenstein, proposed that the usual function of laws be delegated to rules for the derivation of predictions. But I would not say that I am right and Schlick is wrong. The whole controversy is essentially not a question of true or false beliefs, but rather a question of the choice of the form of language, or the form of the whole system of science. At any rate, there can be no doubt that we can derive predictions and also determine their probability on the basis of given evidence, no matter which of the two system forms we use.

Although, from the point of view of practical application, the prediction of concrete observable events and the determination of their probabilities are the main results we obtain from science, I suppose we all agree in the view that practical application is by far not the only purpose of science. We appreciate science highly because it helps us to understand the processes of the world in which we live, from the micro-cosmos to the macro-cosmos. And this includes the processes investigated in astronomy, which we find so fascinating, although they have mostly no practical consequences for us.

(My comments to Bar–Hillel on rules of acceptance are to be found at another place in this volume).

Reply to K. R. Popper

Popper's comment on instance confirmation is based on misunderstandings which were completely cleared up by Bar–Hillel ten years ago (*British Journal for the Philosophy of Science*, VII, 1956, pp. 247f.). What I call the instance confirmation of a universal law l, is a degree of confirmation (and therefore a conditional probability, which satisfies the axioms of the probability calculus) *not* of l itself, but of any future instance h of l. But this value is, though not a probability of l, still an important characteristic of the law. In Popper's example, the law which is in the average satisfied by one half of the instances, has, on the basis of my definition, not the probability $\frac{1}{2}$, as Popper erroneously believes, but 0. This is always the case if a counter-instance has been observed. Suppose a physicist or an engineer says of a law that it is 'well established' or 'reliable' or, more explicitly, 'may be used with confidence'. It seems to me that what is meant by these phrases may be explicated by 'the instance confirmation of the law is high'. I do not know why Popper believes that I have abandoned the concept of instance confirmation. So far I have not seen any convincing objection against my conception, least of all from Popper.

I am in agreement with Popper's view that even observational terms like 'red' and the like have basically a dispositional character, and that therefore there is no 'pure observational language'. I have emphasized repeatedly that the distinction between the observational language and the theoretical language is an artificial oversimplification; actually the whole field of language is continuous. Nevertheless it seems to me practically very useful to draw a boundary between the two parts of the language. In science we have frequently a situation of this kind. For example, all medical men know that every disease affects the whole organism; there is no purely circulatory disease. Nevertheless they find it very useful in practice to distinguish between diseases of the circulatory system, the nervous system, the eyes, and so on.

Since Popper seems allergic to the terms 'inductive' and 'intuition', let us for the moment use neutral terms. Instead of 'inductive' we shall say 'probabilistic' (understood either in the logical or the personalistic sense of 'probability', not the frequency sense); and instead of 'intuition': 'the ability to discriminate (at least in simple cases) between valid and invalid reasoning', or briefly 'discriminative ability'. I can hardly see reasons for serious doubt when I make the following assertion which indeed seems to me rather trivial: we cannot hope to teach someone to use a language and, furthermore, to speak and think in a logically correct way unless he has from the beginning certain basic discriminative abilities; and this holds for the whole field of reasoning, including deductive and probabilistic reasoning. But what I would like to emphasize is the following point, which is not trivial. I believe that deductive discriminative ability, even of a very high degree, is not sufficient as a basis for the whole field of reasoning, including probabilistic reasoning. An individual X of the following kind is conceivable. (For psychological reasons it would not be easy to find a living example; but it would be easy to construct a robot of this kind.) X has a very high discriminative ability for deductive reasoning, but only a very low, defective ability for probabilistic reasoning. For example, X is rarely found to make deductive (including arithmetical) mistakes, but he constantly makes mistakes in probability assignments and, consequently, in his betting behaviour. He might, for example, often violate one or all of the three principles of probabilistic reasoning which I have stated in my lecture: the principles of coherence, of strict coherence, and of symmetry with respect to individuals. As an example, let us assume that X knows the following things and nothing else about Mr. Brown: Mr. Brown is a male white American, living in Texas, his age is between 40 and 50 years, and he has tuberculosis; about Mr. Smith he has exactly the same information, no more and no less; but he assigns to the proposition that Brown will die within ten years the probability of one fifth, and at the same time he assigns to the corresponding proposition about Smith the probability of one tenth; and he persists in these assignments in spite of all counter-arguments. I only assert that it is not self-contradictory, i.e. it is logically conceivable that a person be in deductive reasoning absolutely perfect, but in probabilistic reasoning completely erratic and inaccessible to rational argumentation. In contrast, the assumption that an individual is perfect in deductive reasoning, but cannot be dissuaded from his belief that $17 + 5 = 21$, is inconceivable.

By the way, Popper finds it 'interesting' that I give in my lecture an example of deductive inference, but no example of inductive inference. Since in my conception probabilistic ('inductive') reasoning consists essentially not in making inferences, but rather in assigning probabilities, he should instead have required examples of principles for probability assignments. And this request not made but reasonable, was anticipated and satisfied.

Reply to J. Hintikka

The questions raised by Hintikka are very interesting, but their discussion would lead to complicated technicalities for which there is no time here. I shall restrict myself to some brief indications concerning some of the questions, as they look to me from my present point of view. This point of view has of course often been modified in the course of years and will presumably change still further as long as I work in this field.

An important point of change consists in taking into account the fact that, strictly speaking, all evidence is uncertain. For me and my friends, this is an old problem. But now Richard Jeffrey has offered a first solution (in his *Logic of Decision*, 1966). His system takes as the basic concept not credibility, as my system does, but credence, like the systems of De Finetti and Savage. I have now found a way, suggested by the guiding idea of Jeffrey's solution, for modifying my method so as to make it applicable to uncertain evidence. My previous form of evidence was a sequence K_n of observation statements in the form of atomic sentences of the observational language L, each of them ascribing to a certain thing a certain directly observable property. In the new form of the evidence, K'_n, the observer attaches to each observational statement a number representing his credence in the statement at the moment immediately after the observation. (In the usual cases, where we feel practically certain, the number may for instance be 0.999.) Then I have defined a generalized kind of credibility function applicable to evidence of this new form. And the (rational) credence of the observer in a hypothesis H is now defined as the credibility of H with respect to the total evidence given in the new form K'_n. The evidence sequence is always assumed to be finite, since any observer at any time point of his life has observed only a finite number of things. But the class of those propositions with respect to L to which my probability functions are applicable is very much more comprehensive than the class of the sentences in the language L. The class of these propositions, the possible hypotheses, is rather the σ-field generated by the (Boolean) field of the molecular sentences, based on the class of the atomic sentences with respect to the universe of the language, which is a denumerable set of individuals (observable things) and the predicates of the language. Let L be a language with a denumerable sequence of individuals and one family F of k attributes P_j ($j = 1, 2, ..., k$). Let Y be any random variable with respect to L. (For example, Y may be the limit R_j of the relative frequency of P_j or it may be the degree of order (uniformity) in the universe of individuals, defined in some way or other on the basis of the k R_j-values, or it may be anything else.) Then for any real numbers u_1 and u_2, irrespective of the expressibility of these numbers in some given language, the class of propositions on L includes a proposition which says that $Y = u_1$, and also a proposition saying that Y belongs to the interval between u_1 and u_2.

In his last paragraph, Hintikka comments on the problem of the choice of a credibility function and, in particular, on the choice of a value for the parameter λ. Years ago I investigated ways of choosing λ on the basis of given evidence in the form of a sample description E. (My particular tentative method consisted in determining the estimate (expectation value) for the degree of order in the universe, based on E, and then to choose as λ the optimum λ-value λ^Δ for the estimated degree of order[1].) Maybe Hintikka is alluding to this attempt of mine; at any rate he suggests that the choice of λ could not be made on a purely *a priori* basis. However, I found later that making λ dependent either upon the number s of individuals in a sample E, or upon the numbers s_j ($j = 1, 2, ..., k$) of the attributes P_j in E, leads to a violation of the basic axioms. We cannot use in the same inductive method probability values based in certain cases on one λ-value and in other cases on another value. The situation is of course different if somebody decides to abandon his whole inductive method, maybe on the basis of experience or for whatever reason, and then to use from now on another inductive method based on a fixed but different λ-value. In this case, of course, working with a new method does not involve a violation of the axioms. But I also have doubts

---

[1]   I have defined the optimum λ in *The Continuum of Inductive Methods*, 1952, section 22.

about this procedure. Today I am inclined to base the choice of an inductive method, and in particular the choice of a value of λ, not on observed facts, but only on *a priori* considerations. The considerable narrowing of the range of admissible λ-values which, we have achieved in the course of the last ten years was obtained exclusively by *a priori* arguments. (Some of these arguments appear as compelling, others as merely plausible.)

At the present moment it seems to me that within any given inductive method, represented here by a credibility function, only the two following procedures are legitimate for the change of credence values: (1) a change in the credence of an atomic proposition A, prompted by an observation of the individual involved in A, and (2) a change in the credence of other propositions by conditionalization based on changes of the kind (1). I believe that I am here essentially in agreement with Richard Jeffrey, in spite of the differences between our approaches, for example, by my referring always to the total evidence. Against this procedure of mine the objection has repeatedly been raised that it is unrealistic because nobody is actually able to remember the enormous number of observational results he has experienced (and, in the new form indicated above, in addition, the credence values of these observation propositions immediately after the observation). In response, I should like to point out that in Jeffrey's method the observer has to keep in mind the enormous number of credence values not only for all atomic propositions with respect to individuals previously observed, but also with respect to all the individuals not yet observed, whose number may be infinite. (By the way, the number of items of the second kind could be considerably reduced by the acceptance of my principle of symmetry with respect to individuals.)

CHANGES IN THE PROBLEM OF INDUCTIVE LOGIC *

I. LAKATOS

University of London

Introduction.

1. The two main problems of classical empiricism: inductive justification and inductive method.

2. The one main problem of neoclassical empiricism: weak inductive justification (degree of confirmation).

2.1. The weak and strong atheoretical theses.

   (*a*) Carnap abandons the Jeffreys–Keynes postulate. Qualified instance confirmation versus confirmation.

   (*b*) The weak atheoretical thesis: confirmation theory without theories.

   (*c*) The conflation of the weak and the strong atheoretical theses.

   (*d*) The interconnection between the weak and strong atheoretical theses.

   (*e*) A Carnapian logic of discovery.

2.2. Probability, evidential support, rational belief and betting quotients.

   (*a*) Are degrees of evidential support probabilities?

   (*b*) Are 'degrees of rational belief' degrees of evidential support or are they rational betting quotients?

   (*c*) Are rational betting quotients probabilities?

---

* This paper grew out of a comment on Professor Carnap's address. The author is indebted for criticisms of previous versions to Y. Bar–Hillel, P. Feyerabend, D. Gillies, J. Hintikka, C. Howson, R. Jeffrey, I. Levi, A. Musgrave, A. Shimony and J. W. N. Watkins, but most of all to Carnap and Popper who both spent days on criticising previous versions and thereby contributed immensely to my understanding of the problem and its history. However I am afraid that Carnap – and possibly also Popper – may disagree with the position at which I have arrived. None of them have seen the latest version.

Introduction.

A successful research programme bustles with activity. There are always dozens of puzzles to be solved and technical questions to be answered; even if *some* of these – inevitably – are the programme's own creation. But this self-propelling force of the programme may carry away the research workers and cause them to forget about the problem background. They tend not to ask any more to what degree they have solved the original problem, to what degree they gave up basic positions in order to cope with the internal technical difficulties. Although they may travel away from the original problem with enormous speed, they do not notice it. Problem-shifts of this kind may invest research programmes with a remarkable tenacity in digesting and surviving almost any criticism [1].

Now problem-shifts are regular bedfellows of problem-solving and especially of research programmes. One frequently solves very different problems from those which one has set out to solve. One may solve a more interesting problem than the original one. In

---

[1] For a general discussion of research programmes, problem-solving versus puzzle-solving, problem-shifts, cp. Lakatos: 'Criticism and the methodology of scientific research programmes', in Lakatos–Musgrave (eds): *Criticism and the Growth of Knowledge*, 1968.

such cases we may talk about a 'progressive problem-shift' [1]. But one may solve some problems less interesting than the original one; indeed, in extreme cases, one may end up with solving (or trying to solve) no other problems but those which one has oneself created while trying to solve the original problem. In such cases we may talk about a *degenerating problem-shift* [2].

I think that it can do only good if one occasionally stops problem-solving, and tries to recapitulate the problem background and assess the problem-shift.

In the case of Carnap's vast research programme one may wonder what led him to tone down his original bold idea of an *a priori*, analytic inductive logic to his present caution about the epistemological nature of his theory [3]; why and how he reduced the original problem of rational degree of belief in hypotheses (principally scientific theories) first to the problem of rational degree of belief in particular sentences [4], and finally to the problem of the probabilistic consistency ('coherence') of systems of beliefs.

I shall start with a potted version of the problem background of inductive logic.

1. *The two main problems of classical empiricism: inductive justification and inductive method.*

Classical epistemology in general can be characterized by its two main problems: (1) the problem of the *foundations* of – epistemic, i.e. perfect, infallible – knowledge (the *logic of justification*); and

---

[1] A simple example of a 'progressive problem-shift' is when we explain more than, or even something inconsistent with, what we set out to explain. This indeed is one of Popper's adequacy requirements for a good solution of an explanatory problem ('The Aim of Science', *Ratio*, 1, 1957, pp. 24–35).

[2] The 'degenerating problem-shift' can again be illustrated by the example of explanatory problems. An explanation constitutes a degenerating problem-shift if it was arrived at by 'conventionalist' (i.e. content-reducing) stratagems. Cp. *below*, p. 378.

[3] Cp. *below*, footnote 2 on pp. 361–2.

[4] By 'particular sentences' I mean truth-functional compounds of sentences of the form $r(a_1, a_2, ..., a_n)$ where r is an n-ary relation and a_i individual constants. Carnap calls such sentences 'molecular'. (*Logical Foundations of Probability*, 1950, p. 67.)

(2) the problem of the growth of – perfect, well-founded – knowledge
or the problem of heuristic, or of method (the *logic of discovery*).

The *empiricist brand of classical epistemology* in particular
acknowledged only one *single* source of knowledge about the
external world: the natural light of experience [1]. But this light
can illuminate at best the meaning and truth-value of propositions
expressing 'hard facts': of 'factual propositions'. Theoretical
knowledge is left in darkness.

The logics of justification of all kinds of classical epistemology
– whether empiricist or rationalist – maintained some strict,
black-and-white appraisal of propositions. This amounted to a
sharp demarcation between knowledge and non-knowledge. They
equated knowledge – *epistēmē* – with the proven; unproven *doxa*
was 'sophistry and illusion' or 'meaningless gibberish'. This is how
theoretical, non-factual knowledge was bound to become the central
problem for classical empiricism: it *had* to be justified – or else
scrapped [2].

In this respect the first generation of empiricists was divided.
Newtonians, who soon became the most influential, believed that
true theories *can* be proved ('deduced' or 'induced') infallibly
from factual propositions but from nothing else. In the seventeenth
and eighteenth centuries there was no clear distinction between

---

[1]   *The rationalist brand of classical epistemology*, on the other hand, was
less monolithic: Cartesians admitted the evidence of reason, sense-experience,
and faith, on a par. As for Bacon, he was a confused and inconsistent
thinker, and a rationalist. The Bacon–Descartes controversy is a myth
invented by the Newtonians. Most empiricists, however – surreptitiously
or explicitly – admitted that at least logical knowledge (knowledge about
the transmission of truth) was *a priori*.

[2]   Characteristic of classical epistemology is the sceptic–dogmatist controversy. The sceptical trend in classical empiricism invokes the restriction
of the sources of knowledge to sense-experience only to show that there
is no authoritative source of knowledge whatsoever: even sense-experience
is deceptive, and therefore there is no such thing as knowledge. In the
context of the present discussion I neglect the sceptical pole of the classical
justificationist dialectic.

This analysis of the classical or justificationist theory of knowledge is
one of the main pillars of Karl Popper's philosophy; cp. the Introduction
of his *Conjectures and Refutations*, 1963. For a further discussion cp. my
'Criticism and the methodology of scientific research programmes', *loc. cit.*

'induction' and 'deduction'. (Indeed, for Descartes – *inter alios* – 'induction' and 'deduction' were synonymous terms; he did not think much of the relevance of Aristotelian syllogistic, and preferred inferences which increase logical content. Informal 'Cartesian' valid inferences – both in mathematics and science – increase content and can be characterized only by an infinity of valid patterns. [1])

This is then the logic of justification of classical empiricism: *'factual propositions' and their informal – deductive/inductive – consequences, constitute knowledge: the rest is rubbish.*

Indeed, even meaningless rubbish, according to some empiricists. For, according to an influential trend in empiricism, not only truth but also meaning can be illuminated only by the light of experience. Therefore only 'observational' terms can have primordial meaning; the meaning of theoretical terms can only be derivative, defined (or at least 'partially defined') in terms of observables. But then if theoretical science is not to be branded as altogether meaningless, an inductive ladder not only of propositions but of concepts is needed. In order to establish the truth (or probability) of theories, one first has to establish their meaning. Thus the problem of *inductive definition*, 'constitution' or 'reduction' of theoretical to observational terms, came to be a crucial one for logical empiricism, and the successive failures of its solutions led to the so-called 'liberalisation' of the verifiability criterion of meaning and to further failures [2].

---

[1] Informal mathematical proof and inductive generalization are essentially analogous from this point of view. Cp. my 'Proofs and Refutations', *The British Journal for the Philosophy of Science*, 14, 1963–64; especially footnote 2 on p. 311.

[2] Popper had criticized this trend as early as 1934, in his *Logic of Scientific Discovery*, end of § 25; later he gave an interesting critical exposition of the problem in his *Conjectures and Refutations*, 1963, esp. pp. 258–79. The criticism was either ignored or misrepresented; but, on the whole, the process of 'liberalisation of logical empiricism' has been nothing but a piecemeal and incomplete, independent and not so independent, rediscovery of Popper's 1934 arguments. The historian of thought cannot help but see a general pattern: a school of thought is established; it receives crushing criticism from outside; this external criticism is ignored; internal difficulties set in; 'revisionists' and 'orthodox' fight about them, with the orthodox turning the original doctrine into a 'fairly dried-up petty-foggery'

The *methodological implications of this logic of justification* were clear. Classical method in general demands that the path of knowledge should be cautious, slow progress from proven truth to proven truth, avoiding self-perpetuating error. For empiricism in particular this meant that one had to start from indubitable factual propositions from which, by gradual valid induction, one could arrive at theories of ever higher order. The growth of knowledge was an accumulation of eternal truths: of facts and 'inductive generalizations'. This theory of 'inductive ascent' was the methodological message of Bacon, Newton and – in a modified form – even of Whewell.

Critical practice demolished the classical idea of valid content-increasing inferences in both mathematics and science, and separated valid 'deduction' from invalid 'informal proof' and 'induction'. Only inferences which did not increase logical content came to be regarded as valid [1]. This was the end of the logic of justification of classical empiricism [2]. Its logic of discovery was first shaken by Kant and Whewell, then crushed by Duhem [3], and

by criticism-reducing stratagems and with the revisionists slowly and incompletely discovering and digesting the critical arguments which have been there for decades. From the outside, where these critical arguments have become commonplaces, the 'heroic' struggle of revisionists – whether within marxism, freudism, catholicism or logical empiricism – looks trivial and occasionally even comical. ('Fairly dried-up petty-foggery' was Einstein's description of later logical empiricism; cp. Schilpp: 'The Abdication of Philosophy', *Kant-Studien*, **51**, 1959–60, p. 491.)

[1] A reconstruction of this historical process is one of the main topics of my 'Proofs and Refutations', *loc. cit.*

[2] Of course, classical rationalists may claim that inductive inferences are enthymematic deductive inferences with synthetic *a priori* 'inductive principles' as hidden premises. Also cp. *below*, p. 366.

[3] One of the most important arguments in the history of philosophy of science was Duhem's crushing argument against the inductive logic of discovery which showed that some of the deepest explanatory theories are *fact-correcting*, that they are *inconsistent* with the 'observational laws' on which, according to Newtonian inductive method, they were allegedly 'founded' (cp. his *Aim and Structure of Physical Theory*, 1906; pp. 190–195 of the 1954 English translation). Popper revived and improved Duhem's exposition in his 'Naturgesetze und theoretische Systeme', 1948, and his 'Aim of Science', 1957. Feyerabend elaborated the theme in his 'Expla-

finally replaced by a new theory of the growth of knowledge
by Popper.

2. *The one main problem of neoclassical empiricism: weak inductive
   justification (degree of confirmation).*

Following the defeat of classical empiricism most empiricists
refused to draw the sceptical conclusion that theoretical science
– undefinable from observational terms, unprovable from observational statements – is nothing but sophistry and illusion. They
thought that a good empiricist could not give up science. But
how then could one be a good empiricist – retaining both science
and some basic core of empiricism?

Some thought that the breakdown of induction destroyed science
as knowledge but not as a socially useful instrument. This was
one source of modern instrumentalism.

Others shrank back from this degradation of science to the level
of 'glorified plumbing' (as Popper put it) and set out to save science
as knowledge. Not as knowledge in the classical sense, for that
had to be restricted to mathematical and logical knowledge; but
as knowledge in some weaker sense, as fallible, conjectural
knowledge. There could have been no more radical departure
from classical epistemology: according to classical epistemology
conjectural knowledge was a contradiction in terms [1].

---

nation, reduction and empiricism', 1962. I, for one, showed in 1958 that a
similar argument applies in the logic of mathematical discovery: as in
physics one may not explain what one has set out to explain, so in mathematics one may not prove what one has set out to prove (cp. my 'Proofs
and Refutations', 1963–64).

[1] This switch from the classical epistemology to fallibilism was one of
the great turning points in Carnap's intellectual biography. In 1929 Carnap
still thought that only indubitably true statements could be admitted to
the body of science; Reichenbach's probabilities, Neurath's dialectic,
Popper's conjectures, made him give up his original idea that 'there was
a certain rock bottom of knowledge . . . which was indubitable. Every other
kind of knowledge was supposed to be firmly supported by this basis and
therefore likewise decidable with certainty.' (Cp. Carnap's Autobiography
in Schilpp (ed.): *The Philosophy of Rudolf Carnap*, 1963, esp. p. 57. Also
cp. Reichenbach's amusing recollections in his 'Induction and Probability',
Philosophy of Science, 3, 1936.) It is interesting that the same switch was

But then two new problems arose. The *first* problem was *the appraisal of conjectural knowledge*. This new appraisal could not possibly be a black and white appraisal like the classical one. It was not even clear whether such an appraisal was possible; whether it would have to be conjectural itself; whether there was a possibility of a quantitative appraisal; and so on. The *second* problem was *the growth of conjectural knowledge*. The theories of the inductive growth of (certain) knowledge (or of 'inductive ascent') – from Bacon and Newton to Whewell – had collapsed: they had urgently to be replaced.

In this situation *two schools of thought emerged*. One school – *neoclassical empiricism* – started with the first problem and never arrived at the second [1]. The other school – *critical empiricism* – started by solving the second problem and went on to show that this solution solves the most important aspects of the first too.

The first school – culminating in Carnap's neoclassical empiricism – approached the problem from the classical point of view of the logic of justification. Since it was clear that theories could not be

---

one of the great turning points also in Russell's intellectual biography (cp. my 'Infinite Regress and the Foundations of Mathematics', *Aristotelian Society Supplementary Volume*, **36**, 1962, pp. 167 ff.).

[1] Most 'neoclassicists' were – and some still are – blissfully unaware of the second problem. They thought that even if science does not produce certainty, it produces near-certainty. Ignoring Duhem's master-argument against induction, they insisted that the main pattern of scientific progress is 'non-demonstrative inference' from factual premisses to theoretical conclusions. According to Broad the unsolved problem of *justification of induction* was a 'scandal of philosophy' *because* inductive method was the 'glory of science': scientists proceeded successfully from truths to richer truths (or, at least, to very probable truths) while philosophers toiled unsuccessfully to justify this procedure (cp. his *Ethics and the History of Philosophy*, 1952, pp. 142–3). Russell held the same view. Other neoclassicists occasionally admit that at least *some* of creative science may consist of irrational jumps which then have to be closely followed by severe assessment of the degree of evidential support. (Carnap's position will be analysed in detail below, in **2.2**.) But whether they assume that science proceeds by induction, by irrational insight, or by conjectures and refutations, they assume it unthinkingly: for most neoclassicists have a distinct aversion to taking the problem of the growth of science seriously. Cp. *below*, pp. 326 ff.

classified as provably true or false, they had (according to this school) to be classified as at least 'partially proved', or in other words, as 'confirmed (by facts) to a certain degree'. It was thought that this 'degree of evidential support' or 'degree of confirmation' should somehow be equated with probability in the sense of the probability calculus [1]. The acceptance of this identity suggested a vast programme [2]: to define a – possibly computable – countably additive measure function over the field of the sentences of the complete language of science, satisfying also some further adequacy requirements inspired by the intuitive idea of 'confirmation'. Once such a function is defined, the degree to which a theory h is confirmed by the evidence e can be calculated simply by taking $p(h,e) = = p(h.e)/p(e)$. If there are several different possible functions, further secondary axioms have to be added to Kolmogorov's primary axioms until the function is uniquely determined.

Thus Carnap – following the Cambridge school (Johnson, Broad, Keynes, Nicod, Ramsey, Jeffreys), Reichenbach, and others – set out to solve the following problems: (1) to justify his claim that the degree of confirmation satisfies Kolmogorov's axioms of probability, (2) to find and justify further secondary adequacy requirements for the determination of the sought-for measure function; (3) to construct – piecemeal – a complete, perfect language of science in which all propositions of science can be expressed; and (4) to offer a definition of a measure function which would satisfy the conditions laid down in (1) and (2).

---

[1] Throughout the paper the terms 'probability' and 'probabilistic' will be used in this sense.

[2] In fact, probabilistic inductive logic was a Cambridge invention. It stemmed from W. E. Johnson. Broad and Keynes attended his lectures and then developed his ideas. Their approach rested on a simple logical howler (going back to Bernoulli and Laplace). As Broad put it: '. . . induction cannot hope to arrive at anything more than probable conclusions and *therefore* the logical principles of induction must be the laws of probability' (Review of Keynes' 'Treatise on Probability', *Mind*, N.S., 41, 1932, p. 81; my italics). The premise refers to likelihood or verisimilitude, the conclusion to the mathematical calculus of probability. (It is interesting that before Popper's criticism of Keynes and Reichenbach in 1934 nobody had pointed out this conflation.)

Carnap thought that while science was conjectural, the theory
of probabilistic confirmation would be *a priori* and infallible: the
axioms, whether primary or secondary, would be seen to be true
in the light of *inductive intuition*, and the language (the third
ingredient) would of course be irrefutable – for how can one refute
a language? (At first, he may also have hoped that the measure
function would be computable: that once a machine is programmed
with the perfect language and the axioms, it will churn out
probabilities for any hypothesis relative to the evidence that is
fed in. Science is fallible, but the degree of its fallibility is precisely
and infallibly measurable by a machine. But, of course, he realized
that Church's theorem shows that in general this is impossible [1].)
Now, since according to logical empiricism – I prefer to call it
neoclassical empiricism [2] – only analytic statements can be
infallible, Carnap took his 'inductive logic' to be *analytic* [3].

He also found that the construction of a complete language for
science is a piecemeal and possibly never-ending process – but
then one had better make sure that the gradual construction of

---

[1] Cp. *Logical Foundations of Probability*, 1950, p. 196. Also cp. Hintikka:
'Theory of inductive generalisation', in Bar–Hillel (ed.): *Logic, Methodology
and Philosophy of Science*, 1965, footnote 22, p. 283. *But the function may
be computable for finite languages or for languages without universal statements.*

[2] The main feature of classical empiricism was the domination of the
logic of justification over the logic of discovery. This feature essentially
survived in logical empiricism: partial justification or appraisal, but not
discovery, of theories was its primary interest. On the other hand, in Popper's
treatment of growth without foundations the logic of discovery dominates
the scene: I call this approach 'critical empiricism'; but 'critical rationalism'
(or 'rational empiricism'?) may be even more suitable.

[3] This later led to philosophical troubles, cp. *below*, p. 361, footnote 2,
pp. 401 ff., 412 ff. Also, strictly speaking, throughout this paragraph, 'infallible'
should be replaced by 'practically infallible'; for Carnap, since Gödel's
results, occasionally warns that neither deductive nor inductive logic is
perfectly infallible. But he still seems to think that inductive logic is no
more fallible than deductive logic, which for him includes arithmetic (cp.
his 'Inductive logic and inductive intuition', *this volume*, p. 266). The
fallibility of 'analytic' statements, of course, knocks out a major pillar of
logical empiricism (cp. my 'Empiricism in the Contemporary Philosophy
of Mathematics', *The British Journal for the Philosophy of Science*, 19, 1968–9).

the confirmation function follows closely the gradual construction of this language and that the already established values of the function are not altered in the process of completion. This was, I think, the ideal that Carnap tried to approximate first with his *requirement of* (relative) *completeness* of the language [1], then with his axiom *C6* in his 1952 system [2], and later with *Axiom 11* of his 1955 system [3]. The underlying ideal seems to be a principle that one could call the *principle of minimal language*, that is, the principle according to which the degree of confirmation of a proposition *depends only on the minimal language in which the proposition can be expressed*. Thus the degree of confirmation would remain invariant while the language is being enriched.

It soon turned out that the difficulties involved in the construction of the confirmation function increase steeply with the increasing complexity of the language. Despite the tremendous work done by Carnap and his collaborators during the last twenty years, the research programme of 'inductive logic' still has not produced measure functions on languages including analysis, or physical probability, which, of course, are needed in the formulation of the most important scientific theories. But the work is going on [4].

---

[1] This lays down that the system of predicates should be 'sufficiently comprehensive for expressing all qualitative attributes exhibited by the individuals in the given universe' (*Logical Foundations of Probability*, 1950, p. 75); the requirement also stipulated that 'any two individuals differ only in a finite number of respects' (p. 74).

[2] 'We may assume that it has no influence on the value of $c(h, e)$, where h and e contain no variables, whether in addition to the individuals mentioned in h and e there are still other individuals in the universe of discourse or not' (*The Continuum of Inductive Methods*, 1952, p. 13).

[3] 'The value of $c(h, e)$ remains unchanged if further families of predicates are added to the langugage.' Cp. Schilpp (ed.): *The Philosophy of Rudolf Carnap*, 1963, p. 975, and also the Preface to the Second Edition of his *Logical Foundations of Probability*, 1962, pp. xxi–xxii.

[4] I wonder, will the next interesting development in inductive logic produce impossibility results which may prove that certain elementary adequacy requirements regarding the construction of c-functions cannot possibly be fulfilled for rich – and even for not so rich – languages? (But I am very sceptical whether such results would, as Gödel's did, pave the way to new patterns of growth.)

Submerged in this difficult programme, Carnap and his school completely ignored the problem of scientific *method*. *The classical twin problems of induction were the justification of theories, and the discovery of theories from facts. Carnap's neoclassical solution provides at best a solution of the problem of weak justification. It leaves the problem of discovery, the problem of the growth of knowledge, untouched.* Logical empiricists thus made a very significant *cut* in the empiricist programme. There can be little doubt that neither Carnap nor his associates paid any serious attention to genuine methodological problems. Indeed, Carnap – and Carnapians – do not even seem to have a word for what used to be called 'methodology', 'heuristic', or 'logic of discovery': the rational reconstruction of patterns of growth (or, as Bar–Hillel would put it, 'diachronics'). Carnap says that the concept of confirmation is 'basic in the *methodology* of empirical science' [1]. This expropriation of 'methodology' for the method of justification, for the study of fully fledged theories – and, moreover, the implicit or explicit exclusion from rational investigation of the study of their growth – is widespread [2].

Carnap uses the term 'methodology' primarily to denote the discipline of *applying* inductive logic. Thus 'inductive logic' concerns itself with the construction of the *c*-function while 'methodology of induction' offers advice about *applying* the *c*-function. 'Methodology of induction' is then a chapter within the logic of justification [3].

---

[1] Cp. Schilpp (ed.): *The Philosophy of Rudolf Carnap*, 1963, p. 72 (my italics).

[2] Carnap says, characteristically, in the first sentence of his *Pseudoproblems of Philosophy*, 1928: 'The aim of epistemology is the foundation of a method for the justification of cognitions.' Method, *qua* logic of discovery, disappears – we have nothing but a 'method' of justification.

A similar situation has arisen in the philosophy of mathematics, where 'methodology', 'proof', etc. are all expropriated for concepts in the logic of justification. Cp. my 'Proofs and Refutations', *loc. cit.* In this paper my deliberate *mixed* usage of the justificationist term 'proof' and of the heuristic term 'proof' creates – as I intended – a paradoxical impression.

[3] Cp. Carnap: *Logical Foundations of Probability*, 1950, § 44A: 'Methodological problems'. He remarks that he applies here the term 'methodology' only 'for lack of a better term'; but undeniably his usage is made possible only by the fact that in his philosophy he does not need the term in its

An interesting example of the expropriation of the natural terminology of growth-concepts for use as confirmation-concepts is the Carnapian usage of the term 'inference-making' [1].

To understand the problem we have to go back to classical empiricism. According to *classical empiricism* science proceeds by inductive inference: first one collects some facts and then one 'makes an inductive inference' to a theory which the inductivist perfectly naturally calls a 'generalization'. According to Popper's *critical empiricism*, one starts with speculative theories which one then tests severely. Here there is only deductive inference and no 'generalizations'. Carnap time and again seems to agree with Popper that the facts are not the necessary starting points of discovery. When he uses 'inductive inference', he uses it as a technical term in the sense of the logic of justification but not in the sense of the logic of discovery. For him 'inference-making' is nothing but the assignment of a probability value to an ordered pair $\langle h, e \rangle$. This is certainly a strange terminology, for 'inference-making' is the characteristic term of old-fashioned inductivist logic of *discovery*.

This example is not meant so much to demonstrate the excusable expropriation of the terms of the logic of discovery for use in a logic of justification but also to show the specific dangers inherent in the *non-conscious* character of this expropriation. Occasionally a faint ghost of the logic of discovery appears with confusing consequences. For instance, in his present paper Carnap writes: 'I would not say that it is wrong to regard inference-making as the aim. But from my point of view it seems *preferable* to take as the *essential* point in inductive reasoning the determination of probability values' (my italics) [2]. But what is 'inductive inference-

---

original meaning. (I understand from Bar–Hillel that now Carnap uses instead of the pair 'inductive logic' and 'methodology of induction' the pair *'pure inductive logic'* and *'applied inductive logic'*.)

[1] For another example (Carnap's expropriation of the methodological term 'improvement of guesses') cp. *below*, p. 348, footnote 2; also, for a discussion of his use of 'universal inference', cp. *below*, p. 338.

[2] Cp. his 'Inductive Logic and Inductive Intuitions', *this volume*, p. 258. Also cp. his 'Reply': '... in my conception probabilistic ('inductive')

making' if not 'determination of probability values'? Why does not Carnap say that, indeed, it *is* wrong to regard inference-making as the aim of induction unless it is taken to be determination of the degree to which a hypothesis follows from factual evidence [1]?

Why did logical empiricists have no interest in the logic of discovery? The historian of thought may explain this in the following way. Neoclassical empiricism replaced the old idol of classical empiricism – *certainty* – by the new idol of *exactness* [2]. But one cannot describe the growth of knowledge, the logic of discovery, in 'exact' terms, one cannot put it in formulae: it has therefore been branded a largely 'irrational' process; only its completed (and 'formalized') product that can be *judged* rationally. But these 'irrational' processes are a matter for history or psychology; *there is no such thing as 'scientific' logic of discovery.* Or, to put it in a slightly different way: classical empiricists thought that there are *rules of discovery;* neoclassical empiricists learned (many of

---

reasoning consists *essentially* not in making inferences but *rather* in assigning probabilities . . .' (*this volume,* p. 311; my italics).

[1] I have little doubt that at least part of the answer is that Carnap is frequently too generous to his adversaries, and that he almost always lets them get away as long as they are willing to *share* the disputed area. While being addicted to his own system of ideas, he never follows up the enemy in hostile terrain. It is symptomatic of the Carnap school that while Popper and Popperians have written several essays in the critical history of Carnapian ideas, Carnapians have never even tried to do the same with Popperian ideas. (*'Live and let live'* is not a good rule for the dialectic of intellectual progress. If one does not follow up a critical clash to the bitter end, one may leave uncriticized not only the adversary but also oneself: for the best way to understand critically one's own position is through the relentless criticism of contrary positions.)

[2] 'In this post-rationalist age of ours, more and more books are written in symbolic languages, and it becomes more and more difficult to see why: what it is all about, and why it should be necessary, or advantageous, to allow oneself to be bored by volumes of symbolic trivialities. It almost seems as if the symbolism were becoming a value in itself, to be revered for its sublime 'exactness': a new expression of the old quest for certainty, a new symbolic ritual, a new substitute for religion.' (Popper: *The Logic of Scientific Discovery,* 1959, p. 394).

them from Popper [1]) that there are no such rules; so they thought there was nothing to learn about it. But there are, according to Carnap, rules of *confirmation;* therefore confirmation *is* a subject suitable for 'scientific inquiry' [2]. This also explains why they felt free to expropriate the terminology of the logic of discovery.

All this has never been formulated in such sharp terms; most Carnapians graciously agree that one can say a few informal (and therefore neither very serious nor very significant) things about the logic of discovery, and that Popper has indeed said them. Bar–Hillel, generously, even goes further and suggests a 'division of labour, the Carnapians concentrating mostly on a rational *"synchronic"* reconstruction of science and the Popperians remaining mostly interested in the *"diachronic"* growth of science' [3].

This division of labour seems to imply that the two problems are somehow independent. But they are not. I think the lack of recognition

---

[1] Cp. Carnap: *Logical Foundations of Probability*, 1950, p. 193.

[2] For a further discussion cp. *below*, p. 374.

[3] Cp. his 'Inductive logic as "the" guide of life', *this volume*, p. 66. Bar–Hillel's generosity will be still more appreciated if one remembers that for orthodox logical empiricism even the meaningfulness of 'sloppy' Popperian logic of discovery could be called into question. It is not psychology or history, so it is not empirical. But it would be stretching the concept of analyticity a bit too far to accommodate it. However, Carnap was prepared to do so in order to rescue Popper (although he seemed to think that Popper's usage of the term 'methodology' was a bit idiosyncratic): 'Popper calls the field of his inquiries *methodology*. However, the logical character of the methodological statements and rules is left open. According to Popper (as opposed to the positivist view) there is a third, not precisely characterized field besides the analytical statements of logic and the empirical statements of science; and methodological statements and rules belong to this field. He does not elaborate his position which I regard rather doubtful. But this does not seem to be essential to Popper's general philosophy. Just the other way round: Popper himself says that methodology rests on conventions and its rules should be compared with the rules of chess; but this clearly implies that they are analytic' (Review of Popper's 'Logik der Forschung', *Erkenntnis*, 5, 1935, p. 293). Indeed, Popper himself, in § 82 of his book, says that his appraisal of theories is analytic. While distrusting the logical empiricists' dogma that all meaningful statements are either analytic or synthetic (§§ 10–11), he never elaborated an alternatvie position.

*of this interdependence is an important short-coming of logical empiri-
cism in general and of Carnap's confirmation theory in particular.*

The most interesting phenomenon in this proposed 'division of
labour' is the thesis, implicit in Carnap's work (at least between
1945 and 1956 [1]), that theories certainly play an important role
in the growth of science but none in the logic of confirmation.
This is why the whole problem can be best approached through
a discussion of Carnap's elimination of universal hypotheses in
his 1950 theory of confirmation and of Popper's criticism of it.
This discussion will also try to explain why and how the central
problem of classical empiricism, the (strong or weak) justification
of *theories*, has disappeared from Carnap's programme.

2.1. *The weak and strong atheoretical theses.*

(*a*) *Carnap abandons the Jeffreys–Keynes postulate. Qualified
instance confirmation versus confirmation.* The original problem of
confirmation was no doubt the confirmation of *theories* rather than
that of *particular predictions*. It was the burning epistemological
problem of empiricism to 'prove' theories at least partially from
'the facts' in order to save theoretical science from the sceptics.
It was agreed that a crucial adequacy requirement for confirmation
theory was that it should *grade* theories according to their evidential
support. Broad, Keynes, Jeffreys – indeed everybody in Cambridge –
saw clearly that, if confirmation is probability, and if the a *priori*
confirmation of a hypothesis is zero, no finite amount of observational
evidence can lift its confirmation above this level: this is why
they assigned zero prior probability only to impossible propositions.
According to Wrinch and Jeffreys: 'However sceptical we may be
about the finality of a particular law, we should say that its
probability is finite'. We shall refer to this as the Jeffreys–Keynes
postulate [2].

---

[1]   For Carnap's present position cp. *below*, p. 337, footnote 1 and pp. 360–
61; also p. 370, footnote 2.

[2]   See Wrinch–Jeffreys: 'On Certain Fundamental Principles of Scientific
Inquiry', *Philosophical Magazine*, **42**, 1921, especially pp. 381–2. This is the
problem background of the well-known Wrinch–Jeffreys simplicity ordering;

It is clear from Carnap's *Testability and Meaning* that in the thirties he had similar ideas about degree of confirmation [1] (which he had not yet definitely identified with probability [2]). But in the early forties Carnap found that in his newly-developed theory the degree of confirmation of all *genuinely* universal propositions (i.e. those which refer to infinitely many individuals) was zero. This was clearly inconsistent with the adequacy requirements of his two main forerunners, Jeffreys and Keynes, and also with his own original adequacy requirements. Now he had several possible ways of solving this inconsistency:

(*1*) By regarding $c(l) = 0$ [3] as absurd since it clashes with the Jeffreys–Keynes thesis. But since $c(l) = 0$ follows from $p(l) = 0$ and $c = p$, at least one of these two theses has to be given up [4]. One has either (*1a*) to design a probability function which takes positive values on universal propositions or (*1b*) to abandon $c = p$.

(*2*) By regarding $c(l) = 0$ as acceptable and abandoning the Jeffreys–Keynes postulate, and with it the idea that a theory can ever be made even probable. But this may seem to many a counter-intuitive solution and certainly shows the need also for some *other* degree of confirmation.

(*3*) By reducing the domain of the confirmation function to particular propositions, and claiming that this function solves all the problems of confirmation theory: theories are dispensable for confirmation theory. In a Pickwickian sense this solution may be said to leave the Jeffreys–Keynes thesis valid in the restricted

---

this served to solve the problem of how one can learn 'inductively' about theories. (For a critical discussion cp. Popper: *The Logic of Scientific Discovery*, 1959, Appendix *viii.)

[1] 'Instead of verification we may speak ... of gradually increasing confirmation of the law' ('Testability and Meaning', *Philosophy of Science*, 3, 1936, p. 425).

[2] *Ibid*, pp. 426–7.

[3] Following Carnap throughout the rest of this paper I use *l* for universal, *h* primarily for particular propositions. (*My term 'particular' corresponds to his 'molecular'*.)

[4] It is to be remembered that throughout this paper p refers to countably additive measure functions (cp. p. 323, footnote 1).

domain[1]. But here again one needs a serious and persuasive argument before one accepts that all confirmation theory is in fact about particular propositions.

Carnap tried possibilities (*1a*), (*2*), and (*3*), *but never* (*1b*): to give up $c = p$ was for him inconceivable. First he chose (*2*) and put forward an interesting argument in its defence. This was his theory of 'qualified instance confirmation'. He then seemed to be inclined to entertain (*3*). And now, one understands, he is working on a solution on the lines of (*1a*).

Popper, on the other hand, thought that (*1a*), (*2*), and (*3*) had to be ruled out: (*1b*) *was the only solution*. Both (*2*) and (*3*) were inconceivable for him because he thought that no worthwhile confirmation theory could fail to explain how we can learn about theories and how we can grade them according to their empirical support. As for (*1a*) he claimed to have barred that by proving that $p(l) = 0$ for *all* 'acceptable' probability functions[2]. But if

---

[1] In a Pickwickian sense, since the Jeffreys–Keynes thesis refers, primarily if not exclusively, to *genuinely* universal hypotheses. (Also, one has to remember that not only universal but also precise particular numerical predictions would have zero measure in Carnap's 1950 approach; but, of course, one could again argue that such predictions can never be confirmed in a strict sense, and that confirmation theory should be further restricted to predictions within some finite interval of error of measurement: precise predictions also are dispensable for confirmation theory.) For Popper (and for me) without *genuinely universal* propositions there can be no scientific theories. Of course, if one postulates that the universe can be described in a finite language then the theories themselves are ('L-') equivalent to particular propositions. In defence of Carnap's 1950 theory one may set up a philosophy of science based on the idea of such a 'finite' universe. For a critical discussion of such an idea cp. Nagel: 'Carnap's theory of induction', in Schilpp (ed.): *The Philosophy of Rudolf Carnap*, 1963, pp. 799–800.

[2] Cp. *The Logic of Scientific Discovery*, 1959, appendices *vii and *viii. (According to Popper a probability function in this context is 'acceptable' if, roughly, (*a*) it is defined on a language containing infinitely many individual constants (say, names of moments of time) and (*b*) it is defined for particular statements as well as for universal statements.) Good claimed (in his review of Popper's book, *Mathematical Reviews*, **21**, 1960, p. 1173) that the proof was incorrect, but this interesting problem has unfortunately not been discussed since, in spite of some recently proposed systems with

$c(l)$ must *not* be uniformly zero and $p(l)$ *is* uniformly zero, then $c \neq p$.

But is $c(l) = 0$ so absurd? Carnap, following a hint by Keynes and Ramsey, gave a spirited defence of it.

The main point of Carnap's defence is that naive intuition was misguided into $c(l) \neq 0$. He indicates that 'degree of confirmation' is a vague concept, but if we substitute for it the concept of 'rational betting quotient', the mistake transpires at once [1]. For – Carnap argues – when a scientist or engineer says that a scientific theory is 'well-founded' or 'reliable' he does *not* mean that he would bet that the theory was true for all its instances in the whole universe and for eternity. (In fact, he would always bet against such a preposterously daring proposal, exactly according to $c(l) = 0$.) What he means is that he would bet that the next instance of the theory will comply with it. But this second bet is really on a particular proposition. The scientist's and, still more, the engineer's phrase 'confirmation of a law', according to Carnap, refers to the next instance. He called this 'confirmation of the next instance' the 'qualified instance confirmation' of the law. Of course the qualified instance confirmation of a law is not zero; but, on the other hand, qualified instance confirmation or 'reliability' of a law is *not* probability [2].

---

positive probabilities for universal propositions. Also, one should here point out that for Popper $p(l) = 0$ was important because it purported to show that the neoclassical rule '*Aim at highly probable theories*' was hopelessly utopian – as had been the classical rule: '*Aim at indubitably true theories*'. (For Popper's charge that Carnap adopts this neoclassical rule cp. *below*, pp. 340–43).

Also cp. Ritchie's 1926 proof that inductive generalizations, 'as such', have zero probability, *below*, p. 334.

[1] Carnap does not put it as clearly as this. But his argument is an interesting anticipation of his later problem-shift from degree of confirmation to betting quotients (cp. *below*, 2.2).

[2] Carnap, of course, must have realized this, but did not care to say so. It was Popper who first pointed this out in his ' "Content" and "Degree of Confirmation" '; a reply to Dr. Bar–Hillel', *The British Journal for the Philosophy of Science*, **6**, 1955–6, p. 160. Also cp. Popper: 'Theories, Experience and Probabilistic Intuitions', *this volume*, p. 289.

Carnap's argument is very interesting. It had already been proposed by Keynes, who had grave doubts whether any reasonable grounds could be found for his $p(l) > 0$. This led him to this aside: 'Perhaps our generalisation should always run: "It is probable that any given φ is f", rather than, "It is probable that all φ are f". Certainly, what we commonly seem to hold with conviction is the belief that the sun will rise *tomorrow*, rather than the belief that the sun will *always* rise . . .' [1]. Keynes' doubts about his postulate were soon followed by Ritchie's disproof. Ritchie offered a proof that the probability of any inductive generalisation – as such, in the absence of *a priori considerations* – is zero [2]. This, of course, did not disturb Broad and Keynes who did not mind metaphysical speculation; but it seems to have disturbed Ramsey. Replying to Ritchie, he pointed out that 'we can agree that inductive generalisations need have no finite probability, but particular expectations entertained on inductive grounds undoubtedly do have a high numerical probability in the minds of all of us . . . If induction ever needs a logical justification it is in connection with [such probabilities].' [3]

However, the idea of qualified instance confirmation creates an awkward difficulty. It ruins the programme of a *unified* theory of probabilistic confirmation of laws. It looks as if there are *two* important and utterly different measures of confirmation at least for ('empirical') laws (i.e. 'low-level' theories) [4]: $c_1(l) = 0$ for any theory whatsoever – and a non-probabilistic measure of confirmation oriented towards 'reliability' ($c_2(l) \approx 1$ if l has overwhelming verifying evidence).

Popper's main criticism of Carnap's qualified instance con-

---

[1]   Keynes: *A Treatise on Probability*, 1921, p. 259.

[2]   Ritchie: 'Induction and Probability', *Mind*, N.S., 35, 1926; esp. pp. 309–10 and 318.

[3]   'Truth and Probability', 1926; published posthumously in Ramsey: *Foundations of Mathematics*, 1931 (cp. pp. 183–4).

[4]   In Carnap's 1950 system the only theories that figured were 'empirical generalizations' which could be expressed in his 'observational language' and contained only monadic predicates. The generalization of the concept of qualified instance confirmation to theories in general could be extremely difficult if not impossible.

firmation was that the explanation was '*ad hoc*', introduced by
Carnap only 'in order to escape from an unintended result', namely
that '[Carnap's] theory has not supplied us with an adequate
definition of "degree of confirmation" [for theories]' [1]. In particular,
he pointed out that according to Carnap's 'reliability measure' a
refuted theory scarcely loses its reliability by refutation; indeed,
there is no guarantee that a *refuted* law obtains a lower qualified
instance confirmation than any of those which have stood up to
tests. 'More generally, if a theory is again and again falsified, on
the average, in every n-th instance, then its (qualified) "instance
confirmation" approached $1 - 1/n$ instead of 0, as it ought to do,
so that the law "All tossed pennies always show heads" has the
instance confirmation $\frac{1}{2}$ instead of 0. In discussing in my *L. Sc. D.*
a theory of Reichenbach's which leads to mathematically equivalent
results, I described this unintended consequence of his theory as
"devastating". After 20 years, I still think it is' [2].

But Popper's argument would only hold if Carnap maintained
– as Reichenbach indeed did – that 'qualified instance confirmation'
had anything to do with 'confirmation'. But according to Carnap
it had *not;* and he indeed agrees with Popper that the law 'All
tossed pennies always show heads' – while having $\frac{1}{2}$ reliability – has
zero confirmation. Carnap introduced his 'reliability measure' only
to explain why engineers think, mistakenly, that $c(l) \neq 0$: because
they conflate confirmation measure with reliability measure, because
they confuse betting on a law with betting on its next instance.

(*b*) *The weak atheoretical thesis: confirmation theory without
theories.* Since the term 'qualified instance confirmation of *theories*'
was only a *manner of speech* for the confirmation of certain particular
propositions (of the 'next instances'), it was, strictly speaking,
redundant. In 1950 Carnap still kept 'qualified instance confirmation'
for the sake of those who found it difficult to get rid of the old-
fashioned idea that the main problem of inductive logic is the
partial justification of *theories* by evidential support; but after

---

[1]   *Conjectures and Refutations*, 1963, p. 282.

[2]   *Ibid.*, p. 283. He repeats this statement in his 'Theories, Experience
and Probabilistic Intuitions', *this volume*, p. 290.

1950 he abandoned qualified instance confirmation, 'reliability', altogether – he did not mention it either in his 'Replies' in the Schilpp volume or in his present paper. (This elimination of the theory of reliability also solved the awkward problem of having *two* confirmation theories, especially since one of the two was not probabilistic.) In addition he decided to omit the 'ambiguous' term 'degree of confirmation' (and 'evidential support') and use exclusively 'rational betting quotient' [1].

But this decision was more than terminological. It was partly motivated by Popper's 1954 criticism which showed that Carnap's intuitive idea of confirmation was inconsistent [2], and partly by the reconstruction and strengthening in 1955 of an earlier result of Ramsey and de Finetti by Shimony (and following him by Lehmann and Kemeny) [3].

According to the Ramsey–De Finetti theorem a betting system is 'strictly fair' or as Carnap puts it, a system of beliefs is 'strictly coherent', if and only if it is probabilistic [4]. Thus, at the time when Popper showed that there is something wrong with Carnap's idea of evidential support and when Carnap himself felt that his original arguments even for equating rational betting quotients and logical probability were 'weak' [5], this result seemed to provide solid foundations for his inductive logic: at least rational betting quotients and degrees of rational belief were proved to be probabilistic. The final solution of the problem of evidential support in terms of rational betting quotients could then be left for later. But Carnap had to pay a price for the support offered by the Ramsey–De Finetti theorem: he had to abandon *any* reference in his theory

---

[1] Cp. his 'Replies' in Schilpp (ed.): *The Philosophy of Rudolf Carnap*, 1963, p. 998 (written about 1957); and the Preface to the Second Edition of his *Logical Foundations of Probability*, 1962, p. xv.

[2] Cp. *below*, pp. 353–56.

[3] Cp. Shimony, 'Coherence and the axioms of confirmation: *Journal of Symbolic Logic*, **20**, 1955; Lehman: 'On confirmation and rational betting', *ibid.*, **20**, 1955; Kemeny: 'Fair bets and inductive probabilities', *ibid.*, **20**, 1955.

[4] For a clear explanation of the terms 'strict fairness' or 'strict coherence' see Carnap's 'Inductive logic and inductive intuition', *this volume*, pp. 260–2.

[5] *Ibid.*, p. 266.

to universal propositions, for the proof of this theorem hinges on the lemma that $p(h) \neq 0$ for all contingent propositions [1].

So first $p(l) = 0$ led to a uniform, trivial appraisal of universal propositions; then $p(h) \neq 0$, as a condition of the Ramsey–De Finetti theorem, led to their total exclusion. What finally emerged was a 'confirmation theory' which (*1*) was *essentially concerned with betting on particular predictions*. But this theory had also another important feature: (*2*) *the rational betting quotient for any particular prediction was to be independent of the available scientific theories* [2].

I shall refer to these two theses – which make *theories dispensable in the logic of confirmation* – jointly as the '*weak atheoretical thesis*'; I shall refer to the thesis that *theories are dispensable both in confirmation theory and in the logic of discovery*, as the '*strong atheoretical thesis*'.

The shift from the original problem about confirmability and confirmation of *theories* to the weak atheoretical thesis is not a minor shift. Carnap seems to have taken a long time to make it. This is indicated by his original hesitation among three views about confirmation theory: should the confirmation of theories or of predictions play the primary role, or should they be on a par? 'Some believe that, with respect to the evidence at hand, our primary judgments concern the reliability of theories, and that judgments as to the reliability of predictions of single events are derivative in the sense that they depend upon the reliability of the theories used in making the predictions. *Others believe that judgments about predictions are primary, and that the reliability of a theory cannot mean anything else than the reliability of the predictions to which the theory leads.* And according to a third view, there is a general concept of the reliability of a hypothesis of any form with

---

[1]   In his present paper, 'Inductive logic and inductive intuition', he bases his theory on the Ramsey–De Finetti theorem (cp. *above*, p. 260), but does not mention that it does not apply to universal propositions at all as long as $p(l) = 0$. [Shimony, in his important paper (*loc. cit.*, pp. 18–20), indicates that it may be impossible to extend the field of applicability of the Ramsey–de Finetti theorem to countably additive fields at all even if one experiments with other probability metrics.]

[2]   'Scientific' is meant here in Popper's sense.

respect to given evidence. Theories and molecular predictions are in this case regarded as merely two special kinds of hypotheses.' [1] He then decided to opt for the second view [2]. But we find some trace of hesitation even in his *Logical Foundations of Probability*, for the explicit announcement of his final decision comes rather unexpectedly at the very end of the book, where he introduced $c(l) = p(l) = 0$ and its far-reaching consequences. Some subtle formulations in the book now, of course, with hindsight, appear significant [3]. But nowhere does he indicate before p. 571 in the *Appendix* that probabilistic appraisal applies only to particular predictions, and not to theories. But he knew the result all along, since he had already published it in 1945 in his paper in *Philosophy of Science*, 'On Inductive Logic'. The clearest account of what happened is already contained in this early publication: 'The universal inductive inference is the inference from a report on an observed sample to a hypothesis of universal form. Sometimes the term "induction" has been applied to this kind of inference alone, while we use it in a much wider sense for all non-deductive kinds of inferences [4]. The universal inference is not even the most important one; it seems to me now that the role of universal sentences in the inductive procedures of science has generally been over-estimated ... The predictive inference is the most important inductive inference.' [5]

---

[1] 'Theory and Prediction in Science', *Science*, **104**, 1946, p. 520; my italics.

[2] A particularly clear statement of this can be found in his recent 'Probability and Content Measure' (Feyerabend–Maxwell (eds.): *Mind, Matter, and Method*, 1966, p. 252): 'Once we see clearly which features of predictions are desirable, then we may say that a given theory is preferable to another one if the predictions yielded by the first theory possess on the average more of the desirable features than the predictions yielded by the other theory.'

[3] E.g.: 'The *two* arguments [of logical probability] in general refer to facts' (p. 30; my italics).

[4] Of course this is a rather misleading way of putting it; for Carnap's 'universal inductive inference' is not an 'inference *from* a sample *to* a universal hypothesis', but a metalinguistic statement of the form $c(l, e) = q$. Cp. *above*, pp. 327 ff.

[5] Also cp. *Logical Foundations of Probability*, 1950, p. 208: 'The term "induction" was in the past often restricted to universal induction. Our

So Carnap first 'widens' the classical problem of inductive justification and then omits the original part.

One cannot help wondering what persuaded Carnap to resign himself to this radical problem-shift. Why did he not at least *try*, perhaps following the Wrinch–Jeffreys idea of simplicity ordering (expounded in 1921)[1], to introduce *immediately* a system with positive measures for universal propositions? A tentative answer is of course that when he would have encountered many more technical difficulties and he first wanted to try a relatively easier approach. There is, of course, nothing wrong with such a consideration: it is understandable that one tries to simplify the technical difficulties of one's research programme. But one still might be more cautious and not shift one's philosophical position *too* hastily under such temptation[2]. (This is of course not to say that problem-cuts and problem-shifts – and feedbacks from technical difficulties to basic philosophical assumptions – are *not* inevitable companions of any major research programme.)

Calling attention to a problem-shift, even critically, does not imply that the shifted problem may not be very interesting and correctly solved. Therefore the critic's next step should be to appraise Carnap's solution of the problem of rational betting quotients on particular propositions. But before we do this (in **2.3.**), it will be worthwhile to make a few comments on the two main lines of Popper's attack on Carnap's programme: (*a*) his criticism of Carnap's alleged strong atheoretical thesis (in the remaining sections of **2.1**) and (*b*) his criticism of Carnap's identification of evidential support and logical probability (in **2.2**).

---

later discussion will show that actually the predictive inference is more important not only from the point of view of practical decisions but also from that of theoretical science.' Again, this problem-shift goes back to Keynes: 'Our conclusions should be in the form of inductive correlations rather than of universal generalisations' (*A Treatise on Probability*, 1921, p. 259).

[1] Cp. *above*, p. 330, footnote 1.

[2] However, according to Popper, Carnap's 'antitheoretical turn' was rather a *return* to his old antitheoretical position of the late twenties. Cp. *below*, pp. 340–41.

(c) *The conflation of the weak and the strong atheoretical theses.* In the *Appendix* of his *Logical Foundations* Carnap concludes the section 'Are Laws Needed for Making Predictions?' with this statement: 'We see that the use of laws is not indispensable for making predictions. Nevertheless it is expedient, of course, to state universal laws in books on physics, biology, psychology, etc.'

This is certainly a sharp statement of an unusual position. As we shall see, it was intended to express nothing more than Carnap's 'weak atheoretical thesis'. But the unfortunate formulation made some readers think that it did express more, that it expressed the 'strong thesis': theories are *altogether* dispensable in science. They thought that if Carnap had meant only the weak thesis he would have said: 'Nevertheless universal laws are vital ingredients in the growth of science', instead of referring only to their (mnemonical?) expediency in textbooks [1]. And very few people could realize that for Carnap 'making predictions' is not predicting unknown facts from known facts but rather assigning probability values to such predictions already made [2].

It was this passage that provoked Popper into his onslaught on Carnap's alleged strong atheoretical thesis and into neglecting the criticism of the 'weak thesis'. Popper, of course, remembered his old heroic Vienna days when he fought the Vienna Circle in order to prevent them from banning theories on the grounds that they could not be strictly justified *('verified')*. He thought he had won that battle. Now, to his horror, he thought that Carnap was going to ban them again because they could not be at least probabilistically justified *('confirmed')*: 'With his doctrine that laws may be dispensed with in science, Carnap in effect returns to a position very similar to the one he had held in the heyday of verificationism and which he had given up in the *Syntax* and in *Testability*. Wittgenstein and Schlick, finding that natural laws are non-verifiable, concluded from this that they are not genuine

---

[1] Even some of his closest collaborators misunderstood this passage. Bar–Hillel – agreeing with Watkins' interpretation of it – describes it as expressing an 'overly instrumentalistic attitude' ('Bunge and Watkins on inductive logic', *this volume*, p. 284).

[2] Cp. *above*, pp. 327 f.

sentences. Not unlike Mill they described them as rules for the derivation of genuine (singular) sentences – the *instances* of the law – from other genuine sentences (the initial conditions). I criticized this doctrine in my *Logik der Forschung*; and when Carnap accepted my criticism in the *Syntax* and in *Testability*, I thought that the doctrine was dead . . .' [1].

Carnap, in his reply, unfortunately, ignored Popper's desperate protest and did not clear up the misunderstanding. But, on many other occasions, Carnap *did* try to avoid any impression that he should have thought that theories were dispensable in the logic of discovery.

At least since the *Logik der Forschung* Carnap agreed with Popper's logic of discovery and with its emphasis on the central role played by theories in the growth of science. For instance, in 1946 he wrote: 'From the purely theoretical point of view, the construction of a *theory* is the end and goal of science . . . the theory is not *discovered* by a wholly rational or regulated procedure; in addition to knowledge of the relevant facts and to experience in working with other theories, such nonrational factors as intuition or the inspiration of genius play a decisive role. Of course, once a theory is proposed, there may be a rational procedure for *examining* it. Thus it becomes clear that the relation between a theory and the observational evidence available is, strictly speaking, not that of *inferring* the one from the other but rather that of *judging* the theory on the basis of the evidence when both are given' [2]. Carnap kept stressing that all that he was interested in was how to *judge* ready theories, not how to *discover* them, that even if judging theories could be reduced to judging particular predictions, *discovering* theories could not be reduced to discovering particular predictions: 'The task of inductive logic is not to find a law for the explanation of given phenomena. This task cannot be solved by any mechanical procedure or by fixed rules; it is rather solved through the intuition, the inspiration, and the good luck of the scientist. The function of inductive logic begins *after*

---

[1] Schilpp (ed.): *The Philosophy of Rudolf Carnap*, 1963, p. 217.
[2] 'Theory and Prediction in Science', *Science*, **104**, 1946, p. 520.

a hypothesis is offered for examination. Its task is to measure
the support which the given evidence supplies for the tentatively
assumed hypothesis.'[1]

A recent passage in Carnap's Intellectual Autobiography shows
interestingly Carnap's reluctant, restricted, but undeniable ap-
preciation of the role of theories in the *growth* of science: '. . . the
interpretation of theoretical terms is always incomplete, and the
theoretical sentences are in general not translatable into the
observation language. These disadvantages are more than balanced
by the great advantages of the theoretical language, viz. the great
freedom of concept formation and theory formation, and the
explanatory and predictive power of a theory. These advantages
have so far been used chiefly in the field of physics; the prodigious
growth of physics since the last century depended essentially
upon the possibility of referring to unobservable entities like atoms
and fields. In our century other branches of science such as biology,
psychology, and economics have begun to apply the method of
theoretical concepts to some extent.'[2]

Why then Carnap's misleading formulation in the *Appendix?*
*The explanation, I think, lies in the conflation of the conceptual and
terminological frameworks of the logics of justification and discovery,
caused by Carnap's neglect of the latter. This led then to the subsequent
– unintended – conflation of the weak and strong atheoretical theses.*

(*d*) *The interconnection between the weak and strong atheoretical
theses.* But why was Popper misled by Carnap's slip? I think
because he could not imagine how one could possibly combine a
Popperian logic of discovery with Carnap's logic of justification.
For him the weak and strong theses were inseparable. He, mistakenly,
thought that 'those who identify confirmation with probability
must believe that a high degree of probability is desirable. They
implicitly accept the rule: "Always choose the most probable

---

[1] Carnap: 'Inductive Logic and Science', *Proceedings of the American
Academy of Arts and Sciences*, **80**, 1953, p. 195. Carnap does not draw the
attention of the unsuspecting reader to the fact that according to his theory
(*anno* 1953) the measure of support which any evidence can supply for
a tentatively assumed *universal* hypothesis is zero.

[2] P. A. Schilpp (ed.): *The Philosophy of Rudolf Carnap*, 1963, p. 80.

hypothesis".' [1] Why *must?* Why must Carnap *implicitly accept* the rule which he *explicitly rejects?* (He even says – following Popper – that scientists devise 'daring guesses on slender evidence' [2].)

To be fair to Popper, one has to point out that his assertion that 'those who identify confirmation with probability ... implicitly accept the rule: "Always choose the most probable hypothesis" ' may have applied to Jeffreys, Keynes, Russell, and Reichenbach – to those whom he criticized in 1934. And this is no coincidence: there is, indeed, a deep connection between confirmation theory and heuristic. In spite of his mistake about Carnap's actual beliefs, *Popper touched here on a basic weakness of Carnap's philosophy: the loose, and even paradoxical, connection between his elaborate logic of confirmation (or reliability) and neglected logic of discovery.*

What sort of connection is there between a theory of confirmation and a logic of discovery?

A theory of confirmation assigns marks – directly or indirectly [3] – to theories, it gives a *value-judgment*, an *appraisal* of theories. Now the appraisal of any finished product is bound to have decisive pragmatic consequences for the method of its production. Moral standards, by which one judges people, have grave pragmatic implications for education, that is, for the method of their production. Similarly, scientific standards by which one judges theories, have grave pragmatic implications for scientific method, the method of their production. An important pattern of criticism of moral standards is to show that they lead to absurd educational consequences (for instance utopian moral standards may be criticized by pointing to the hypocrisy to which they lead in education). There should be an analogous pattern of criticism for confirmation theory.

The methodological implications of Popperian appraisals are relatively easily discernible [4]. Popper wants the scientist to *aim*

---

[1] K. R. Popper: *Conjectures and Refutations*, 1963, p. 287.

[2] 'What is Probability?', *Scientific American*, **189**, 1953, p. 128.

[3] Indirectly with the help of qualified instance confirmation.

[4] Cp. *below*, 3.

at highly falsifiable bold theories [1]. He wants him to *aim* at very severe tests of his theories. But would Carnap want the scientist to *aim* at theories of, say, high qualified instance confirmation? Or should he only *rely on* them but not *aim at them?* It can be shown by a simple example that he not only *should not* aim at them, but *must not* aim at them.

Let us take Carnap's principle of 'positive instantial relevance', that is, in the language of qualified instance confirmation,

$$c_{qi}(l, e) < c_{qi}(l, e \ \& \ e')$$

where e' is the 'next instance' of l. According to Carnapians, this principle is a precise version of an axiom of informal inductive intuition [2].

But to Nagel it is not: 'According to the formulae Carnap obtains for his system, the degree of confirmation for a hypothesis is in general increased if the confirming instances for the hypothesis are multiplied – even when the individuals mentioned in the evidence cannot be distinguished from each other by any property expressible in the language for which the inductive logic is constructed . . .' [3]

Indeed, Carnap's reliability theory puts a premium on the completely mechanical repetition of the same experiment – indeed, a decisive premium, for such mechanical repetitions may make the qualified instance confirmation of any statement of the form

---

[1] By the way, Popper's occasional slogan: '*Always choose the most improbable hypothesis*' (e.g. *Logic of Scientific Discovery*, 1959, p. 419; or *Conjectures and Refutations*, 1963, p. 218), is a careless formulation, since according to Popper *all* universal hypotheses have the same improbability, namely 1; this gives no guidance on which to choose; the guidance is only provided by his non-quantitative theory of 'fine structure of content' in appendix *vii of his *Logic of Scientific Discovery*.

[2] Carnap–Stegmüller: *Induktive Logik und Wahrscheinlichkeit*, 1959, p. 244.

[3] E. Nagel: 'Carnap's theory of induction', in Schilpp (ed.): *The Philosophy of Rudolf Carnap*, 1964, p. 807. Nagel had already put this argument forward against Reichenbach (*Principles of the Theory of Probability*, 1939, § 8).

'All A's are B's' not merely constantly increase but actually converge to unity [1].

Now this inductive judgment seems to lead to strange pragmatic consequences. Let us have two rival theories such that both 'work' in certain well-defined experiments. We programme two machines to perform and record the two experiments respectively. Will the victory go to the theory whose machine works faster in producing confirming evidence?

This is connected with what Keynes called the problem of the 'weight of evidence'. Indeed, it is a simple *paradox of weight of evidence*. Keynes noticed (as some of his predecessors already had) that the *reliability* and the *probability* of a hypothesis may differ. On our paradox, no doubt, he would have simply commented: 'The *probabilities* of the two theories, of course, differ, but the *weight of evidence* in their favour is the same'. Keynes emphasized that 'weight cannot, then, be explained in terms of probability' [2] and that 'the conclusion that the "weight" and the "probability" of an argument are independent properties, may possibly introduce a difficulty into the discussion of the application of probability to practice' [3].

Of course this criticism does not hit Popper who admits as evidence only results of sincere attempts at refutation [4]. Carnap, however, can escape this criticism only by insisting that his appraisal of theories in respect of supporting evidence must have no methodological implications as to how to collect such evidence. *But can one completely sever the appraisal of theories from its methodological implications? Or perhaps several different appraisals are needed, some appraising theories from the point of view of methodology, others from the point of view of confirmation?*

---

[1]   Cp. formula 17 in Carnap's *Logical Foundations of Probability*, 1950, p. 573.

[2]   Keynes: *A Treatise on Probability*, 1921, p. 76.

[3]   *Ibid.* The intuitive discrepancy between the 'weight of evidence' and probability does not only introduce a mere 'difficulty', as Keynes would have it, but is alone 'difficult' enough to destroy the very foundations of inductive logic. For another paradox of the weight of evidence cp. *below*, p. 345, footnote 3.

[4]   Cp. e.g. *The Logic of Scientific Discovery*, 1959, p. 414.

(e) *A Carnapian logic of discovery.* Is there then a 'Carnapian' logic of discovery which would be married as naturally to Carnap's inductive logic as Popper's logic of discovery is to his theory of empirical content and corroboration (or as the classical logics of discovery are married to their corresponding logics of justification)?

It so happens that Kemeny *did* offer such a Carnapian heuristic.

Kemeny's heuristic is not simply 'Aim at *theories* with high Carnapian marks' – for he does not seem to regard theory-construction as a task of science. According to Kemeny [1], the task of the theoretical scientist is to explain 'certain data collected through careful observations' with the help of 'scientifically acceptable' hypotheses. 'The selection of such hypotheses can be analysed into three stages: (*1*) The choice of a language in terms of which the hypothesis is to be expressed ... (*2*) The choice of a given statement from this language, which is to serve as the hypothesis. (*3*) The determination of whether we are scientifically justified to accept the hypothesis on the given evidence.' Then Kemeny continues: 'It is the last step that Carnap is interested in' (and which he solves by his *c*-functions). It can be seen that if Carnap succeeds in solving (*3*), he makes (*2*) superfluous: 'Given the language, we can consider any meaningful statement of it as a potential theory. Then the "best confirmed hypothesis relative to the given evidence" is well defined and may be selected. (Uniqueness is assumed for convenience only; it is easy to modify the argument by the addition of an arbitrary selection among equally confirmed hypotheses.)'

Kemeny says these are the three stages of 'selecting an acceptable hypothesis'. But could not these three stages represent a full *account of scientific method?* There would then be three stages in the growth of science: (*1'*) the construction of languages (and the determination of λ), (*2'*) the calculation of the *c*-values for non-universal hypotheses, and (*3'*) the application (interpretation) of the *c*-functions [2]. The second stage, since h and e are not universal

---

[1] 'Carnap's Theory of Probability and Induction', Schilpp (ed.): *The Philosophy of Rudolf Carnap*, 1963, p. 711 ff.

[2] According to Carnap, in the construction of languages one has to follow an inductive path, starting with observation-language. Cp. e.g. his

statements, could be programmed on an inductive machine [1]. The third seems to be trivial. But, Kemeny consoles us, this 'would not put the scientist out of business'; he would be occupied with the first stage, devising languages which 'would remain as the truly creative step'.

Let us now look more closely at Kemeny's methodology. First we devise a language. Then we define a probability distribution over the Boolean algebra of its (possibly only particular) sentences. Then we perform experiments and calculate, according to the Bayes formula, $p(h, e^k)$ where e^k is the conjunction of the outcomes of k experiments. Our 'improved' distribution resulting from the Bayesian learning process will be $p_k(h) = p(h, e^k)$. So all that we do is to feed $p_k(h)$ into a machine and fit it with a data-recorder: then we read off the 'improved' guesses $p_k(h)$ each evening. This 'learning process', this way of 'improvement of our guesses', is known as 'Bayesian conditionalization'.

What is wrong with 'Bayesian conditionalization'? Not only that it is *'atheoretical'* but that it is *acritical*. There is no way to discard the Initial Creative Act: the learning process is strictly confined to the original prison of the language. Explanations that break languages [2] and criticisms that break languages [3] are impossible in this set-up. The strongest criticism *within* a language – refutation in the hard sense in which one can refute a deterministic theory – is also ruled out, for in this approach *science becomes statistics writ large. But statistics becomes Bayesian conditionalization writ large,* for refutation by statistical rejection methods is ruled out too: no finite sample can ever prevent a 'possible world' from exerting eternal influence on our estimates.

In this method there is no place of honour accorded any more to *theories or laws.* Any sentence is as good as any other, and if

---

'The Aim of Inductive Logic', Nagel–Suppes–Tarski (eds.): *Logic, Methodology and Philosophy of Science,* 1960, p. 312.

[1]   Carnap: *Logical Foundations of Probability,* 1950, p. 196.

[2]   The deepest explanations are exactly the 'fact-correcting' explanations: those which radically reformulate and reshape the explanandum, and change its 'naive' language into 'theoretical' language. Cp. *above,* p. 320, footnote 3.

[3]   A paradigm of language-breaking criticism is concept-stretching refutation; cp. my 'Proofs and Refutations', *loc. cit.*

there is a preferred class, then – at least in Carnap's present
systems – it is the class of particular sentences. The concept of
explanation (again [1]) disappears; though we may retain the term
as a manner of speech for those sentences whose instantiations
have high confirmation. *Testability* disappears too, for there are no
potential falsifiers. No state of affairs is ever excluded. The recipe
is: guesses, with different and changing degrees of probability, but
without criticism. Estimation replaces testing and rejecting. (It is
curious how difficult it is for many people to understand that
Popper's guesswork idea of science means not only a – trivial –
admission of fallibility but also a demand for criticizability [2].)

---

[1]   As it had done once already in the early days of logical empiricism.

[2]   Carnap, in a recent paper ('Probability and Content Measure', in
Feyerabend–Maxwell (eds.): *Mind, Matter, and Method*, 1966), again stresses
his agreement with Popper that 'all knowledge is basically guessing' and
that the aim of inductive logic is 'precisely to improve our guesses and,
what is even more of fundamental importance, to improve our general
methods for making guesses'. The deceptive similarity in the terminology
covers up very different meanings. '*Improvement of a guess*', for Popper,
means refuting a theory and replacing it by an unrefuted one with higher
empirical content and, preferably, in a new conceptual framework. A
Popperian improvement of a guess is then part of his logic of discovery
and, incidentally, a critical, creative and purely theoretical affair.
'*Improvement of a guess*', for Carnap, means taking all the 'alternatives'
to a particular hypothesis available in some given language L, estimating
their probabilities relative to the total (or 'relevant') evidence and then
choosing among them the one which seems the most rational to choose
according to the purpose of one's action. 'Improvement of the general
methods for making guesses' is then an improvement of the methods of
choosing a c-function and possibly also an improvement of the pragmatic
rules of application discussed in § 50 of his *Logical Foundations of Probability*
and in his just quoted 'Probability and Content Measure'. A Carnapian
improvement of a guess is then a mechanical (or almost mechanical) and
essentially pragmatic affair – creativity is shifted to the 'methods' of making
guesses, which then of course are 'of more fundamental importance'. While
in Popper's 'improvement of a guess', refutation – critically throwing a
theory overboard – plays a crucial role, it plays no role in Carnap's 'improvement of a guess'. (Of course, one may ask whether Carnap's 'improvement of a guess' is part of the logic of discovery or part of the logic
of confirmation. It certainly fits well in Kemeny's heuristic framework –
with a pragmatic flavour added to it.)

One can scarcely deny that Kemeny's inductive method (of discovery) is naturally associated with Carnap's inductive method (of confirmation). Carnap's 'weak atheoretical thesis' – no theories in the logic of confirmation – strongly suggests Kemeny's 'strong atheoretical thesis' – no theories in the logic of discovery either. But Carnap himself never followed up this suggestion – even at the price of a stark contrast between his occasionally expressed, almost Popperian views on the method of discovery and his own method of confirmation [1].

Kemeny's heuristic, of course, in a sense vindicates Popper's fears: the 'weak atheoretical thesis' strongly suggests the 'strong atheoretical thesis'. But while the historian of thought must point out the strong connection between the two, he must not condemn the 'weak thesis' for 'guilt by association'. Popper's conflation of the strong methodological thesis and the weak justificationist thesis led him on many occasions to flog the dead horse and spare the live. But the criticism of the weak thesis has to be direct. However, before embarking on this criticism (in **2.3**), let us see how Carnap's programme shifted, not only from theories to particular propositions but also from evidential support to rational betting quotients.

2.2. *Probability, evidential support, rational belief and betting quotients.*

Carnap's shift of the problem of inductive logic from universal to particular propositions was accompanied by a parallel shift from the interpretation of inductive logic as providing primarily degrees of evidential support to its interpretation as providing primarily rational betting quotients. In order to appreciate this important parallel problem-shift, let me give another piece of potted history.

Neoclassical empiricism had a central dogma: *the dogma of the identity of*: (*1*) *probabilities*, (*2*) *degrees of evidential support* (*or*

---

[1]   Carnap in fact praised Kemeny's paper as having been 'very successful in presenting ... the aims and methods of inductive logic' (Schilpp (ed.): *The Philosophy of Rudolf Carnap*, 1963, p. 979). But I do not think he paid serious attention to that part of Kemeny's (by the way, in many respects excellent) paper which I analysed. I should like to stress once again Carnap's *unawareness* of problems concerning the logic of discovery.

confirmation), (3) *degrees of rational belief and* (4) *rational betting quotients*.

This '*neoclassical chain of identities*' is not implausible. For a true empiricist the only source of rational belief is evidential support: thus he will equate the degree of rationality of a belief with the degree of its evidential support. But rational belief is plausibly measured by rational betting quotients. And it was, after all, to determine rational betting quotients that the probability calculus was invented.

This chain was the basic hidden assumption underlying Carnap's whole programme. At first he was, as it transpires from *Testability and Meaning*, primarily interested in evidential support. But in 1941, when he embarked on his research programme, he saw his basic task primarily as that of finding a satisfactory 'explication' of the concept of logical probability. He wanted to perfect the work initiated by Bernoulli, Laplace, and Keynes.

But Bernoulli, Laplace and Keynes developed their theory of logical probability not for its own sake but only because they took logical probability to be identical with rational betting quotients, degrees of rationality of belief and of evidential support.

And so did Carnap. A brief glance at the *order* of his problems (confirmation, induction, probability) on page 1 of his *Logical Foundations of Probability* shows this. Thus his theory of probability was to solve the time-honoured problem of induction, which, according to Carnap, was to judge laws and theories on the basis of evidence. But as long as evidential support = probability, *Logical Foundations of Probability = Logical Foundations of Evidential Support = Logical Theory of Confirmation*. Carnap, after some hesitation, decided to call his *explicatum* for logical probability 'degree of confirmation' – a choice which later turned out to be something of an embarrassment.

(*a*) *Are degrees of evidential support probabilities?* Already at an early stage of his work Carnap came to *feel* that evidential support is the weak point in the chain of neoclassical empiricism. Indeed, the discrepancy between rational betting quotients and degrees of evidential support was so glaring in the case of *theories* that he had to split the two already in his 1950 exposition. For the rational betting quotient for any theory is zero, but its 'reliability' (that is, its evidential support) varies. Therefore he split his concept of confirmation for theories into two: their 'degree of confirmation', he claimed, was zero, but their degree of confirmation (i.e. qualified instance confirmation) was positive [1].

This throws new light on Carnap's first step in his 'atheoretical' problem-shift: the first atheoretical move was due to the first crack in the neoclassical chain.

But very soon he found that even by formulating his philosophy of science completely in terms of particular propositions he could not prevent further cracks. The identity of degrees of evidential support and rational betting quotients for particular propositions is not self-evident either: the probabilistic character of the second may seem to be clear, but the probabilistic character of the first is anything but clear. This is what he had in mind when he wrote: 'Although this explanation [i.e. explanation of logical probability as evidential support] may be said to outline the primary and simplest meaning of probability$_1$, it alone is hardly sufficient for the clarification of probability$_1$ as a quantitative concept' [2]. Since Carnap had, at this point, already realised that his argument that evidential support = logical probability, is based on 'entirely arbitrary' assumptions [3], he shifted the emphasis to betting intuition. But he did *not* realise that not only is his argument for the thesis concerning the identity of evidential support and logical probability based on unsatisfactory assumptions but the thesis may be altogether false – even in the case of particular propositions.

Without realising it, he introduced two different concepts in his

---

[1] Cp. *above*, p. 334.

[2] *Logical Foundations of Probability*, 1950, p. 164. This is the first mention in the book of this insufficiency: indeed, earlier there is a marked confidence that there will be no such insufficiency. But great books are usually characterised by a certain inconsistency – at least in emphases. One modifies, self-critically, one's position when elaborating it, but one seldom rewrites – if only for lack of time – the whole book on each such occasion.

[3] *Ibid.*, p. 165.

Logical Foundations of Probability for rational betting quotients
and for degrees of evidential support. For rational betting
quotients he used $p(h, e)$; for degrees of evidential support he used
$p(h, e) - p(h)$. But he conflated the two: in most of his book
(in his quantitative and comparative theory) he claimed that *both*
rational betting quotients and degrees of evidential support are
$p(h, e)$; in §§ 86, 87, 88 (in his classificatory theory), however, he
slipped into the thesis that *both* are $p(h, e) - p(h)$.

It is the irony of the story that in these sections Carnap criticised
Hempel for having two different *explicanda* for evidential support
in mind [1], and for having, in the main, opted for the wrong, proba-
bilistic-betting approach.

The two conflated notions are, of course, radically different. The
Carnapian bettor's $p(h, e)$ is maximal when h is a tautology: the
probability of a tautology, on any evidence, is 1. The Carnapian
scientist's $p(h, e) - p(h)$ is minimal when h is a tautology: the evidential support of a tautology is always zero. For $p(h, e)$ the following 'consequence condition' holds: $p(h, e)$ can never decrease when
transmitted through deductive channels, that is, if $h \to h'$, then
$p(h', e) \geqslant p(h, e)$. But for $p(h, e) - p(h)$ this condition, in general,
does not hold. The differences are due to the fact that two rival
and mutually inconsistent intuitions are at play. According to our
betting intuition, any conjunction of hypotheses, whatever the evidence, is at least as risky as any of the conjuncts. (That is,
$(h)(h')(e)(p(h, e) \geqslant p(h \& h', e))$.) According to our *intuition of evidential support*, this cannot be the case: it would be absurd to
maintain that the evidential support for a more powerful theory
(which is, in the Carnapian projection of the language of science
onto the distorting mirror of particular hypotheses, a conjunction
of hypotheses) *must not* be more than the evidential support for
a weaker consequence of it (in the case of the Carnapian projection, for any of the conjuncts). Indeed, intuition of evidential
support says that the more a proposition says, the more evidential
support it may acquire. (That is, within Carnap's framework, it
should be the case that $(\exists h)(\exists h')(\exists e)(c(h, e) < c(h \& h', e))$.) But then

---

[1] *Ibid.*, p. 475.

degrees of evidential support cannot be the same as degrees of probability in the sense of the probability calculus.

All this would be trivial if not for the powerful time-honoured dogma of what I called the 'neoclassical chain' identifying, among other things, rational betting quotients with degrees of evidential support. This dogma confused generations of mathematicians and of philosophers [1].

The first philosopher to challenge the dogma was Popper [2]. He set out to break the neoclassical chain by proving that degrees of evidential support cannot possibly be probabilities – whatever the interpretation of the latter. That is, he set out to prove that the function $C(h, e)$, evidential support, confirmation, or corroboration of h by the evidence e, does not obey the formal calculus of probability.

Popper proposed two different critical arguments: one in 1934, and one in 1954. (In 1954 he also proposed a 'rival formula'.)

Popper's 1934 argument was that 'the corroborability of a theory and also the degree of corroboration of a theory . . . stand both,

---

[1] Now we can see that Hempel fell prey to the *same* confusion. He realised that there are two rival subcurrents in the theory of confirmation: one can be characterised primarily by the consequence condition, the other by the condition that if e confirms h, it also confirms any hypothesis that entails h: the entailment or 'converse consequence condition'. He showed that, given some simple, generally accepted assumptions, the two conditions are inconsistent. (Cp. his 'Studies in the logic of confirmation', *Mind*, **54**, 1945, p. 104.) After some hesitation, and indeed, confusion, he rather arbitrarily chose in 1945 the former, in 1965 the latter. (Cp. his Postscript to his 1945 paper in his *Aspects of Scientific Explanation*, 1965, p. 50.) Incidentally, his famous 'paradox of confirmation' looks dramatically different according to which condition one adopts: this is the keynote of the discussion of his paradox between Popperians and Carnapians. (For this point, cp. Mackie: 'The paradox of confirmation', *The British Journal for the Philosophy of Science*, **13**, 1962–3.)

[2] The first statistician to challenge the dogma was Fisher. He equated 'degree of rational belief' with his non-additive likelihood function (cp. his 'On the mathematical foundations of theoretical statistics', *Transactions of the Royal Society of London*, Series A, **222**, 1922, p. 327, footnote *). But he could not argue his position sufficiently clearly since he did not have Popper's idea of empirical content or his theoretical outlook.

as it were, in inverse ratio to its logical probability . . . But the view implied by probability logic is the precise opposite of this. Its upholders let the probability of a hypothesis increase in *direct proportion* to its logical probability – although there is no doubt that they intend their "probability of a hypothesis" to stand for much the same thing that I try to indicate by "degree of corroboration" ' [1]. Or: *degree of evidential support is proportional not to probability but to improbability.*

According to Popper's new footnote, added in 1959 to this passage, these lines 'contain the crucial point of [his] criticism of the probability theory of induction' [2].

But the supporting argument wobbles. It hinges on two points:

(*1*)   The first crucial point of the argument is that corroboration varies inversely with probability, that is, if $p(h) \geqslant p(h')$, then for all e, $C(h, e) \leqslant C(h', e)$. But this unqualified assertion about the direct proportionality of degree of corroboration and of corroborability (or about the inverse proportionality of degree of corroboration and probability) is absurd [3]; so much so that Popper himself, when in 1954 he gave a detailed list of his adequacy requirements, postulated that, at least when h and h' imply e, the degree of corroboration must vary *directly, not inversely*, with (prior) probability, that is, if $p(h) \geqslant p(h')$, then for all e, $C(h, e) \geqslant C(h', e)$ [4].

(*2*)   The second crucial point of the argument is that 'posterior probability', unlike corroboration, varies directly with 'prior probability', that is, if $p(h) \geqslant p(h')$, then for all e, $p(h, e) \geqslant p(h', e)$ [5]. But

---

[1]   *The Logic of Scientific Discovery*, 1934, § 83.

[2]   *The Logic of Scientific Discovery*, 1959, p. 270, footnote *3.

[3]   One wonders whether it was this assertion that misled Carnap into believing that Popper seems to use the term 'degree of corroborability' as synonymous with the term 'degree of corroboration'. (Cp. his Reply to Popper in Schilpp (ed.): *The Philosophy of Rudolf Carnap*, 1963, p. 996).

[4]   Cp. his 1954 desideratum *viii (c)*, *The Logic of Scientific Discovery*, 1959, p. 401. Incidentally, Popper used to accuse Carnap of 'choosing' the most probable theory. But *then* he himself could be accused, on the ground of his *viii (c)*, of 'choosing' the most probable theory from among those which can explain a given piece of evidence.

[5]   For another formulation of this same point see his *Logic of Scientific Discovery*, 1959, p. 363: 'The laws of the probability calculus demand that,

this, as Bar–Hillel pointed out to me, is false, and counterexamples can easily be constructed.

Nevertheless the heart of Popper's argument is sound and can easily be corrected in the light of his later work. First, while one has to abandon his first thesis about the direct ratio between degree of corroboration and empirical content, one may keep his weaker thesis about the direct ratio between degree of corroborability and empirical content: if we increase the content of a theory, its corroborability also increases. This can be achieved for instance by fixing the upper bound of degree of corroboration of a hypothesis at its empirical content [1], and by allowing evidence to raise the corroboration of the more informative theory above the maximum level of the corroboration of the less informative one. That is, if h implies h' and the empirical content of h is greater than of h', then $C(h, e) > C(h', e)$ should be possible for some e. This indeed *is* excluded by Carnap's inductive logic, according to which probability can only increase when transmitted through deductive channels: if h implies h', then for all e, $p(h, e) \leqslant p(h', e)$. But then corroboration (or confirmation or evidential support) cannot be probability.

Popper's 1954 argument, like Popper's 1934 argument, was an important one. But, as in the previous case, his formulation suggested a stronger thesis than the one he had actually proved; and thereby, as in the previous case, he weakened and delayed its impact.

What he claimed to have established was once more 'a mathematical refutation of all those theories of induction which identify the degree to which a statement is supported or confirmed or corroborated by empirical tests with its degree of probability in the sense of the calculus of probability' [2]. But what he in fact proved was that Carnap's 1950 'grand theory' was inconsistent.

---

of two hypotheses, the one that is logically stronger, or more informative, or better testable, and thus the one which can be *better corroborated*, is always *less probable* – on any given evidence – than the other.'

[1]   Cp. the third of Popper's 1954 *desiderata*, *The Logic of Scientific Discovery*, 1959, p. 400.

[2]   *Ibid.*, pp. 389–90. Also cp. pp. 396–8.

I call Carnap's 'grand theory' the trinity of classificatory, comparative, and quantitative concepts of confirmation soldered into one 'grand theory' by the requirement that they should be related as the concepts, Warm, Warmer, and Temperature [1]. Popper's argument showed that the inconsistency was due to the fact that Carnap had inadvertently two different *'explicanda'* in mind, namely, evidential support (something like Popper's degree of corroboration) and logical probability [2]. Popper claimed that Carnap fell prey to the historical 'tendency to confuse measures *of* increase or decrease with the measures *that* increase and decrease (as shown by the history of the concepts of velocity, acceleration and force)' [3].

By now Carnap and most Carnapians have accepted the gist of Popper's criticism. Carnap, in 1962, in the Preface to the second edition of his *Logical Foundations of Probability*, separated the two explicanda and decided that, in the future, he would call $p(h, e)$ not 'degree of confirmation' but 'rational betting quotient' or, simply, 'probability'. But together with the *term* 'confirmation', went his *theory* of confirmation, that is, his theory of evidential support. Popper rightly stated in 1955: 'there is no "current [Carnapian] theory of confirmation"' [4]. Bar–Hillel was the first Carnapian who proposed a new theory of confirmation and suggested what I would call a 'vectorial' instead of a 'scalar' appraisal of hypotheses, consisting of an ordered pair: ⟨'initial informative content', 'degree of confirmation'⟩ [5]. In 1962 Carnap decided to take Bar–Hillel's advice [6]. But now he seems to have changed his mind again and returned to his old idea of a 'scalar' rather than a 'vectorial' confirmation theory; he now suggests $p(h, e) \cdot (1 - p(h))$

---

[1]   Cp. Carnap: *Logical Foundations of Probability*, 1950, p. 15.

[2]   *The Logic of Scientific Discovery*, 1959, p. 393.

[3]   *Ibid.*, p. 399.

[4]   Cp. his ' "Content" and "Degree of Confirmation": A Reply to Dr. Bar–Hillel', *The British Journal for the Philosophy of Science*, 6, 1955–6, p. 158.

[5]   'Comments on "Degree of Confirmation" by Professor K. R. Popper', *The British Journal for the Philosophy of Science*, 6, 1955–56.

[6]   Cp. his 'Probability and Content Measure' in Feyerabend–Maxwell: *Mind, Matter and Method*, 1966.

for degree of confirmation. Bar–Hillel interprets this as a symptom of Carnap's incurable 'acceptance syndrome' [1].

However, Carnap – and his followers – certainly do not panic at this disarray. As they see it, inductive logic is primarily concerned with the explication of logical probability, and not with the problem of evidential support, which will eventually be solved with its help. It was a mistake, they assert, but only a slight and primarily *terminological* mistake to call the *explicatum* of logical probability 'degree of confirmation'.

No doubt Carnap's research programme of inductive logic had sufficient tenacity to survive the shattering blow to its *direct* interpretation as a theory of evidential support [2]. But while he may claim that his 'theory of confirmation' does not collapse with his original theory of confirmation (mistakenly christened 'theory of confirmation'); while Bar–Hillel and he also may correctly challenge Popper and his followers to criticise his inductive logic interpreted as a theory of rational betting quotients rather than as a theory of evidential support [3], there is not much point in retorting to Popper's demolition of Carnap's theory of confirmation that Popper's interpretation of 'degree of confirmation' as degree of confirmation is a 'misinterpretation' [4].

(*b*)   *Are 'degrees of rational belief' degrees of evidential support or are they rational betting quotients?* Even if Carnapians found a new, satisfactory theory of evidential support, they would face a new problem. Since Popper broke the chain between degrees of evi-

---

[1]   Cp. Bar–Hillel: 'The acceptance syndrome', *this volume*, p. 153.

[2]   When Carnap finally understood that Popper's criticism contains a valid point, he saved his *programme*, if not his 1950 *theory*, on a mere two pages of the Preface of the 1962 edition of his *Logical Foundations*. Popper underestimated the tenacity of research-programmes when he thought that the 'contradictoriness [of Carnap's 1950 theory] is not a minor matter which can be easily repaired' (*The Logic of Scientific Discovery*, 1959, p. 393).

[3]   Bar–Hillel: 'Remark on Popper's Note on Content and Degree of Confirmation', *The British Journal for the Philosophy of Science*, 7, 1956–7, p. 248; and Carnap's Reply to Popper, in Schilpp (ed.): *The Philosophy of Rudolf Carnap*, 1963, p. 998.

[4]   *Ibid.*

dential support and probabilities (and hence, according to Carnap, rational betting quotients), to which side, if any, should 'degrees of rational belief' belong? Or should rational belief be split into two? Carnap seems to take it for granted that degrees of rational belief are betting quotients. Popper seems to take it for granted that degrees of rationality of belief be equated with his degrees of evidential support [1].

It has been a cornerstone of empiricism that the only justification, total or partial, of a hypothesis – and therefore the only rational ground for total or partial belief in it – is its evidential support. And there has also been a longstanding dogma about degrees of belief, namely, that their best touchstone is how much one is willing to bet on them. (Carnap attributed this idea to Ramsey [2], but Ramsey himself refers to it as to an 'old-established' thesis [3].) But if evidential support was to determine degrees of belief, and degrees of belief were to be measured by betting quotients, then these three concepts naturally were merged into one. But now this old-established trinity is split. And this rings the death knell of the *one* concept of 'rational belief', 'credence', 'credibility', etc., in any *objective* sense of these terms.

Thus the breaking up of the chain of neoclassical empiricism implies the collapse also of its theory of rational belief. Already in 1953 Kemeny and Oppenheim distinguished 'degrees of inductive support' (which were identical with Carnap's rational betting quotients or degrees of 'firmness') and 'degrees of factual support' (which were related to Carnap's degrees of 'increase of firmness') [4]. Which should measure the rationality of belief?

There are some obvious arguments for $p(h, e)$. But those philosophers who still take logical empiricism seriously but have become convinced that Carnap's inductive logic contains aprioristic

---

[1] Cp. *The Logic of Scientific Discovery*, 1959, p. 415. But see *below*, p. 412, footnote 6.

[2] Cp. his 'Inductive logic and inductive intuition', *this volume*, p. 259.

[3] Cp. his 'Truth and Probability', 1926, in his *Foundations of Mathematics and other Logical Essays*, edited in 1950 by R. B. Braithwaite, p. 172.

[4] Cp. Kemeny–Oppenheim: 'Degree of factual support', *Philosophy of Science*, 20, 1953, pp. 307–24.

metaphysical assumptions [1], are bound to ask whether it is not a betrayal of true empiricism to claim that $p(h, e)$ should determine the rational degree of belief? For the true empiricist surely there must be no other source of rational belief but empirical evidence (and, of course, genuinely tautological logic). But why should the true empiricist take $p(h, e)$ for evidential support, rather than $p(h, e) - p(h)$, when it is obvious that a large ingredient of the value of $p(h, e)$ is simply the putative probability of h in the light of no evidence whatever?

Proliferation of more or less different formulae with more or less different name-tags does not solve the problem. In one paper we read:

'The upshot is essentially as follows: (A) Carnap is concerned to analyze the measure inherent in the question: "How sure are we of p if we are given q as evidence?" (B) Popper and Kemeny–Oppenheim deal with the question: "How much surer are we of p given q than without q?" (C) The present measure of evidential relevance deals with the question: "How much is our confidence in the truth of p increased or decreased if q is given?" ' [2]. But there is no critical discussion of the rights or wrongs of any of these different measures: instead, we are told that it is 'impolite' to deny that each of them measures *something* [3].

(c) *Are rational betting quotients probabilities?* The safest link in the neoclassical chain seemed to be the one between probabilities and rational betting quotients, supported by the Ramsey–De Finetti theorem. But several arguments undermine this support. For instance Putnam pointed out that in scientific predictions 'we are not playing against a malevolent opponent but against nature, and nature does not exploit "incoherencies" ' [4]. Indeed, if we assume, for the sake of the argument, that betting quotients do measure degrees of rational belief, but also that the only rational

---

[1] Cp. *below*, p. 361, footnote 2.

[2] Rescher: 'A theory of evidence', *Philosophy of Science*, 25, 1958, p. 87.

[3] *Ibid.*, p. 94.

[4] 'Probability and confirmation', in Morgenbesser (ed.): *Philosophy of Science Today*, 1967, p. 113.

source of belief is evidential support, and finally that evidential support is not probabilistic, then what is the correct conclusion from the Ramsey–De Finetti theorem? The correct conclusion is that it is irrational to base our theory of rationality on the manichean assumption that if we do not arrange our bets (or degrees of belief) probabilistically an evil power will catch us out by a shrewdly arranged system of bets. If once this unrealistic assumption is abandoned, we may just as well have another look at non-probabilistic theories of rational betting quotients, like Wald's minimax method or even possibly formulae akin to Popper's degree of corroboration [1], etc., which are now being regarded by Carnapians as conclusively refuted by the Ramsey–De Finetti theorem alone.

Putnam's argument in itself is enough to shake the universal validity of Carnap's theory of rational belief and of rational betting quotients. But I shall propose also a different, independent argument. This argument will not question that rational betting quotients should be probabilistic; it will not question that rational betting quotients be restricted to particular hypotheses; but it will question the second clause of the weak atheoretical thesis underlying Carnap's theory of rational betting quotients (or of degrees of rational belief) for particular propositions, that is, the thesis that restricts even the domain of the second argument of his c-functions to particular propositions and forbids taking into account the appraisal of theories altogether [2]. However, I shall show that in calculating rational betting quotients of particular hypotheses one cannot escape appraising (genuinely universal) *theories*. Now Carnap's inductive logic cannot appraise theories, because theories, the vehicles of scientific growth, cannot be satisfactorily appraised without a theory of scientific growth. But if so, Carnap's inductive logic fails not only as a theory of evidential support, but also as a theory of rational betting quotients.

[In his 'Replies' in Schilpp (ed.): *The Philosophy of Rudolf Carnap*, 1963, Carnap writes that he has now constructed new, probabilistic,

---

[1]   Popper's *desideratum viii* (c) incorporates a crucial element of betting intuition into his theory of evidential support (cp. *The Logic of Scientific Discovery*, 1959, p. 401).

[2]   Cp. *above*, p. 337.

c-functions in which theories may have positive measures (p. 977). But since these new c-functions are, as I understand, still probabilistic and therefore invariably obey the consequence condition, they are scarcely suitable for measuring evidential support; since they assign positive values to universal hypotheses, they cannot possibly mean rational betting quotients in view of Keynes', Ramsey's and Carnap's arguments to the effect that only a fool would bet on the universal truth of a scientific theory. (No wonder that in Hintikka's recent papers, in which he too develops metrics with $c(l) > 0$, the term 'betting' never occurs.) But then a strange situation may arise: Carnap may have to leave the definition *both* of rational betting quotients and of degrees of evidential support (in terms of his c-function) for later and elaborate an inductive logic hanging completely in the air. Of course, as already mentioned, there is no *logical* limit to the tenacity of a research programme – but one may come to doubt whether its shift was 'progressive'.]

2.3   *The collapse of the weak atheoretical thesis.*

(a)   *'Correctness of language' and confirmation theory*[1]. Carnap's atheoretical confirmation theory rests on a number of theoretical assumptions, some of which, in turn, will be shown to depend on the available scientific theories. The epistemological status of these theoretical assumptions – the axioms governing the c-functions, L, the value of λ – has not been sufficiently clarified; Carnap's original claim that they were 'analytic' may have now been abandoned but has not yet been replaced. For instance, λ may be interpreted either as a measure of the degree of complexity of the world[2], or as the speed at which one is willing to modify one's

---

[1]   Throughout this section 'confirmation theory' stands for 'inductive logic' as Carnap *now* interprets it: as a theory of rational belief, of rational betting quotients. Of course, once we have shown that there can be no atheoretical 'confirmation theory', that is, no atheoretical inductive logic, we also have shown that there can be no atheoretical confirmation theory, that is, no definition of degrees of evidential support in terms of atheoretical betting quotients.

[2]   Cp. Popper's and Nagel's papers in Schilpp (ed.): *The Philosophy of Rudolf Carnap*, 1963, especially pp. 224–6 and pp. 816–25. Carnap did not

a priori assumptions under the influence of empirical evidence [1].
I shall concentrate on *L*.

*The choice of a language for science implies a conjecture as to what
is relevant evidence for what, or what is connected, by natural necessity,
with what.* For instance, in a language separating celestial from
terrestrial phenomena, data about terrestrial projectiles may seem
irrelevant to hypotheses about planetary motion. In the language
of Newtonian dynamics they become relevant and change our
betting quotients for planetary predictions.

Now how should one find the 'correct' language which would
state correctly what evidence is relevant for a hypothesis? Although
Carnap never asked this question, he implicitly answered it: in
his 1950 and 1952 systems 'the observational language' was expected
to fulfil this requirement. But Putnam's and Nagel's arguments
imply that the 'observational' language cannot be 'correct' in my
sense [2].

However, both Putnam and Nagel discussed this problem as

---

comment, although in his *Autobiography* he seems to say that *λ* depends
on the 'world structure', which, however, the 'observer is free to choose'
according to his degree of 'caution'. (*Ibid.*, p. 75.) But already in an earlier
paper he had said that *λ* 'somehow corresponds to the complexity of the
universe' ('Remarks to Kemeny's paper', *Philosophy and Phenomenological
Research*, 13, 1953, p. 376). In his present paper he argues that 'for fruitful
work in a new field it is not necessary to be in possession of a well-founded
epistemological theory about the sources of knowledge in the field' ('Inductive
logic and inductive intuition', *this volume*, p. 258). No doubt, he is right.
But then the programme of inductive logic, which originally was deeply
embedded in austere empiricism, in fact presupposed, if Popper's and Nagel's
arguments are correct, an apriorist epistemology.

[1]   Kemeny seems to favour the latter interpretation. He calls *λ* an 'index
of caution' which puts a brake on modifying one's position too fast under
the influence of empirical evidence (cp. his 'A contribution to inductive
logic', *Philosophy and Phenomenological Research*, 13, 1952–3, p. 373 and
his 'Carnap on Probability and Induction' in Schilpp (ed.): *The Philosophy
of Rudolf Carnap*, 1963, p. 728). But which is the *rational* index of caution?
With infinite caution one never learns, so this is irrational. Zero caution
may come under criticism. But otherwise the inductive judge seems to
refuse to pronounce on *λ* – he leaves its choice to the scientist's instinct.

[2]   Schilpp (ed.): *The Philosophy of Rudolf Carnap*, 1963, pp. 779 and
804 f.

if there were some unique theoretical language opposed to *the* observation language, so that this theoretical language would be the correct one. Carnap countered this objection by promising to take *the* theoretical language into account [1]. But this does not solve the general problem, the problem of 'indirect evidence' (I call *'indirect evidence relative to L in L*'* an event which does not raise the probability of another event when both are described in *L*, but does so if they are expressed in a language *L**). In the examples given by Putnam and Nagel *L* was Carnap's 'observational language' and *L** the superseding theoretical language. But a situation of the same kind may occur whenever a theory is superseded by a new theory couched in a new language. Indirect evidence — a common phenomenon in the growth of knowledge — makes the degree of confirmation a function of *L* which, in turn, changes as science progresses. Although growth of the evidence *within* a fixed theoretical framework (the language *L*) leaves the chosen *c*-function unaltered, growth of the theoretical framework (introduction of a *new* language *L**) may change it radically.

Carnap tried his best to avoid any 'language-dependence' of inductive logic. But he always assumed that the growth of science is in a sense cumulative: he held that one could stipulate that once the degree of confirmation of *h* given *e* has been established in a suitable 'minimal language', no further argument can ever alter this value. But scientific change frequently implies change of language and change of language implies change in the corresponding *c*-values [2].

This simple argument shows that Carnap's (implicit) 'principle of minimal language' [3] does not work. This principle of gradual construction of the *c*-function was meant to save the fascinating ideal of an eternal, absolutely valid, *a priori* inductive logic, the ideal of an inductive machine that, once programmed, may need an *extension of the original programming* but *no reprogramming*.

---

[1] *Ibid.*, pp. 987–9.

[2] Where theories are, there is fallibility. Where scientific fallibility is, there is refutability. Where refutability is, refutation is nearby. Where refutation is, there is change. How many philosophers go to the end of the chain?

[3] Cp. *above*, p. 325.

Yet this ideal breaks down. The growth of science may destroy any particular confirmation theory: the inductive machine may have to be reprogrammed with each new major theoretical advance.

Carnapians may retort that the revolutionary growth of science will produce a revolutionary growth of inductive logic. But how can inductive logic grow? How can we change our whole betting policy with respect to hypotheses expressed in a language L whenever a new theory couched in a new language L^* is proposed? Or should we do so only if the new theory has been – in Popper's sense – corroborated?

Obviously we do not always want to change our c-function on the appearance of a fancy new theory (in a fancy new language) which has no better empirical support than the extant ones. We certainly would change it if the new theory has stood up to severe tests, so that it could be said that 'the new language has empirical support' [1]. But *in this case we have reduced the Carnapian problem of confirmation of languages (or, if you prefer, of the choice of a language) to the Popperian problem of corroboration of theories.*

This consideration shows that *the essential part of 'language planning' far from being the function of the inductive logician is a mere by-product of scientific theorising* [2]. The inductive logician can, at best, say to the scientist: 'if *you* choose to accept the language L, then *I* can inform you that, in L, $c(h, e) = q'$. This, of course, is a complete retreat from the original position in which the inductive judge was to tell the scientist, on the sole basis of h and e, how much h was confirmed on the basis of e: 'All we need [for calculating $c(h, e)$] is a logical analysis of the meanings of the two sentences' [3]. But if the inductive judge needs to get from the scientist in addition to h and e also the language of the most advanced, best-corroborated theory, what then does the scientist need the inductive judge for?

Yet the situation of the Carnapian inductive judge becomes

---

[1] In this case we might even talk about the 'refutation of a language'.

[2] It is interesting that some inductive logicians, still unaware of this fact, think that language planning is only 'formalization' and therefore a mere 'routine' (though quite possibly laborious) job for the inductive logician.

[3] Carnap: *Logical Foundations of Probability*, 1950, p. 21.

still more precarious if there are two or more rival theories formulated in completely different languages. In this case there does not seem to be any hope of the inductive judge deciding between them – unless he asks some super-judge to set up a secondary c-function in order to appraise languages. But how should that be done [1]? Perhaps the 'best' they can do is – instead of getting into an infinite regress of metaconfirmation functions – to ask *the scientist* for those degrees of belief which he cares to attach to his rival theories, and weight the values of the rival functions accordingly.

Inductive justice is perhaps at its weakest in the prescientific stage of 'empirical generalizations' or 'naive conjectures' [2]. Here inductive judgements are bound to be highly unreliable, and the language of such conjectures will in most cases soon be replaced by some radically different new language. However, present-day inductive judges may give very high c-values to predictions couched in a naive language which the scientist's instinctive 'hunch' may rate very low [3]. The inductive judge has only two ways out: either by appealing to some super-judge with a request for an appraisal of languages, or by appealing to the scientist's instinctive rating. Both courses are fraught with difficulty.

To sum up, it seems that rational betting quotients can best be provided to customers who – at their own risk and left to their

---

[1] Bar–Hillel, pointing out that 'there exist no generally accepted criteria for the comparison of two language-systems', says that 'here lies an important task for present-day methodology' ('Remarks on Carnap's Logical Syntax of Language' in Schilpp (ed.): *The Philosophy of Rudolf Carnap*, 1963, p. 536). Also cp. L. J. Cohen: 'An argument that confirmation functors for consilience are empirical hypotheses', *this volume*, pp. 247 ff.

[2] Cp. my 'Proofs and Refutations', *loc. cit.*, Part IV, § 7.

[3] This is, in fact, a further paradox of the 'weight of evidence' (cp. *above*, p. 345). Curiously, according to Carnapians, it is exactly this prescientific domain where inductive logic can be most successfully applied. This mistake stems from the fact that probability measures have been constructed only for such 'empirical' (or, as I prefer putting it, 'naive') languages. But unfortunately such languages express only very accidental, superficial features of the world and therefore yield particularly uninteresting confirmation estimates.

own devices – specify the language in which the quotients are to be calculated.

All this shows that there is here something that makes inductive logic dramatically different from deductive logic: if A is a consequence of B, no matter how our empirical knowledge develops, A will remain a consequence of B. But with the increase of our empirical knowledge, $c(A, B)$ may change radically. Since we opt for a new language usually in the wake of a victorious theory *corroborated by empirical facts*, Carnap's claim that 'the principal characteristic of the statements in both fields [i.e. in deductive and inductive logic] is their independence of the contingency of facts' [1] is shattered, and thereby also the justification of applying the common term 'logic' to both fields.

A historical consideration of the notorious 'principles of induction' may throw some more light on this situation. The main problem of classical epistemology was to *prove* scientific theories; the main problem of neoclassical empiricism is to *prove* degrees of confirmation of scientific hypotheses. One way of trying to solve the classical problem was to reduce the problem of induction to deduction, to claim that inductive inferences are enthymematic and that in each of them there is a hidden major premiss, a synthetic *a priori* '*[classical] principle of induction*'. Classical inductive principles would then turn scientific theories from mere conjectures into proven theorems (given, of course, the certainty of the minor premiss, expressing the factual evidence). This solution, of course, was incisively criticised by empiricists. But neoclassical empiricism wants to *prove* statements of the form $p(h, e) = q$; therefore neoclassical empiricism too needs some indubitably true premiss (or premisses), that is, a '*[neoclassical] principle of induction*'. Keynes, for instance, refers to this neoclassical principle when he assumes 'some valid principle darkly present to our minds, even if it still eludes the peering eyes of philosophy' [2]. Unfortunately in the literature the two different kinds of inductive principles have been persistently conflated [3].

---

[1] *Logical Foundations of Probability*, 1950, p. 200.

[2] Keynes: *A Treatise on Probability*, 1921, p. 264.

[3] An interesting example is the difference between the classical and

That inductive logic must depend on metaphysical principles was a commonplace for Broad and Keynes; they had no doubt that for deriving a probability metric they needed such principles. But in trying to work out these principles they became very sceptical about whether they could find them and if they did find them whether they could justify them. In fact, both, but especially Broad, gave up hope of the latter; Broad thought that all such principles could achieve would be to *explain* rather than to *prove* some probability metric which one would have to take for granted [1]. But he must have thought that this was a scandalous retreat: we may call it the neoclassical scandal of induction. The '*classical scandal of induction*' was that the inductive principles, needed to *prove* theories (from facts), could not be justified [2]. The '*neoclassical scandal of induction*' is that the inductive principles, needed to *prove* at least the degree of confirmation of hypotheses, could not be justified either [3]. The neoclassical scandal of induction meant that since the inductive principles could not serve as proving but only as explanatory premisses, *induction could not be part of logic*

---

neoclassical Principle of Limited Variety. Its main classical version is the Principle of Eliminative Induction: 'there are only n possible alternative explanatory theories'; if factual evidence refutes $n-1$ of them, the n-th is *proved*. Its main neoclassical version is Keynes' principle 'that the amount of variety in the universe is limited in such a way that there is no one object so complex that its qualities fall into an infinite number of independent groups' – unless we assume this, no empirical proposition whatsoever can ever become highly probable (*loc. cit.*, p. 258). Also while classical principles of induction may be formulated in the object language (for instance, by postulating the disjunction of the 'limited variety' of theories), neoclassical principles of induction can be formulated *only* in the metalanguage (cp. *below*, p. 400, footnote 1).

[1] Cp. his 'A reply to my critics' in Schilpp (ed.): *The Philosophy of C. D. Broad*, 1959, p. 751.

[2] Cp. above, p. 321, footnote 1. In order to appreciate the 'scandal' one should read Keynes (or Russell) rather than Broad. In setting out his programme Keynes had two uncompromisable, absolute basic requirements: the certainty of evidence and the logically proven certainty of statements of the form $p(h, e)=q$. (*A Treatise on Probability*, 1921, p. 11.) If these cannot be satisfied, inductive logic cannot fulfil its original aim: to save scientific knowledge from scepticism.

[3] These two 'scandals' have also been conflated in the literature.

but only of speculative metaphysics. Carnap, of course, could not admit *any* metaphysics, whether 'proven' or speculative: so he solved the problem by hiding the rattling metaphysical skeleton in the cupboard of Carnapian 'analyticity'. This is how the diffident metaphysical speculation of the Cambridge school turned into confident Carnapian language-construction.

Now Carnap's 'analytical' inductive principles consist partly of his explicit axioms, partly of his implicit meta-axioms about the correctness of L and λ. We showed that as far as the correctness of a chosen L is concerned, it is not only an unprovable but a refutable premiss. But then confirmation theory becomes no less fallible than science itself.

(b)   *The abdication of the inductive judge.* We saw that since the inductive judge cannot appraise languages, he cannot pass judgment without asking the scientist to perform this task for him. But on further scrutiny it turns out that the scientist is asked to participate still more actively in fixing degrees of confirmation. For even after a language (or several languages and their respective weights) has been agreed on, difficult situations may still arise.

What if there is a very attractive, very plausible theory in the field, which so far has little or no evidence to support it? How much should we bet on its next instance? The sober advice of the inductive judge is that no theory should be trusted beyond its evidential support. For instance, if the Balmer formula is proposed after only three lines of the hydrogen spectrum have been discovered, the sober inductive judge would keep us from becoming over-enthusiastic and prevent us – against our hunch – from betting on a fourth line as predicted by the formula.

The inductive judge is then unimpressed by striking theories without sufficient factual backing. But he may be unimpressed also by dramatic refutations. I shall show this by another example. Let us imagine that we already have c-functions defined on very complex languages. For instance, let us postulate a language in which all Newtonian and Einsteinian mechanics and theories of gravitation are expressible. Let us imagine that hitherto all the (billions of) predictions from both theories have been confirmed, except for the predictions concerning the perihelion of Mercury where only Einstein's theory was confirmed while Newton's theory failed. The numerical predictions from the two theories differ in general but because of the smallness of their difference or the imprecision of our instruments the difference was measurable only in the case of Mercury. Now new methods have been devised, precise enough to decide the issue in a series of crucial experiments. How much should we then bet on the Einsteinian predictions h_E^i versus the corresponding Newtonian h_N^i? A scientist would take into account that Newton's theory had after all been refuted (in the case of Mercury) while Einstein's theory survived, and would therefore suggest a very daring bet. A Carnapian however, cannot, with his weak atheoretical thesis, take Newton's or Einstein's theories (and the refutation of the former) into account. Thus he would find little difference between $c(h_N^i, e)$ and $c(h_E^i, e)$, and might therefore suggest a very cautious bet: he would regard a high bet on Einstein's theory against Newton's, under these circumstances, as a bet on a mere hunch.

Now the interesting point is that although a Carnapian might be prevented by the weak atheoretical thesis from taking theories (and their refutations) into account in calculating c-values, he may suggest that it would be wise in such cases to ignore the calculated 'rational betting quotient' and rather bet on the 'hunch'. Carnap himself explains that 'it is true that many non-rational factors affect the scientist's choice, and I believe that this will always be the case. The influence of some of these factors may be undesirable, for instance a bias in favour of a hypothesis previously maintained publicly or, in the case of a hypothesis in social science, a bias caused by moral or political preferences. But there are also non-rational factors whose effect is important and fruitful; for example, the influence of the "scientific instinct or hunch". Inductive logic does not intend to eliminate factors of *this* kind. Its function is merely to give the scientist a clearer picture of the situation by demonstrating to what degree the various hypotheses considered are confirmed by the evidence: This logical picture supplied by inductive logic will (or should) influence the scientist, but it does not uniquely determine his decision of the choice of hypothesis. He will be helped in this decision in the same way a tourist is helped by a good map. If he uses inductive logic, the decision still remains his; it will however, be an enlightened decision rather than a more or less blind one'[1].

But if inductive logicians agree that 'hunches' may frequently overrule the exact rules of inductive logic, is it not misleading in the extreme to stress the rule-like, exact, quantitative character of inductive logic?

Of course, the inductive judge, instead of abdicating his resposibilities to the scientist's hunches, may try to strengthen his legal code. He may construct an inductive logic that throws the atheoretical thesis overboard and makes his judgments dependent on the theories proposed in the field. But then he would have to grade these theories according to their trustworthiness prior to constructing his main c-function [2]. If this falls through, he again will have no alternative but to ask the scientist to provide him

---

[1] 'Inductive Logic and Science', *Proceedings of the American Academy of Arts and Sciences*, **80**, 1953, pp. 195–6. Of course, some scientists may protest against calling even an untested speculation a 'non-rational factor' in prediction-appraisal; though perhaps they would not mind taking it to be a 'non-empirical factor'.

[2] Indeed, Carnap, in one of his new and yet unpublished systems, has already made a first step in this direction. He is referring to this system in his reply to Putnam: 'In inductive logic, we might consider treating the postulates although they are generally synthetic, as "almost analytic" ([Logical Foundations of Probability, 1950], D58–1a), i.e., assigning to them the m-value 1. In this connection it is to be noted that only the fundamental principles of theoretical physics would be taken as postulates, no other physical laws even if they are "well established". What about those laws which are not logical consequences of the postulates, but are "proposed" in Putnam's sense? In my form of inductive logic I would assign to them the m-value 0 (for another alternative see my comments on (10), § 26 III); but their instance confirmation may be positive. As mentioned earlier, we could alternatively consider here, in analogy to Putnam's idea, making the rules such that the d.c. of a singular prediction would be influenced not only by the form of the language and thereby by the postulates, but also by the class of proposed laws. At the present moment, however, I am not yet certain whether this would be necessary.' (Schilpp (ed.): *The Philosophy of Rudolf Carnap*, 1963, pp. 988–9; for his reference to '(10), § 26 III' cp. *ibid.*, p. 977).

with these grades. If the inductive judge, in addition, recognizes that one cannot take (as Carnap may have hoped originally) evidence statements as at least practically certain [1], then he will have to ask the scientist for still more information about his hunches: he will have to ask also for the scientist's (changing) degrees of belief attached to each evidence statement.

Indeed, this further step was inevitable. After Popper's 1934 argument concerning the theoretical character of 'basic statements' there could be no doubt that any evidence statement was theoretical [2]. To insist on their 'molecular' character is misleading: in a 'correct' language all 'observation statements' appear as logically universal statements, whose 'trustworthiness' would have to be measured by the 'trustworthiness' of the background theories to which they belong [3]. And this trustworthiness may occasionally be remarkably low: whole bodies of accepted evidence statements may be overthrown when a new theory throws new light on the facts. The growth of the body of 'evidence statements' is no more cumulative and peaceful than the growth of explanatory theories.

But then, in the light of these considerations, the following picture emerges. The weak atheoretical thesis has collapsed. Either (1) the atheoretical c-functions have to be overruled in each single case by the scientist's hunches or else (2) new 'theoretical' c-functions must be constructed. The latter case again gives rise to two possibilities: either (2a) a method can be designed to provide

---

[1] Not that Carnap would not have preferred to find a way to deal with uncertain evidence: 'For many years I have tried in vain to correct this flaw in the customary procedure of inductive logic . . .' (Cp. his 'On rules of acceptance', *this volume*, p. 146).

[2] Keynes still thought that inductive logic *had* to be based on the *certainty* of evidence statements; if evidence statements are inevitably uncertain, inductive logic is pointless (cp. his *Treatise on Probability*, 1921, p. 11). The need for taking into account the uncertainty of evidence statements in inductive logic was first mooted by Hempel and Oppenheim ('A definition of "degree of confirmation" ', *Philosophy of Science*, 12, 1945, pp. 114–5), but only Jeffrey made the first concrete step in this direction (cp. his 'Probable Knowledge', *this volume*, pp. 166–80).

[3] For further discussion of this point cp. my 'Criticism and the methodology of scientific research programmes', *loc. cit.*

both a 'prior' *c*-function (that is a function assessing the trust-worthiness of theories prior to the construction of the final language) and the 'proper' *c*-function for calculating the degree of confirmation of the 'particular' statements of the final language: or, (*2b*) if such a method cannot be designed, the new 'theoretical' *c*-function will have to depend on the scientist's hunches about the trustworthiness of his languages, theories, evidence and about the rational speed of the learning process. But in this case (*2b*), it is no business of the inductive judge to criticize these 'hunches'; for him these are data about the scientist's *beliefs*. His judgment will be: if *your* beliefs (rational or irrational) about languages, theories, evidence, etc., are such and such, then *my* inductive intuition provides you with a calculus of 'coherent' beliefs about all the other hypotheses within the given framework.

There is really not much to choose between an 'atheoretical' inductive logic whose verdicts are to be freely overruled by the scientist's theoretical considerations (which fall beyond its legislation) on the one hand, and, on the other, a 'theoretical' inductive logic which is based on theoretical considerations fed in from outside. In both cases the inductive judge abdicates his historic responsibilities [1]. All that he can do is to keep coherent the scientist's beliefs; so that if the scientist should bet on his beliefs against a shrewd and inimical divine bookmaker, he would not lose merely because his betting system was incoherent. The abdication of the inductive judge is complete. He promised to hand down judgment on the rationality of beliefs; now he is ending up by trying to supply a calculus of coherent beliefs on whose rationality he cannot pronounce. The inductive judge cannot claim any longer to be a 'guide of life' in any relevant sense.

(Carnapians, while accepting the gist of this evaluation, may not regard all this as a failure. They may argue that what is happening is perfectly analogous to what happened in the history of deductive logic: originally it was devised for *proving* propositions and only later had to confine itself to *deducing* propositions from others. Deductive logic was originally intended to establish both firm

---

[1] Nobody has yet tried (*2a*); and I bet nobody will.

truth-values and also safe channels for their transmission; the fact that it had to abdicate proving and concentrate on deducing liberated its energy rather than clipped its wings and reduced it to irrelevance. Inductive logic was originally intended to establish both objective, rational degrees of beliefs and their rational coordination; now, forsaking the former and concentrating wholly on the 'rational' coordination of subjective beliefs, it can still claim to be *a* guide of life. I do not think this argument holds water but I have little doubt that it will be taken up and eagerly and ingeniously defended.)

With the abdication of the inductive judge even the last tenuous threads are severed between inductive logic and the problem of induction. A mere calculus of coherent beliefs can at best have marginal significance relative to the central problem of the philosophy of science. Thus, in the course of the evolution of the research programme of inductive logic its problem has become much less interesting than the original one: the historian of thought may have to record a 'degenerating problem-shift'.

This is not to say that there are no interesting problems to which Carnap's calculus might apply. In some betting situations the basic beliefs may be specified as the 'rules of the game'. Thus (*1*) a language *L* may be laid down which is 'correct' by decree: indirect evidence is excluded as violating the rules of the game; (*2*) nothing may be permitted to influence the events from unspecified, not previously agreed, sources – such influence constitutes a breach of the rules; (*3*) there may be an absolutely mechanical decision procedure for establishing the truth-values of the evidence statements. If conditions such as these are fulfilled, inductive logic may provide useful service. And, indeed, these three conditions are essentially fulfilled in some standard betting situations. We could call such betting situations '*closed games*'. (It can easily be checked that the Ramsey–De Finetti–Shimony theorem applies only to such 'closed games'.) But if science is a game, it is an *open game*. Carnap was mistaken in claiming that the difference between the usual (closed) games of chance and science was only in degree of complexity [1].

---

[1] Cp. his *Logical Foundations of Probability*, 1950, p. 247.

Carnap's theory may also apply to 'closed statistical problems', where for practical purposes both the 'correctness' of the language and the certainty of the evidence may be taken for granted.

The programme of inductive logic was overambitious. The gap between rationality and formal rationality has not narrowed quite as much since Leibniz as Carnapians seem to have thought. Leibniz dreamt of a machine to decide whether a hypothesis was true or false. Carnap would have been content with a machine to decide whether the choice of a hypothesis was rational or irrational. But there is no Turing machine to decide either on the truth of our conjectures or on the rationality of our preference.

There is then an urgent need to look again at those fields in which the inductive judge has abdicated his responsibilities: first of all, at problems concerning the appraisal of theories. Solutions to these problems had been offered by Popper – even before Carnap started his programme. These solutions are methodologically oriented and unformalizable. But if relevance is not to be sacrificed on the altar of precision, the time has come to pay more attention to them.

Moreover, it will be shown with the help of Popper's approach that the appraisal of theories has a fine structure unnoticed by Carnap; and that, using this fine structure, one can offer a rival even to Carnap's theory of rational betting quotients for particular hypotheses. But the difference between the Popperian and the Carnapian approach cannot be put simply as a difference between different solutions of the same problem. Solving the problem interestingly always involves reformulating it, putting it in a fresh light. In other words: an interesting solution always *shifts* the problem. *Rival solutions of a problem frequently imply rival problem-shifts.* The discussion of the rival Popperian problem-shift will also throw further light on Carnap's problem-shift. As Carnap and his school shifted the original centre of gravity of the problem of induction away from informality to formality, away from methodo-logy to justification, away from genuine theories to particular propositions, away from evidential support to betting quotients, so Popper and his school shifted it in exactly the opposite direction.

3. *The one main problem of critical empiricism: method.*

While neoclassical empiricism inherited from classical empiricism only the problem of a monolithic, all-purpose appraisal of hypotheses, Popper's critical empiricism focussed attention on the problem of their discovery. The Popperian scientist makes *separate* appraisals corresponding to the separate stages of discovery. I shall use these methodological appraisals ('acceptability$_1$', 'acceptability$_2$', etc.) to construct an appraisal even of the *trustworthiness* of a theory ('acceptability$_3$'). This 'acceptability$_3$' comes closest to Carnap's degree of confirmation. But since it is based on Popper's *methodological* appraisals, I shall first have to discuss these at some length.

3.1. *'Acceptability$_1$'.*

The first, prior appraisal of a theory immediately follows its proposal: we appraise its *'boldness'*. One of the most important aspects of 'boldness' may be characterized in terms of *'excess empirical content'* [1], or, briefly, *'excess content'* (or *'excess information'* or *'excess falsifiability'*): a bold theory should have some novel potential falsifiers which none of the theories in the extant body of science has had; in particular, it should have excess content over its *'background theory'* (or its *'touchstone theory'*), that is, over the theory it challenges.

The background theory may not have been articulated at the time when the new theory is proposed; but in such cases it can easily be reconstructed. Also, the background theory may be a double or even a multiple theory in the following sense: if the relevant background knowledge consists of a theory T_1 and of a falsifying hypothesis T'_1 of it, then a challenging theory T_2 is bold only *if it entails some novel factual hypothesis* which had not been entailed either by T_1 or T'_1 [2].

---

[1] For the all-important concept of 'empirical content' cp. Popper: *The Logic of Scientific Discovery*, 1934, § 35: the empirical content of a theory is its set of 'potential falsifiers'. Incidentally, Popper, with his two 1934 theses that (*1*) the empirical information a sentence conveys is the set of states of affairs which it forbids and that (*2*) this information can be measured by improbability rather than probability, founded the semantic theory of information.

[2] My 'background theory' and 'background knowledge' should not be

A theory is the bolder the more it revolutionizes our previous picture of the world: for instance, the more surprisingly it unites fields of knowledge previously regarded as distant and unconnected; and even possibly the 'more inconsistent' it is with the 'data' or with the 'laws' it set out to explain (so that if Newton's theory had not been inconsistent with Kepler's and Galileo's laws, which it set out to explain, Popper would give it a lower grade for boldness [1]).

If a theory is judged 'bold', scientists '$accept_1$' it as a part of the 'body of science' of the day. On acceptance into the body of science several things may happen to the theory. Some may try to criticize it, test it; some may try to explain it; others may use it in the determination of the truth-values of potential falsifiers of other theories; and even technologists may take it into consideration. But above all, this $acceptance_1$ is acceptance for serious criticism, and in particular for testing: it is a certificate of testworthiness. If a 'testworthy' theory is explained by a new 'bold' higher level theory, or if some other theory is falsified with its help, or again, if it becomes shortlisted for technological use, then its testing becomes still more urgent.

We may call $acceptance_1$ *'prior acceptance'* since it is *prior* to testing. But it is *usually not prior to evidence*: most scientific theories are designed, at least partly, to solve an explanatory problem.

One may be tempted to characterise the boldness of a theory merely by its 'degree of falsifiability' or 'empirical content', that is, by the set of its potential falsifiers. But if a new theory T_2 explains some available evidence already explained by some extant

---

confused with Popper's 'background knowledge'. Popper's 'background knowledge' denotes 'all those things which we accept (tentatively) as *unproblematic* while we are testing the theory', such as initial conditions, auxiliary theories, etc. etc. (*Conjectures and Refutations*, 1963, p. 390, my italics). My 'background theory' is *inconsistent* with the tested theory, Popper's is *consistent* with it.

[1] Popper calls such 'fact-correcting' explanations *'deep'* – which is another word for a certain type of outstanding boldness (cp. his 'The aim of science', *Ratio*, 1, 1957, p. 29). It goes without saying that it is impossible to compare at all, let alone numerically, 'degrees' of 'depth'.

theory T_1, the 'boldness' of T_2 is gauged not simply by the set of potential falsifiers of T_2 but by the set of those potential falsifiers of T_2 which had not been potential falsifiers also of T_1. A theory which has no more potential falsifiers than its background theory has then at most zero 'excess falsifiability'. Newton's theory of gravitation has very high excess falsifiability over the conjunction of its background theories (Galileo's theory of terrestrial projectiles and Kepler's theory of planetary motions): therefore it was bold, it was scientific. However, a theory akin to Newton's theory, but applying to all gravitational phenomena except the orbit of Mercury has negative excess empirical content over Newton's original, unrestricted theory: therefore this theory, proposed after the refutation of Newton's theory, is not bold, is not scientific. *It is excess empirical content, that is, the increase in empirical content, rather than empirical content as such, that measures the boldness of the theory.* Clearly, one cannot decide whether a theory is bold by examining the theory in isolation, but only by examining it in its historico-methodological context, against the background of its available rivals.

Popper proposed in 1957 that theories should not only be 'testable' (that is, falsifiable) but also 'independently testable', that is, they should have 'testable consequences which are different from the *explicandum*' [1]. This requirement, of course, corresponds to 'boldness' as here defined: it suggests that in the prior appraisal of theories falsifiability should be supplemented by excess falsifiability.

But it transpires already from his *Logic of Scientific Discovery*, 1934, that falsifiability without excess falsifiability is of little importance. His demarcation criterion draws a line between 'refutable' (scientific) and 'irrefutable' (metaphysical) theories. But he uses 'refutable' in a rather Pickwickian sense: he calls a theory T 'refutable' if *two* conditions are satisfied: (*1*) if it has some 'potential falsifiers', that is, one can specify statements conflicting with it whose truth-value can be established by some generally accepted

---

[1] 'The aim of science', *Ratio*, 1, 1957, p. 25; also cp. his *Conjectures and Refutations*, 1963, p. 241.

experimental technique of the time [1], and (2) if the discussion
partners agree not to use 'conventionalist stratagems' [2], that is,
not to replace T, following its refutation, by a theory T' which
has less content than T. This usage, although explained very
clearly in several sections of Popper's *Logic of Scientific Discovery*,
is responsible for many misunderstandings [3].

My terminology is different, and nearer to ordinary usage. I call
a theory 'refutable' if it satisfies Popper's *first* condition. Corre-
spondingly, I call a theory *acceptable₁ if it has excess refutability*
over its background theory. This criterion stresses the Popperian
idea that it is growth that is the crucial characteristic of science.
The crucial characteristics of growing science are excess content rather
than content, and, as we shall see, excess corroboration rather than
corroboration.

We must distinguish carefully between the concept of boldness,
based on Popper's 1957 concept of independent testability, and
Popper's 1934 concept of testability or scientificness. According
to his 1934 criterion a theory, arrived at, after the refutation of
its background theory, by a 'content-decreasing stratagem' [4] may
still be 'scientific', if it is agreed that this procedure will not be
repeated. But such a theory is not independently testable, not
bold: according to my model it cannot be accepted (accepted₁) into
the body of science.

It should be mentioned that Popper's Pickwickian usage of 'refutability' leads to some queer formulations. For instance, according
to Popper, 'once a theory is refuted, its empirical character is
secure and shines without blemish' [5]. But what about Marxism?
Popper, correctly, says that it is *refuted* [6]. He also holds, in his

---

[1] For further discussion of this condition cp. my 'Criticism and the
methodology of scientific researchprogrammes', *loc. cit.*

[2] Cp. his *Logic of Scientific Discovery*, 1934, §§ 19–20.

[3] For the clearest discussion of Popper's demarcation criterion cp.
Musgrave, 'On a demarcation dispute', in Lakatos–Musgrave (eds.): *Problems
in the Philosophy of Science*, 1968, pp. 78 ff.

[4] I prefer this term to Popper's term 'conventionalist stratagem'.

[5] *Conjectures and Refutations*, 1963, p. 240.

[6] *Ibid.*, pp. 37 and 333.

usage correctly, that it is *irrefutable* [1], that it has lost its empirical character because its defenders, after each refutation, produce a new version of it with *reduced empirical content*. Thus in Popper's usage irrefutable theories may be refuted. But of course, content-reducing stratagems do not, in the ordinary sense of the term, make a *theory* 'irrefutable': they make rather *a series of theories* (or a 'research programme') irrefutable. The series, of course, consists of non-bold theories and represents a degenerative problem-shift; but it still contains *conjectures and refutations* – in the 'logical' sense of 'refutations'.

Finally, let me say that I also tried to avoid the possibly misleading expression 'degree' of excess falsifiability or of falsifiability. In general, as Popper frequently stresses, the (absolute) empirical contents of two theories are not comparable. One can state in the case of rival theories that one has excess content as compared with the other, but again, the excess is in no sense measurable. If one grants, with Popper, that all theories have equal logical probability, namely zero, logical probability cannot show the difference between the empirical content of theories. Moreover, a theory T_2, of course, may have excess content relative to T_1 while its (absolute) content may be much less than that of T_1; also, T_2 may be bold relative to T_1 and T_1 at the same time bold relative to T_2. Thus boldness is a binary, transitive but not antisymmetrical relation (a 'pre-ordering') among theories. However, we might agree to say that 'T_2 has higher empirical content than T_1' if and only if T_2 has excess empirical content over T_1 but not *vice versa*. Then *'has higher empirical content than'* is a partial ordering relation, although *'bold'* is not.

3.2. *'Acceptability₂'*.

Bold theories undergo *severe tests*. The 'severity' of tests is assessed by the difference between the likeliness of the positive outcome of the test in the light of our theory and the likeliness of its positive outcome in the light of some rival 'touchstone theory' (already articulated in the extant body of science, or only articulated on

---

[1] *Ibid.*, pp. 34–5 and 333.

the proposal of the new theory). Then there are only two types of 'severe' tests: (1) those which refute the theory under test by 'corroborating' [1] a falsifying hypothesis of it and (2) those which corroborate it while refuting the falsifying hypothesis. If all the hundreds of millions of ravens on earth had been observed and all had been found to be black, these observations would still not add up to a single severe test of the theory A: 'All ravens are black': the 'degree of corroboration' of A would still be zero. In order to test A severely one must use some 'bold' (and, still better, some already corroborated) touchstone theory, say, A': 'a specified substance a injected into the liver of birds always turns their feathers white without changing any other genetic characteristic'. Now if a, injected in ravens, turns them white, A is refuted (but A' corroborated). If it does not, A is corroborated (but A' refuted) [2]. Indeed, in Popper's ruthless society of theories, where the law is the (shortlived) survival of the fittest, a theory can become a hero only through murder. A theory becomes testworthy on presenting a threat to some extant theory; it becomes 'well-tested' when it has proved its mettle by producing a new fact that realises the threat and liquidates a rival.

This Popperian jungle contrasts starkly with Carnap's civilised society of theories. The latter is a peaceful welfare state of fallible but respectably aging theories, reliable (according to their qualified instance confirmation) to different but always positive degrees, which are registered daily with pedantic precision in the office of the inductive judge. Murders are unknown – theories may be undermined but never refuted [3].

---

[1]   The definition of 'corroboration' follows *below*, p. 381.

[2]   It is clear from this that there is nothing psychologistic about 'severity'.

[3]   It is another characteristic example of the 'dramatic' air of Popper's theory that while he would regard the first observation of relativistic light deflection in 1919 as a severe test of Einstein's theory, he does not regard repetitions of the 'same' test as severe (since the result of the first test has now become background knowledge), and does not allow them to contribute to the corroboration achieved by the first test (cp. his *Logic of Scientific Discovery*, 1934, § 83). Popper rejects slow inductive 'learning$_{ind}$', which is based on long chains of evidence: in a dramatic 'learning$_{popp}$' process one learns in a flash.

Bold theories, after having been severely tested, undergo a second 'posterior' appraisal. A theory is *'corroborated'* if it has defeated *some* falsifying hypothesis, that is, if *some* consequence of the theory survives a severe test. It then becomes 'accepted$_2$' in the body of science. A theory is *'strictly corroborated at time t'* if it has been severely tested and not refuted in any test up to time t [1].

A severe test of T relative to a touchstone theory T' tests, by definition, the *excess* content of T over T'. But then *a theory T is corroborated relative to T' if its excess* content *over T' is corroborated, or if it has 'excess corroboration' over its touchstone theory.* We may also say that *a theory is corroborated or accepted$_2$ if it is shown to entail some novel facts* [2]. Thus, just as 'acceptability$_1$' is related to excess content, 'acceptability$_2$' is related to excess corroboration. This, of course, is in keeping with the (Popperian) idea that it is the progressing problematic frontiers of knowledge, and not its relatively solid core, which give science its scientific character; according to justificationism it is just the other way round.

Just as T_2 may have excess content over T_1 and *vice versa*, T_2 may have excess corroboration over T_1 and *vice versa*. Excess corroboration, like boldness, is a transitive but not an anti-symmetrical relation. However, just as we defined a partial ordering on the basis of the pre-ordering 'has higher content than', we may define a partial ordering on the basis of the pre-ordering 'has excess corroboration over': *'T_2 has a higher degree of corroboration than T_1'* if T_2 has excess corroboration over T_1 but not *vice versa* [3].

Popper's 1934 concept of the severity of a test of T was related to the concept of a sincere effort to overthrow T. In 1959 he still

---

[1] The two concepts are somewhat different. Popper's 'well-tested' is closer to my 'strictly corroborated'. Cp. *below*, p. 385.

[2] Or, more precisely, some novel factual hypotheses which stand up to severe tests.

[3] According to these definitions, T_2 may have 'higher degree of corroboration than' T_1 but T_1 may be 'bold' with respect to T_2 – although T_1 cannot have 'higher content than' T_2. I indulge in these pedantries if only to show how absurd it is to dream of an all-purpose monolithic appraisal of theories.

wrote: 'The requirement of sincerity cannot be formalised' [1]. But in 1963 he said that 'the severity of our tests can be objectively compared; and if we like, we can define a measure of their severity' [2]. He defined severity as the difference between the likelihood of the predicted effect in the light of the theory under test together with background knowledge *and* the likelihood of the predicted effect in the light of background knowledge only, where Popper's 'background knowledge' is, unlike my 'background knowledge', the *unproblematic* knowledge we assume while testing [3]. That is, while my degree of severity of a test-evidence e of a theory T relative to a touchstone theory T' might be symbolised by $p(e, T) - p(e, T')$, Popper's degree of severity of e of T relative to unproblematic background knowledge b might be symbolised by $p(e, T \& b) - p(e, b)$. In my interpretation initial conditions are *part* of a theory; indeed, Popper's b is part both of my T and of my T'. The difference is only very slight; my definition, I think, gives an additional stress to the Popperian idea that methodological concepts should be related to competitive growth. Thus for Popper a novel test *of Einstein's theory* may be 'severe' even if its result also corroborates Newton's theory. In my framework such a test is a 'severe' test *of Newton's* rather than Einstein's theory. But in both formulations the degree of severity of a test depends on the extant body of science, on some conception of the available background knowledge.

The scientist '$accepts_2$' a theory for the *same* purposes as he $accepted_1$ the bold theory before the tests. But $acceptance_2$ lends an added distinction to the theory. An $accepted_2$ theory is then regarded as a supreme challenge to the critical ingenuity of the best scientists: Popper's starting point and his paradigm of scientific achievement was the overthrow and replacement of Newtonian physics. (Indeed, it would be very much in the spirit of Popper's philosophy to issue only temporary certificates of acceptance: if a theory is accepted₁ but does not become accepted₂ within n years,

---

[1] *The Logic of Scientific Discovery*, 1959, p. 418.

[2] *Conjectures and Refutations*, 1963, p. 388.

[3] Cp. *above*, p. 375, footnote 2.

it is eliminated; if a theory is accepted$_2$ but has had no lethal duels for a period of m years, it is also eliminated.)

It also follows from the definitions of acceptance$_1$ and acceptance$_2$ that a theory may be accepted$_1$ but already, at the time of its acceptance, be known to be false. Again, a theory may be accepted$_2$ but may have failed *some* severe tests. That is, one should accept bold theories into the body of science whether or not they have been refuted. One should accept them for further criticism, for further testing, for the purpose of explaining them etc., at least *as long as* there is no new bold superseding theory. This methodology allows the 'body of science' to be inconsistent, since some theories may be 'accepted$_1$', together with their falsifying hypotheses. Thus consistency (and, in view of 'acceptance$_0$', refutability [1]) should be construed as a regulative principle rather than a precondition of acceptance. (An important consequence of this consideration is that since the body of science may be inconsistent, it cannot be an object of rational belief. This is yet another argument for Popper's thesis that 'belief-philosophy' has nothing to do with the philosophy of science.)

The rule – 'keep testing and explaining even a refuted theory until it is superseded by a better one' – suggests a counterpart to our criteria of acceptance: a theory T_1 is '*superseded*' and *eliminated* from the body of science ('*rejected$_1$*') on the appearance of a new theory which has corroborated excess content over T_1 while T_1 has no corroborated excess content over T_2 [2].

A bold theory always challenges some theory in the extant body

---

[1]   Theories like the conservation principles, which are not 'bold' in our technical sense, and may not even be testable, may also be accepted ('*accepted$_0$*') into the body of science as regulative principles or scientific research programmes. For detailed discussion and literature on this '*acceptance$_0$*' cp. my 'Criticism and the methodology of scientific research programmes', *loc. cit.* (Three similar 'acceptances' are discussed by J. Giedymin, in his 'Empiricism, refutability, rationality', in Lakatos–Musgrave (eds.): *Problems in the Philosophy of Science*, 1968, pp. 70 ff.)

[2]   The 'rules of elimination' may be varied; their actual form does not matter much. But *it is vital that there be some procedures for eliminating theories from the body of science* in order to save it from following for too long a track that may lead nowhere.

of science; but the *supreme* challenge is when it not only claims that the challenged theory is false but that it can explain all the truth-content of the challenged theory. Thus *refutation alone is not sufficient reason to eliminate the challenged theory.*

Because of deeply ingrained justificationist prejudices against refuted theories, scientists frequently play down refuting instances and do not take a falsifying hypothesis seriously before the latter gets embedded into a higher-order rival theory which explains also the partial success of the refuted theory. Until then falsifying hypotheses are usually kept out of the *public* body of science. But it also happens that a theory is publicly refuted though not yet replaced: the theory, known to be false, continues to be explained and tested. In such cases the theory is officially recorded as one which, in its extant version, applies only to 'ideal' or 'normal' etc. cases, and the falsifying hypotheses – if mentioned are recorded as 'anomalies' [1].

But such 'ideal', 'normal' cases, of course, frequently do not even exist. For instance it was always known that 'ideal' hydrogen 'models' like the ones described by Bohr's first theory do not exist – not to mention 'models' in economic theories. But this shows that theories rarely pass severe tests of their new content with flying colours; even some of the best theories may never get 'strictly

---

[1]   A detailed heuristic analysis of such situations is to be found in my 'Proofs and Refutations', *loc. cit.*, and in my 'Criticism and the methodology of scientific research programmes', *loc. cit.* One of the *leitmotivs* of my 'Proofs and Refutations' is that a refuted hypothesis may not be expelled from the body of science: that, for instance, *one may bravely – and profitably – go on to 'explain' a hypothesis known to be false.* My original case study was taken from informal mathematics but only to show that such patterns are characteristic not only of the growth of science but also of the growth of mathematics.

One may use the expression 'explain T_1 with the help of T_2' in the sense of 'explain with the help of T_2 what looks like the truth-content of T_1 in the light of T_2'. The semantics of ordinary language is unsuitable in discussing these matters, since it is based on false theories of scientific growth according to which one only explains what are alleged to be true reports of facts. Agassi's 'Sensationalism' (*Mind*, N.S., **75**, 1966) also discusses this problem.

corroborated' [1]. But such theories, even if in a strict sense they fail all their tests, may have some of their excess empirical content, namely some weaker but still interesting consequences, corroborated; thus they may still entail novel facts and thus be accepted$_2$. For instance, Bohr's first theories of the hydrogen atom were immediately falsified by the fact that spectral lines were multiplets [2]; but the subsequent discovery of Lyman's, Brackett's, and Pfund's series corroborated, and indeed, strictly corroborated, the weaker but still novel, previously undreamt of, consequence of Bohr's theory that there are spectral lines in the immediate neighbourhood of predicted wavelengths. Theories, while failing all their tests quantitatively, frequently pass some of them 'qualitatively': and if they lead to novel facts, then according to our definition they can still be 'accepted$_2$'.

[According to Popper's definition of corroboration a theory is *either* corroborated *or* refuted. But even some of the best theories have failed to be corroborated by Popper's austere 'strict' standards; indeed, most theories are born refuted.]

These considerations make us revise our previous criterion of *elimination* of a theory from the body of science [3]. Refutation is definitely not *sufficient* for the elimination of a theory – but its becoming 'superseded' by a more powerful theory is not *necessary* either. For if a theory, however bold, has no excess corroboration, that is, if it entails no novel *facts* [4], we may eliminate it from the body of science without its becoming superseded by a challenger. But, of course, it may be much more difficult to establish that a

---

[1]   A theory is 'strictly corroborated' if it is corroborated but has not been refuted (cp. *above*, p. 381).

[2]   The 'fine structure' of the hydrogen spectrum – amounting to a refutation both of Balmer's series and of Bohr's first models – was discovered by Michelson in 1891, twenty-two years before the publication of Bohr's theory.

[3]   Cp. *above*, p. 383.

[4]   It should be stressed again that we never *know* that a theory entails novel facts. All we may know is that it entails novel corroborated hypotheses. Corroborated hypotheses are the fallible (epistemological-methodological) counterparts of (ontological) facts; corroborated hypotheses may not be 'truly corroborated'.

theory is in this sense 'fully refuted' (in the sense that *all* its novel consequences are refuted) than to establish that it is corroborated, that is, that at least *one* of its novel consequences is corroborated. It is easier to establish acceptance$_2$ than this (full) rejection$_2$.

Acceptance$_2$ then draws a methodologically important demarcation between bold theories: while a first-class (accepted$_2$) theory is eliminated from the body of science only when it is superseded by a bold new theory, a second-class theory (with no excess corroboration) is eliminated on mere refutation, there being nothing in it that had not been explained before: the (putative) truth-content of the body of science will not be decreased by such 'rejections$_2$', just as it will not be decreased by 'rejections$_1$'. A theory without excess corroboration has no excess explanatory power [1].

All this serves as a good illustration of the Popperian problem-shift: the decisive difference between the corroboration and the refutation of a theory is primarily a matter for the logic of discovery and not for the logic of justification. *Thus one may accept$_1$ and accept$_2$ theories even if they are known to be false, but reject (reject$_1$) theories even if there is no evidence against them* [2]. This conception of acceptance and rejection is a feature totally alien to the classical outlook. We accept theories if they indicate *growth* in truth-content ('progressive problem-shift'); we reject them if they do not ('degenerative problem-shift'). This provides us with rules for acceptance and rejection even if we assume that all the theories we shall ever put forward will be false.

---

[1]   Incidentally, it is interesting that for universal propositions Popper's formulae for explanatory power and for degree of corroboration coincide: one gets the formula for degree of corroboration by multiplying the formula for explanatory power by $1+p(h)p(h, e)$. But $p(h)$ for universal propositions, according to Popper, is zero. Therefore if e is interpreted as the total *test*-evidence, explanatory power and degree of corroboration will become synonymous. (Cp. Popper: *The Logic of Scientific Discovery*, 1959, p. 401).

[2]   Perhaps at this point we should mention that the 'body of science' as a body of deductively perfectly organised theories with crystal clear rules of acceptance$_1$ and acceptance$_2$, rejection$_1$ and rejection$_2$, is an *abstraction*. I neither assume that such a 'body of science' has existed at any time or that even as an abstraction it is useful for *all* purposes. For many purposes, it is better to construe science – as Popper stresses in his later philosophy – rather as a *body of problems* than a body of theories.

One of the most important features of the two methodological appraisals of theories is their *'historical character'* [1]. They depend on the state of background knowledge: the prior appraisal on the background knowledge at the time of the proposal of the theory and the posterior appraisal also on the background knowledge at the time of each test.

The 'historical character' of these appraisals has interesting implications. For instance, a theory explaining three hitherto seemingly unrelated lower level well-corroborated theories but nothing more would have no excess empirical content over the conjunction of its predecessors, and therefore both its prior and posterior appraisal may turn out to be unfavourable. But if the theory had followed the first two lower level theories but preceded the third, it would have had 'excess falsifiability' and would also have had excess corroboration; it would have ranked high on both counts. The Bohr–Kramers–Slater theory ranked high on the first appraisal but it failed its first test and never became corroborated. But had it been put forward earlier, it could have survived a few first tests and thus it would have gained also high posterior ranking before its death [2]. Agassi points out that such examples indicate

---

[1] After having stated that prior and posterior appraisal are mere corollaries to methodology, this should be no surprise. Methodology is wedded to history, since methodology is nothing but a rational reconstruction of history, of the growth of knowledge. Because of the imperfection of the scientists, some of the actual history is a caricature of its rational reconstruction; because of the imperfection of the methodologists, some methodologies are caricatures of actual history. (And, one may add, because of the imperfection of historians, some histories of science are caricatures both of actual history and of its rational reconstruction.)

[2] Similarly, the theory T_0, that at dusk flying saucers fly over Hampstead Heath is, I guess, 'fully refuted' if put forward in 1967. But let us imagine that we have never before seen any flying objects – animate or inanimate; and that according to our theories it is *impossible* that objects should fly. Now if T_0 is put forward in such historical circumstances and is carefully tested, it might well be corroborated by the observation of some flying owls. The theory then has led to the discovery of a revolutionary new fact: that there exist (well specifiable) flying objects. Flying saucers would have entered the history of science rather as Newton's forces acting at a distance did.

that the second appraisal – at least in some cases – may remunerate a 'prior' virtue of the theory, namely that it was proposed boldly and *quickly*, before its whole true 'factual' content was discovered without its stimulus [1]. One might have thought that while a positive prior appraisal indirectly applauds the inventor of the theory, a positive posterior appraisal can show nothing but his luck; one can aim at bold theories but one cannot *aim* at well-corroborated theories. It is up to us to devise bold theories; it is up to Nature whether to corroborate or to refute them. But Agassi's analysis shows that this is not *entirely* correct: the bolder the theory, the more chance it has of excess corroboration. Thus *prior and posterior appraisal appraise conjointly the growth of our knowledge produced by the theories rather than the theories in themselves.*

Popper never actually introduced the requirement of 'acceptability$_2$'; nevertheless, 'acceptability$_2$' is only an improved version of his new *'third requirement'* that a satisfactory theory should pass some independent tests *and* should not fail on the *first* one [2]. It was careless of Popper to attach importance to the *first* test being failed.

Popper's supporting arguments can also, I think, be improved. In order to do so, let me first contrast *two models of scientific growth.*

In the *'Popperian model'* the growth of science is regulated by the rules of acceptance and rejection as outlined above. The *'Agassite model'* differs from this in one single aspect: complete lack of excess corroboration is no reason for rejection$_2$, and if a theory explains all the truth-content of its predecessor, it may 'supersede' it even without having excess corroboration.

Now let us take the following sequence of theories and refutations:

(*1*)   A major theory T_0, accepted$_2$, is refuted by a minor falsifying hypothesis f_1, which is also accepted$_2$ [3]. The (relevant part of the) body of science in both models consists of T_0 and f_1.

---

[1]   Cp. his most interesting paper on 'The role of corroboration in Popper's methodology', *The Australasian Journal of Philosophy*, **39**, 1961, pp. 87–8.

[2]   *Conjectures and Refutations*, 1963, pp. 240–48.

[3]   'Major' means comprehensive, having a huge content; 'minor' means a low-level, factual hypothesis.

(2) T_1 is proposed. T_1 is bold, explains all the truth-content of T_0 as well as f_1; its excess content is e_1. But e_1 is 'fully refuted', T_1 is rejected$_2$. The refuting hypothesis is f_2 and it is accepted$_2$.

In the Popperian model the body of science now consists of T_0, f_1, f_2. In the Agassite model it consists of T_1 and f_2.

(3) T_2 is proposed. T_2 is bold, explains all the truth-content of T_1 as well as f_2; its excess content is e_2. But e_2 is 'fully refuted', T_2 is rejected$_2$. The refuting hypothesis is f_3 and it is accepted$_2$.

In the Popperian model the body of science now consists of T_0, f_1, f_2, f_3. In the Agassite model it consists of T_2 and f_3. And so on.

This shows that Popper rejects theories T_1 and T_2 as *ad hoc* [1], while Agassi does not. For Popper such growth is *pseudo-growth* which does not live up to his *ideal of growth*. He would agree that T_1 and T_2 are heuristically stimulating since they 'led' to f_2 and f_3; but according to him, in such growth theories are mere stimulants, 'mere instruments of exploration' [2]. For Popper there is no 'growth of knowledge' without at least a chance of growth in verisimilitude [3]; in the Agassite model verisimilitude seems to stagnate or even decrease in the sequence $\{T_0, T_1, T_2\}$, which, therefore, for Popper, represents a degenerating shift. The verisimilitude of the sum of the increasing number of falsifying hypotheses may of course increase; but, for Popper, this is an 'inductivist' disintegration of science into a collection of isolated phenomena.

But, following the line of Agassi's argument, let us imagine that after T_0 and f_1, T_2 is immediately proposed. T_2 will then be accepted$_1$ and also accepted$_2$, for f_2 is part of its excess content. Now why should $\{T_0, T_1, T_2\}$ represent a degenerative shift when $\{T_0, T_2\}$ represents a progressive shift?

---

[1] Popper uses his pejorative term '*ad hoc*' in two clearly distinguishable senses. A theory without excess content is '*ad hoc*' (or rather '*ad hoc*$_1$'): cp. his *Logic of Scientific Discovery*, 1934, § 19 and his *Conjectures and Refutations*, 1963, p. 241. But since 1963, he has also called a theory without excess corroboration '*ad hoc*' (or rather '*ad hoc*$_2$'): cp. his *Conjectures and Refutations*, 1963, p. 244.

[2] Cp. his *Conjectures and Refutations*, 1963, p. 248, footnote 31.

[3] In Popper's philosophy 'verisimilitude' denotes the difference between the truth-content and falsity-content of a theory. Cp. Chapter 10 of his *Conjectures and Refutations*, 1963.

The argument is interesting. But instead of being an argument *against* the 'Popperian model', it gives a final touch to its clarification. According to Popper the essence of science is growth: *fast potential growth* (acceptability$_1$) and *fast actual growth* (acceptability$_2$). Slow growth is not good enough to live up to Popper's ideal image of science. If imagination does not fly fast enough ahead of the discovery of facts, science degenerates [1]. The Popperian model exposes this degeneration, the Agassite model covers it up.

Whether science will be able to live up to these wonderful standards is, of course, a different matter. If it does, then it will have proceeded not simply through conjectures and refutations, but through (bold) *conjectures, verifications and refutations* [2].

3.3. *'Acceptability$_3$'*.

Popper's methodological appraisals contrast sharply with the classical and neoclassical tradition. Since 'ordinary' thinking and 'ordinary' language are saturated with this tradition, laymen (and also 'ordinary' philosophers and scientists) find Popper's ideas difficult to digest. No doubt, they will find my use of the term 'acceptance' for his concepts of acceptance$_1$ and acceptance$_2$ particularly idiosyncratic. What is so unusual for most people is the underlying idea that one may 'accept' a statement into the body of science before even looking at the evidence; that the degree to which it has transcended (or even negated!) the accepted evidence should count in its favour instead of to its disadvantage. Ac-

---

[1]   Mary Hesse was then wrong when she claimed that Popper's 'third requirement' was 'not consistent with the main planks of Popper's anti-inductivist position' ('Induction and theory-structure', *Review of Metaphysics*, 17, 1964, p. 118). So was, in this respect, Agassi, who, as Popper tells us, regarded Popper's third requirement as 'a residue of verificationist modes of thought'; but so was Popper, who, in spite of his right instinct, 'admitted' that 'there may be a whiff of verificationism here' (*Conjectures and Refutations*, 1963, p. 248, footnote 31). In fact, this requirement can be regarded as a main plank of Popper's anti-inductivist position, since, without it, by Popper's standards, science would degenerate into a collection of facts. Moreover this is one of the most typical examples of how independent Popper's methodology is of 'inductive' considerations.

[2]   'Verification' stands here for 'excess corroboration'.

ceptance$_1$ runs counter to the classical dogma that 'to discover is to prove', and to the neoclassical dogma that the degree of scientific 'acceptance' of a hypothesis increases when the gap between hypothesis and evidence decreases. Moreover, the idea that hypotheses which are false and even known to be false may, under certain strange conditions, be 'accepted', sounds totally incredible to traditional empiricists. Also they may find it difficult to comprehend that for acceptance$_2$ the facts which the theory was devised to explain (i.e. which had been discovered before testing began) are irrelevant; and so are all further observations unless they represent severe tests between the theory and some competitor. All this runs counter to the classical and neoclassical dogma according to which each confirming instance counts, however little [1].

But, apart from the details, Popper's spectrum of appraisals confuses the 'justificationists'. For them – whether orthodox or revisionist – there is only one unique, monolithic, all-purpose *'scientific acceptance'*: acceptance of a theory into the body of science *to the degree to which it has been proved* [2].

Such an idea has always been rejected by Popper. Nonetheless, many philosophers, even if they agree that Popper *did* open up a gamut of important appraisals, would still contend that there are vital problems for the solution of which even he needs *some* concept of *'acceptability$_3$'* ('inductive acceptability', 'trustworthiness', 'reliability', 'evidential support', 'credibility', etc.). This 'acceptability$_3$' – in whatever particular version – is required for an appraisal of the *future performance* of the theory, and it is alleged that it cannot be estimated without *some* inductive principle.

---

[1] Recently, under the influence of Popper's arguments, Hintikka constructed an inductive logic, which, in this respect – and also in some others – deviates from neoclassical dogma (cp. his 'Induction by enumeration and induction by elimination', *this volume*, pp. 191 ff.).

[2] This is the historical explanation of what Bar–Hillel very aptly calls the *'acceptance syndrome'* which results from the assumption that ' "to accept" has one unique meaning in all contexts'. The idea of degree of provenness may have been tacitly discarded by many philosophers, but the syndrome of all-purpose acceptance – 'truly amazing in its lack of sophistication' – still lingers on. (Cp. Bar–Hillel: 'The acceptance syndrome', *this volume*, pp. 150 ff.)

Acceptability$_3$ was originally the dominating aspect both of the classical and of the neoclassical all-purpose appraisal. A theory was 'accepted' primarily if it was judged to yield reliable predictions.

The reason for the paradoxical air of Popper's methodological appraisals is that for all philosophers before him there had been one single conception of acceptability: acceptability$_3$. But for Popper acceptability meant primarily acceptability$_1$ and/or acceptability$_2$.

One example of this confusion is the widespread argument purporting to show that Popper's scientific method rests on inductive considerations concerning acceptability$_3$. The argument proceeds as follows:

(1) Let a theory T be falsified in 1967. Nobody would regard its falsification as a sign of good future prospects for a theory, as a sort of infantile disease which even the healthiest hypotheses could be depended upon to catch, but which then rendered them immune to future attack. Hence, we reject the 'counterinductive policy' of replacing a theory T_1, refuted in 1967, by a modified version T_2 of it which restricts its validity to the period after 1967.

(2) But the *only* possible rationale for rejecting such a 'counterinductive policy' is the tacit inductive principle that theories refuted in the past will continue to be refuted in future, that is, that T_2 is untrustworthy, that it is not *acceptable$_3$*.

(3) Since Popper too would reject T_2, he *must* hold this inductive principle: he must regard T_2 as *not acceptable$_3$*. But then his methodology rests on an inductive principle, contrary to his claims. Q.E.D.' [1]

But (2) is false; and so is the concluding part of (3). Popper does not bar T_2 because it is unacceptable$_3$, but because it has no excess empirical content over T_1: because it is unacceptable$_1$. In formulating Popper's methodology there is no need to refer to acceptability$_3$.

(a) *'Total corroboration' as a measure of 'acceptability$_3$' of theories.* It seems obvious to me that the *basis* for a definition (or 'expli-

---

[1] Cp. Ayer: *The Problem of Knowledge*, 1956, pp. 73–4. Also cp. J. O. Wisdom: *Foundations of Inference in Natural Science*, 1952, p. 225.

Please note my continuation order for the following series:

☐ **North-Holland Series in Applied Mathematics and Mechanics, from vol.** ....
onwards.

☐ **Studies in Logic, from month:** .... **year:** .... **onwards**

Please send prospectuses in the following fields:

Name (*block letters please*): ....

☐	Applied Mathematics
☐	Pure Mathematics
☐	Logic
☐	Statistics
☐	Information Processing
	Non Linear Programming
	Operation Research
☐	Computer Science
☐	....

Full Address:

Please mention your institute or organisation and position held.

P. 25M.168M

cation', as Carnap would put it) of the intuitive idea of acceptability$_3$ should be Popper's 'verisimilitude': the difference between the truth-content and falsity-content of a theory. [1] For surely a theory is the more acceptable$_3$, the nearer it is to the truth, that is, the greater its verisimilitude.

Verisimilitude is Popper's reconstruction of non-probabilistic 'probability' [2]: but while Carnap claims to be able to calculate *his* probability infallibly, Popperian 'probability' – verisimilitude – cannot be infallibly known, for in Popper's philosophy there is no way of discovering with certainty the truth-values of propositions.

But which are the most 'verisimilar' theories? I think that these can (tentatively) be constructed in the following way: we take the extant 'body of science' and replace each refuted theory in it by a weaker unrefuted version. Thus we increase the putative verisimilitude of each theory, and turn the inconsistent body of scientific theories (accepted$_1$ and accepted$_2$) into a consistent body of accepted$_3$ theories, which we may call, since they can be recommended for use in technology, the 'body of technological theories' [3]. Of course, some accepted$_3$ theories will not be acceptable$_1$ or acceptable$_2$ since we arrived at them by content-reducing stratagems; but here we do not aim at scientific growth but at reliability.

This simple model is a rational reconstruction of the actual practice of choosing the most reliable theory. Technological choice follows scientific choice: acceptable$_3$ theories are modified versions of acceptable$_1$ and acceptable$_2$ theories: the way to the acceptable$_3$ theories leads through acceptable$_1$ and acceptable$_2$ theories. *For the appraisal of trustworthiness the methodological appraisals are indispensable.*

---

[1] *Conjectures and Refutations*, 1963, Ch. 10, esp. pp. 233–4; also cp. Watkins: 'Hume, Carnap and Popper', *this volume*, pp. 271 ff.

[2] *Conjectures and Refutations*, 1963, esp. pp. 236–7 and second edition, 1965, pp. 399–401.

[3] If we have two rival, inconsistent theories in the body of science such that neither of them has superseded the other, then their 'trimmed', 'technological' versions may still be inconsistent. In such cases we may either cautiously choose the maximal consistent subset of the propositions of the two theories, or daringly choose the theory with the more empirical content.

We may try to assess acceptability$_3$ also in terms of 'degree of corroboration'. Severity and corroboration (or rather 'excess corroboration') as we defined them, are binary relations between the tested theory T and some touchstone theory T' (or possibly even ternary relations between T, T' and some test-evidence e). Because of this, corroboration turned out to have 'historical character'. But it may seem that the verisimilitude of a theory in the light of evidence must be independent of its prehistory. Indeed, it is a deeply entrenched dogma of the logic of justification that evidential support depends only on the theory and the evidence and certainly not on the growth that they represent in relation to former knowledge [1]. As Keynes put it: 'The peculiar virtue of prediction . . . is altogether imaginary . . . the question as to whether a particular hypothesis happens to be propounded before or after [the] examination of [its instances] is quite irrelevant' [2]. Or, as a recent critic of Popper put it: '[To enquiries concerning evidential support] it is quite irrelevant whether in fact scientists always or usually or never make their observations before conceiving their theories or *vice versa*' [3]. However, the dogma of independence of evidential support from prehistory is false. It is false because the problem of the *weight of evidence* cannot be solved without historico-methodological criteria for 'collecting' theories and evidence [4]. Both the truth-content and the falsity-content of any theory contains infinitely many propositions. How can we minimise the bias of the sample? Most of those people who were aware of this problem suggested the *tabula rasa* solution: evidence must be collected without theoretical bias. The final destruction of this solution was achieved by Popper. *His* solution was that only evidence which was the result of severe tests, 'test-evidence',

---

[1]   There have been notable exceptions, e.g. Whewell: see Agassi's 'The role of corroboration in Popper's methodology', *loc. cit.*, pp. 84 and 87. Popper's requirement for 'independent testability' has a long – and interesting – prehistory.

[2]   *A Treatise on Probability*, 1921, p. 305.

[3]   Cp. Stove's review of Popper's 'Logic of Scientific Discovery', *Australasian Journal of Philosophy*, **38**, 1960, p. 179.

[4]   Also cp. *above*, p. 345.

should count: the only admissible positive evidence for a theory are the corpses of its rivals. Evidential support *is* a historico-methodological concept.

But here one has to be careful. Evidential support for a theory obviously depends not just on the *number* of the corpses of its rivals. It also depends on the *strength* of the killed. That is, evidential support is, as it were, a hereditary concept: it depends on the total number of rival theories killed by the killed rivals. Their set, *in toto*, determines the *'total corroboration'* of a theory [1]. In the assessment of the reliability of a theory *all* the corpses on the long road leading from the most naive expectations to the theory should be taken into consideration [2]. (The conflation of excess corroboration (the tentative estimate of growth) and total corroboration (the tentative estimate of reliability) is a confusing element in Popper's – and Agassi's – presentation [3].)

This argument shows that Popper's 'best-corroborated' theories (in the 'total' sense) almost exactly coincide with our accepted$_3$ theories.

But whichever criterion of acceptability$_3$ we choose, it will have *two very serious shortcomings*. The first is that *it gives us very limited guidance*. While it offers us a body of 'most reliable' theories we cannot compare with its help the reliability of any two theories among these 'most reliable' ones. One cannot compare Popper's (total) 'degrees of corroboration' for two unrefuted theories which have stood up to severe tests. All that we can know is that the theories in our latest body of accepted$_3$ theories have higher degrees of corroboration than their 'predecessors' in any past, discarded body of accepted$_3$ theories. A theory T_2 that supersedes T_1, inherits

---

[1] *Throughout the rest of the paper, 'corroboration' stands for 'total corroboration'; 'best-corroborated' stands for 'with maximal total corroboration'.*

[2] We may, alternatively, articulate a 'most naive expectation' as touchstone theory and assess the severity of tests relative to that reconstructed theory. If the theory under test is a statistical theory, we may use some prior Laplacean distribution as a touchstone theory. But this approach may lead to misleading results. (Cp. *below*, pp. 415 ff.)

[3] It is, incidentally, connected with Popper's failure to distinguish sharply between the merits of excess content and content, discussed *above*, pp. 377 ff.

from T_1, the set of theories which T_1 had defeated: the corroboration of T_2 will clearly be higher than the corroboration of T_1. But the corroborations of two theories T_1 and T_2 can only be compared when the set of defeated theories in T_1's past is a subset of the set of defeated theories in T_2's past: that is, when T_1 and T_2 represent different stages of the same research programme. This circumstance reduces drastically the practical, technological use of corroboration as an estimate of reliability for competing technological designs. For each such design may be based on some theory which, in its own field, is the most advanced; therefore each such theory belongs, in its own right, to the 'body of technologically recommendable theories', of theories accepted$_3$; and therefore their degrees of corroboration will not be comparable. There is not, and cannot be, any *metric* of 'degree of corroboration' – indeed the expression 'degree of corroboration', in so far as it suggests the existence of such a metric, is misleading [1].

But where corroborations of two theories are incomparable, so are their reliabilities. This is entirely plausible. We can only judge the reliability of eliminated theories from the vantage point of our present theories. For instance, we can give a detailed estimate of the reliability, or verisimilitude, of Newton's theory from the point of view of Einstein's theory: we may issue the warning that it is particularly unreliable for high velocities, etc. Even so, the estimate will be fallible, since Einstein's theory is fallible. But we cannot give even a fallible absolute estimate of Einstein's theory itself before it, in turn, is superseded by another theory. *Thus we cannot grade our best available theories for reliability even tentatively, for they are our ultimate standards of the moment.* Only God could give us a correct, detailed estimate of the absolute reliability of *all* theories by checking them against *his* blueprint of the universe. Inductive logicians, of course, do offer such an estimate: but their estimate depends upon an *a priori* superscientific inductive knowledge [2].

---

[1] For a criticism of Popper's metric for degree of corroboration of statistical theories see *below*, pp. **413** ff.

[2] Cp. *below*, p. **400**.

The *second serious shortcoming* of our criterion of reliability is that it is unreliable. Even where comparisons are possible, one can easily conceive of conditions which would make the estimate of verisimilitude by corroboration false. The successive scientific theories may be such that each increase of truth-content could be coupled with an even larger increase in hidden falsity-content, so that the growth of science would be characterised by increasing corroboration and decreasing verisimilitude. Let us imagine that we hit on a true theory T_1 (or on one with very high verisimilitude); in spite of this we manage to 'refute' it with the help of a corroborated falsifying hypothesis f [1], replace it by a bold new theory T_2 which again gets corroborated, etc., etc. Here we would be following, unknowingly, the twists and turns of a disastrous problem-shift, moving even further from the truth – while assuming that we are soaring victoriously towards it. Each theory in such a chain has higher corroboration and lower verisimilitude than its successor: such is the result of having 'killed' a true theory.

Alternatively, let us imagine that in 1800 somebody proposed a stochastic law that in natural processes entropy decreases. This was corroborated by a few interesting facts. Then somebody else discovered that the facts were only due to fluctuations, each with zero probability, and set up the second law of thermodynamics. But what if the decrease of entropy is indeed a natural law, and

---

[1] If a theory is refuted, it is not necessarily false. If God refutes a theory, it is 'truly refuted'; if a man refutes a theory, it is not necessarily 'truly refuted'. Ordinary language does not distinguish sufficiently between truth and alleged truth, between methodological concepts and their metaphysical counterparts. The time is ripe for purifying it of such sacrilegious usages.
Corroborated falsifying hypotheses (or 'falsifying facts') are widely believed to be particularly hard facts; nevertheless they too are frequent casualties of scientific growth. However, it so happens that even if a corroborated falsifying hypothesis of T is refuted, it always has enough strength left to keep T refuted. If not for this incomprehensible feature of the growth of knowledge, Popper could not have ruled that falsification is (methodologically) 'final', that 'a corroborative appraisal made at a later date . . . can replace a positive degree of corroboration by a negative one, but not *vice versa*' (*The Logic of Scientific Discovery*, 1934, § 82).

only our small space-time corner of the universe is characterised by such a major, very unlikely fluctuation [1]? The most rigorous observance of Popperian method may lead us away from truth, accepting false and refuting true laws.

Thus the estimates of reliability or verisimilitude by Popper's 'degree of corroboration' may be false – and therefore, of course, they are unprovable. Certainly, *if science, as it progresses, approximated to truth* (in the sense that its verisimilitude increased with increasing corroboration) *then our estimates would be correct.* The question immediately arises, is *this* assumption the inductive principle on which our philosophy of technology hinges? But in my view, whether or not a proposition is an 'inductive principle' depends not only on the proposition in itself, but also on its epistemic status and function: the truth of an inductive principle must be established *a priori*, because its function is to be the premiss in a *proof* or justification. It is certainly interesting to ask what metaphysical conditions would make our estimates of verisimilitude correct. But the metaphysical statements (*not inductive principles*) specifying these conditions will not *prove* the thesis that the ordering generated by degree of corroboration necessarily equals the ordering generated by degree of verisimilitude: they will rather call attention to the possibility that they might not be satisfied and thereby *undermine* its universal validity. *There is nothing wrong with fallible speculative metaphysics, but only with interpreting some such metaphysical statements as infallible inductive principles* [2].

For instance, there is nothing wrong with speculating about the conditions for a body – and in particular, a growing body – of scientific (or technological) theories to come into existence – and stay in existence (one of the many possible conditions would be that there be natural laws), or about the conditions necessary for

---

[1]   This again may seem to many people very unlikely. Boltzmann actually thought it likely, as it transpires from his *Lectures on Gas Theory*, § 90. (I owe this reference to Popper.)

[2]   It should be stressed that in my usage 'inductive principle' is not restricted to principles which imply a *probabilistic* confirmation function, but is any principle claimed to be *a priori* true which implies a confirmation function – whether the latter is probabilistic or not.

our survival while acting upon our best theories. One possibility is that *our best-corroborated theories happen to have relatively large verisimilitude in the set of those of their consequences which are related to the small spatio-temporal corner of the universe which is our 'home', and their verisimilitude grows with the advancement of science.* This simple but crucial metaphysical assumption would explain mankind's technological success, but it may be false. But since it is irrefutable, we can never discover that it *is* false, if it is: the biggest disasters cannot disprove it (just as the biggest successes cannot prove it). We may 'accept$_0$' this assumption into our body of 'influential' metaphysical theories [1] *without believing it*, just as we keep accepting$_1$ and accepting$_2$ false and even mutually inconsistent theories into our body of science.

These considerations show that even technology can do, or *rather, must do* without 'inductive principles' although it may 'rely' on some (technologically) influential metaphysics.

But there is an immense difference between the ordinary (classical) and probabilistic (neoclassical) conceptions of reliability on the one hand, and our Popperian conception of 'reliability' on the other.

The *classical conception* regards a theory as reliable if it is true, unreliable if it is false. Rationality is acting on true theories; and rational action is unfailingly rewarded by success. The ultra-dogmatist wing of classical empiricism maintains that it can recognise – like God – the truth or falsehood of theories; the ultra-sceptical wing that knowledge, and therefore, rational action, is impossible.

The *neoclassical conception* regards a theory as reliable to a certain degree – in Carnap's 1950 view according to its 'qualified instance confirmation'. To each theory, at any time, there belongs a number between 0 and 1, indicating, with the certainty of logic, its reliability. Thus *reliability has a precise and absolutely reliable proven metric.* The most reliable theory may, however, let one down: the cleavage between rational action and success is larger than in the classical conception. *But we can still know what risk we take*

---

[1] For the idea of (scientifically) 'influential metaphysics' cp. Watkins' important paper: 'Influential and confirmable metaphysics', *Mind*, N.S., **67**, 1958.

and foresee the possible sorts of disaster, together with their respective probabilities. Each proposition has a precise quantitative measure of reliability. In Carnap's approach the super-scientific inductive knowledge needed to determine this metric stems from his (hidden and, indeed, disavowed) claim that he knows the probability distribution of the possible worlds before the blindfolded Creator selected one and turned it into the real world [1].

The *Popperian conception* of 'reliability', as explained here, differs in being a conception of reliability, which, in turn, is itself unreliable. In it we distinguish between *'true reliability'* – unknown to us – and *'estimated reliability'*. This is a direct consequence of the lack of inductive principles in this approach.

It is also evident that in this Popperian approach reliability has nothing to do with 'rational belief': why should it be 'rational' to believe that the universe satisfies all those conditions which would make corroboration a correct estimate of verisimilitude?

The Popperian approach offers no metric, no absolute degrees of reliability, but, at best, a very weak (and, of course, in addition, unreliable) partial ordering among theories. The monadic predicate 'reliable' is replaced by the binary predicate: 'more reliable than'.

Moreover, not only may the most reliable theory let one down, but the theory of reliability is itself unreliable. *We cannot know what risk we are taking and we cannot foresee the possible shapes of disasters and still less their precise probability.* According to Carnap, for instance, even if you rationally predict that you will pull out a blue ball from an urn, you must be prepared (to a well-definable degree) to pull out a white or a red one (according to his metaphysical theory of possible universes, as reflected in his

---

[1] Incidentally, Carnap's programme has at least one superficial similarity to Hilbert's: both gave up intrinsic certainty for propositions in the object-language, but both wanted to re-establish it for propositions in the metalanguage. For Hilbert indubitable metamathematics was to establish – by a feedback-effect, as it were – at least the consistency of mathematics. For Carnap indubitable metascience (inductive logic) was to establish at least the reliability metric of science. (Also cp. my 'Infinite Regress and the Foundations of Mathematics', *Aristotelian Society Supplementary Volume*, **36**, 1962, pp. 156–184.)

language). But for Popper the possible variety of the universe is unlimited: you may equally well pull out a rabbit, or your hand may be caught in the urn, or the urn may explode, or, rather, you may pull out something dramatically unexpected that you cannot possibly understand or even describe. Urn games are poor models of science.

The cleavage between rationality and 'success' is then much wider in the Popperian approach than it was in the previous approaches: so much so that Popperian 'reliability' should always be in quotes.

(b) *Popper's opposition to 'acceptability₃'*. Popper has never cared to devote much attention to the problem of acceptability$_3$. He regards the problem as 'comparatively unimportant' [1]. Indeed, he was right: what one can say about it is not very much. But his casual remarks about the subject are confusing.

On the one hand he stresses time and again that 'the best we can say of a hypothesis is that *up to now* it has been able to show its worth' [2]; one cannot infer from 'degree of corroboration' to trustworthiness. Anyone, then, who interprets his 'degree of corroboration' as having anything to do with degree of corroboration as generally understood, misinterprets him. As Watkins put it: 'A Popperian corroboration-appraisal *is* analytic and does *not* have predictive implications' [3]. Popper's theory of corroboration then maintains a stony silence about the future prospects of the theory. But if all yet unchecked states of affairs were, say, equally possible, the degree of rationality of belief in any yet unchecked particular proposition, would be zero. Indeed, sometimes one wonders, whether Popper and Watkins would regard *any* consideration of acceptability$_3$ as a criminal act of 'induction'.

Salmon rightly points out that if Popper's appraisal of scientific

---

[1] 'On rules of detachment and so-called inductive logic', *this volume*, p. 139.

[2] The quotation is from a note published in *Erkenntnis* 1935 and reprinted in *The Logic of Scientific Discovery*, 1959, p. 315. The italics are mine.

[3] 'Non-inductive corroboration', *this volume*, p. 63.

theories is analytic, then Popper cannot explain how science can be a guide of life [1]. If degree of corroboration does not serve as an estimate, however fallible, of verisimilitude, then Popper cannot explain the rationality of our practical actions, cannot have any practical philosophy and especially, any philosophy of technology which is *based on science*.

One reaction of Popper and some of his colleagues adds up to a curious doctrine that practical rationality is independent of scientific rationality. Popper stresses that for practical purposes 'false theories often serve well enough: most formulae used in engineering or navigation are known to be false' [2]. As Watkins put it: 'Our method of hypothesis-selection in practical life should be well-suited to our practical aims, just as our methods of hypothesis-selection in theoretical science should be well-suited to our theoretical aims; and the two kinds of method may very well yield different answers . . .' [3]. Moreover, Watkins claims that a theory 'may very well be both *better* corroborated by past tests and *less* likely to survive future tests' [4]. So reliability may even be inversely proportional to corroboration! Down with applied science?

On the other hand, we also find strong hints that, even for Popperians, science *is* a guide of life. For instance, Popper writes: 'Admittedly it is perfectly reasonable to believe that . . . well-tested laws will continue to hold (since we have no better assumption to act upon), but it is also reasonable to believe that such a course of action will lead us at times into severe trouble' [5]. Moreover, he even seems to hint that degree of corroboration might be a reasonable estimate of verisimilitude [6]. And I have already mentioned his one statement that 'degree of corroboration' can be interpreted as 'degree of rationality of belief' [7].

---

[1]   Cp. his *Reply, this volume*, pp. 95–7.

[2]   *Conjectures and Refutations*, 1963, p. 57.

[3]   'Non-inductive corroboration', *this volume*, p. 65.

[4]   *Ibid.*, p. 63.

[5]   *Conjectures and Refutations*, 1963, p. 56. Also cp. Watkins' concluding statement, in similar vein, of his 'Non-inductive corroboration', *this volume*, p. 66.

[6]   *Ibid.*, p. 235.

[7]   Cp. *The Logic of Scientific Discovery*, 1959, pp. 414–5 and 418.

Now where does Popper stand? Is *any* sort of 'acceptability₃' an 'inductivist concept' or not? Unfortunately Popper does not define (contemporary) *'inductivism'* with sufficient clarity. As far as I can see he interprets it as a combination of *three doctrines*.

The first doctrine of inductivism is *the doctrine of inductive method*: it postulates the primacy of 'facts' in the logic of discovery. The second doctrine of (contemporary 'neoclassical') inductivism is *the doctrine of the possibility of inductive logic*: it postulates that it is possible to assign – with the certainty of logic – to any pair of propositions a 'degree of confirmation', which characterises the evidential support that the second proposition lends to the first. The third doctrine is that *this 'confirmation function' obeys the probability calculus* [1].

Popper rejects inductive method and replaces it by his theory-dominated logic of discovery. He rejects the possibility of inductive logic, for it would have to rest on some synthetic *a priori* principle. Finally he proves that the statement that the confirmation function is probabilistic is not only unprovable but false [2].

On this interpretation of Popper's position, a theory of acceptability₃ would only be inductivist if it claimed to be *a priori* true and/or if it was probabilistic; and there would be nothing wrong with a conjectural, non-probabilistic estimate of acceptability₃ of theories or with the non-inductive metaphysical speculations which may underly such an estimate. But Popper's insistence, that his degree of corroboration – unlike Reichenbach's or Carnap's degree of confirmation – is analytic and must not be interpreted as being synthetic [3], amounts to an opposition to *any* acceptability₃. This

---

[1]   One may ask: was the three-headed inductivist dragon empiricist or rationalist? The high methodological regard for facts in the first head would suggest an empiricist; the synthetic *a priori* inductive principles in the second head suggest a rationalist. But in the light of Popper's philosophy one can explain the previously paradoxical fact that extreme apriorists are frequently extreme empiricists and *vice versa* (e.g. Descartes, Russell, Carnap): most kinds of empiricism and rationalism are only different variants (or components) of justificationism.

[2]   These three points are summed up already in the first section of his *Logic of Scientific Discovery*, 1934.

[3]   *Ibid.*, § 82.

implies a sharp separation of scientific and practical rationality, which, indeed, both Popper and Watkins seem to advocate. Such a separation may indeed be 'fishy and hypocritical' [1], and leads to misinterpretations of what actually happens in technology [2].

An escalation of the anti-inductivist crusade which makes a target of *any* concept of acceptability₃ can only vitiate its effectiveness. It should be explicitly abandoned, and it should be admitted that science is at least *a* guide of life [3].

(The disarray of Carnap's camp is, in this respect, much worse. Carnap's apriorist metaphysics is hidden under a cloak of analyticity [4]. Carnapians have either to stick bravely to the 'analyticity' of their inductive logic, but then their probability cannot be a guide of life, as Salmon and Kneale keep reminding them [5]; or they can decide that inductive logic *is* a guide of life, but then admit that their inductive logic is an elaborate system of speculative metaphysics [6]).

This concludes the discussion of our three appraisals of theories. The first two appraise the growth achieved by a theory relative to some touchstone theory. Given the two theories, the first appraisal, based on excess empirical content, is a matter of logic, and can

---

[1]   Cp. Watkins: 'Non-inductive corroboration', *this volume*, p. 65.

[2]   In most cases where Popper and Watkins allege that false theories are applied, one can show that the best-corroborated theories are in fact applied. Their argument looks plausible only because in those special examples there happens to be no difference between *applying* the best and the superseded next best theory.

[3]   One has to remember that since it is impossible to compare the degrees of corroboration of our most advanced theories, in many technological decisions pure epistemic considerations play very little part. The fact that theories frequently cannot be compared for reliability makes practical rationality *more independent* of scientific rationality than over-optimistic inductive logic suggests.

[4]   Cp. *above*, pp. 361 and 368.

[5]   Cp. Salmon: 'The justification of inductive rules of inference', *this volume*, especially pp. 40 ff.; and Kneale: 'Confirmation and rationality', *this volume*, pp. 59–61.

[6]   Bar–Hillel, in his 'Inductive logic as "the" guide of life' (*this volume*, pp. 66 ff.) does not, I fear, make it clear where he stands.

be said to be tautologous. The second appraisal has two interpretations: interpreted as a 'tautologous' appraisal it states that the new theory *survived* a test which the touchstone theory did not survive: this alone may serve as an appraisal of growth. Interpreted as a synthetic appraisal (with the fallible metaphysical lemma that excess corroboration means excess truth-content), the second appraisal hopefully guesses that the growth is real, that the new theory, at least in the 'field of application' [1] of the test, is nearer to the truth than its touchstone theory.

The third appraisal compares the total evidential support of theories. If we interpret it as a 'tautologous' appraisal, it merely draws up a balance-sheet of the victories and defeats of the research programmes that led to the compared theories. But then it may be misleading to call this an appraisal of 'evidential support', for why should even the greatest past victories give, without any additional metaphysical assumption, any real 'support' to the theory? They only give 'support' to the theory on the tentative metaphysical assumption that increasing corroboration is a sign of increasing verisimilitude. Thus we have two concepts of 'evidential support': one, 'tautologously', appraises the tests the theory, in its prehistory, (or the 'research programme' leading to it) *has survived*; the other, with the help of metaphysical lemmas, synthetically appraises its *fitness to survive* (in the sense that having more verisimilitude, more of it will be able to 'survive') [2].

3.4. *Theoretical support for predictions versus (test)-evidential support for theories* [3].

The practical rule suggested by our considerations is this: *'Act upon the unrefuted theories which are "contained" in the extant body of science, rather than on theories which are not'*.

---

[1] For 'field of application' cp. Popper's *Logic of Scientific Discovery*, 1934, *passim* (see the index of the English edition).

[2] In Popper's view, of course, *survival* does not imply *fitness for survival*. But, misleadingly, he uses the two terms as synonyms throughout his *Logic of Scientific Discovery* (cp. e.g. pp. 108 and 251 of the English edition).

[3] 'Prediction' is here just shorthand for 'particular hypothesis'.

However this rule offers us – limited – guidance only concerning the choice of the most 'reliable' theory. But what about particular predictions? There we opt for the relevant prediction of the chosen theory.

The 'reliability' of particular propositions may then be characterised in two distinct steps: *first* we decide, if we can, which is the most 'reliable' theory among the relevant ones and *secondly* we decide, on the basis of this chosen theory, which is the most 'reliable' prediction for the given practical problem. Thus while theories may be said to be supported by evidence, 'predictions' are supported by theories.

Let us recall Carnap's important distinction between three possible approaches to defining degrees of confirmation or reliability. The first starts by defining the reliability of theories: the reliability of 'predictions' is derivative. This may be called the *'theoretical approach'*. The second proceeds in the opposite direction: it starts by defining the reliability of predictions: the reliability of theories is derivative. We may call it the *'non-theoretical approach'*. The third, finally, defines the reliability both of theories and predictions in one single formula [1]. This is the *'mixed approach'*. Carnap hesitated between the second and the third [2]. I propose the first, the theoretical approach. This has been consistently ignored by inductive logicians: despite the fact that it is generally used in actual practice. Instead of trusting a prediction according to c-values obtained by a complicated atheoretical method based on some formal language, the engineer will, as a matter of fact, prefer the predictions of the most advanced theory of the day [3].

---

[1] Cp. *above*, p. 337. Carnap, of course, did not then foresee a fourth possibility: where one defines reliability *exclusively* for predictions.

[2] Carnap's 'qualified instance confirmation of theories' belongs to the second approach. But qualified instance confirmation can be defined only for theories of very simple logical form. So Carnap's second approach could not be carried out.

[3] Thus, I think, Carnap is wrong in emphasizing that 'inductive logic does not propose *new* ways of thinking, but merely to explicate *old* ways. It tries to make explicit certain forms of reasoning which implicitly or instinctively have always been applied both in everyday life and science'. ('Inductive logic and science', *Proceedings of the American Academy of Arts*

If the chosen theory is statistical, one can calculate the 'degree of reliability', or 'rational betting quotient' of any particular hypothesis within its range with the help of probability theory: our rational bet on h will be $p(h, T)$, p being logical probability, h being the prediction, and T being the chosen theory, usually of the form $P(h, s) = q$ (h denoting the predicted event, s the stochastic setup, P physical probability) [1].

If the chosen theory is deterministic, one may bet all-or-nothing on the event predicted by the theory – with some reasonable safety margin.

This way of determining rational betting quotients, of course, is not open when there is no scientific theory at our disposal. In such cases one may use Carnap's Bayesian approach; but because of the arbitrariness in the choice of language, the arbitrariness of the prior distribution, and the dubious weight of the sparse accidental evidence, it will only yield an exact but irrational ritual. In cases where scientific theories are at hand, the theoretical approach yields intuitively rational betting quotients where Carnap's non-theoretical approach does not: this can be easily seen if one checks, one by one, our counterarguments to Carnap's values for rational betting quotients in **2.3**.

Of course, my 'theoretical betting quotients' are relative to the theory on which they are based. The *absolute* rational betting quotient on any proposition, whether universal or particular, is zero [2]. 'Theoretical betting quotients' are 'rational' but fallible: they depend on – and fall with – our extant theories. (One may, of course, calculate rational betting quotients for theories and for

---

and Sciences, **80**, 1953, p. 189). But already with his 'non-theoretical approach' Carnap has departed from the reasonings which 'have always been applied . . . in science'. (Of course, there has been no form of reasoning from which somebody at some time has not deviated.)

[1]   In 'closed games' (cp. *above*, p. 373) T is fixed as a 'rule' of the game.

[2]   It should be mentioned here that *all* empirical propositions are universal because of the universal names inevitably recurring in them (cp. Popper: *The Logic of Scientific Discovery*, 1934, § 13, and *Conjectures and Refutations*, 1963, p. 277). Only within the context of a given theory can one distinguish universal and particular propositions.

predictions given a language; but these betting quotients will depend on – and fall with – the language [1]. Moreover, one would need a theory of support – evidential or theoretical – for languages[2]).

Appendix. *On Popper's three notes on degree of corroboration.*

One of the main points of what I called the Popperian approach was that precise, numerical estimates of degrees of 'reliability' are so unreliable as to make any such estimates utopian; moreover, even non-numerical formal expressions are misleading if they suggest that they may lead to *general* comparisons of any real value.

Some students of Popper's work on his 'degree of corroboration', published between 1954 and 1959, may, however, wonder whether Popper himself is, on these terms, a 'Popperian'. Does he not offer *formulae* for his degree of corroboration? Does he not propose a precise, even infallible, *logical metric* in the important case of statistical theories? In view of these results inductive logicians do not know whether to count Popper as one who competes with them in devising *a priori* metrics, or as one who would be against *any* such formulae. Many Carnapians regard Popper's formulae merely as new additions to the fast-growing literature on inductive logic. For instance, Kyburg, in his survey, 'Recent Work in Inductive Logic', lists Popper's formulae along with Carnap's, Kemeny's, and others' in a table and argues that the table 'shows the [large] extent to which the intuitions of these writers coincide' [3]. In one passage he lists Popper as one of the inductive logicians: 'Neither Barker, Popper, Jeffreys, nor any other inductive logician . . .' [4]. In another passage however he states: 'There are writers (Popper, for example) for whom there is no such thing as inductive logic' [5].

---

[1]   For the 'fall' of a language cp. *above*, p. 364, footnote 1.
[2]   Cp. *above*, p. 365.
[3]   *American Philosophical Quarterly*, 1, 1964, p. 258.
[4]   *Ibid.*, p. 269.
[5]   *Ibid.*, p. 249.

In order to clarify this problem, let me first outline Popper's aims in devising his formula for degree of corroboration.

Popper's main aim was to establish with a formal and conclusive argument that even *if* he grants that there can be a quantitative confirmation function defined over all propositions of a language, even *if* he grants that such a function can be expressed in terms of logical probability, then it cannot possibly be probabilistic, that is, it cannot obey the calculus of probability. It was a conversation with Janina Hosiasson in Prague in 1934 (when his book was already in print) which convinced him that such an argument was important [1]. This was the origin of Popper's intermittent work, in the late thirties, on the axiomatisation of probability theory [2].

Popper, in his first note [3], puts this argument in three stages: (*a*) he proposes ten adequacy requirements, or *desiderata*, each one supported by strong arguments, (*b*) he shows that they are consistent by displaying a formula which is expressed in terms of, but not identical with, logical probability and which does satisfy them, and (*c*) he shows that $p(h, e)$ does not satisfy some of them (or even some of Carnap's own *desiderata*). As to (*b*), since Popper has claimed that Carnap's own adequacy requirements were inconsistent, and since he attributed great importance to this inconsistency, he was obliged to produce a formula if for no other purpose than to show that his own *desiderata* were consistent.

But Popper's note makes it clear that *his desiderata are not comprehensive*: 'some intuitive *desiderata* . . . cannot be satisfied by any formal definition . . . one cannot completely formalize the idea of a sincere and ingenious attempt [at refutation].' [4] Inci-

---

[1] *The Logic of Scientific Discovery*, 1934, p. 263, footnote 1.

[2] Kolmogorov's axiomatic system was unsuitable for his purpose: he needed a probability theory based on relative probabilities in order to be able to define $p(x, y)$ even if $p(y) = 0$: this enabled him to cope with universal propositions as second arguments (cp. *The Logic of Scientific Discovery*, 1959, appendix *iv).

[3] 'Degree of Confirmation', *The British Journal for the Philosophy of Science*, 5, 1954–5; reprinted in *The Logic of Scientific Discovery*, 1959, pp. 395–402.

[4] *The Logic of Scientific Discovery*, 1959, pp. 401–2.

dentally, he could have added an eleventh requirement: namely
that there should be at least two *theories* with different degrees
of corroborability and that there should be some possible evidence
on which the more corroborable theory could obtain a higher degree
of corroboration than the less corroborable one. This, of course,
is a vital *desideratum* in the spirit of Popper's philosophy. But if
he measures corroborability by logical improbability the *measure*
of corroborability of *any* universal proposition must be 1, and then
differences in corroborability of theories are not reflected in *differences*
in the measures of corroborability, and, in this sense, this extra
desideratum is not satisfied by his numerical formula. Because of
this, his formula satisfies some of his most important *desiderata*
only trivially for genuine theories, because the 'degree of corroboration' of genuine theories degenerates into their 'explanatory
power' [1]. *This fact does not diminish the value of the formula as*
evidence for consistency, but destroys its value for providing an actual
numerical metric.

---

[1]   Popper's formula for degree of corroboration is

$$C(h, e) = \frac{p(e, h) - p(e)}{p(e, h) + p(e)} (1 + p(h) \, p(h, e)).$$

But if h is universal, $p(h)p(h, e) = 0$, and

$$C(h, e) = \frac{p(e, h) - p(e)}{p(e, h) + p(e)},$$

which he interprets as 'explanatory power': $E(h, e)$.
   As Popper himself points out,

$$\frac{p(e, h) - p(e)}{p(e, h) + p(e)}$$

has 'defects' as degree of corroboration: it 'satisfies the most important of
our *desiderata* but not all'. (*Ibid.*, p. 400).
   Of course, if we do not interpret p as 'ordinary' logical probability but
as a non-numerical function expressing what Popper calls the 'fine structure
of probability', then $p(h)p(h, e)$ need not disappear. Indeed, our 'eleventh
requirement' may be used to show that one cannot define degree of confirmation in terms of logical probability with real numbers as values. (For
the 'fine-structure of probability' see Popper: *The Logic of Scientific Dis-*
covery, 1959, pp. 375-7.)

But Popper, in 1954, did not intend to use his formula for constructing a metric for corroboration. There is not the slightest indication in his first note that Popper might have changed his 1934 position, according to which 'the degree of corroboration of two statements may not be comparable in all cases' and 'we cannot define a numerically calculable degree of corroboration' [1]. Moreover, three years later, in 1957, in his second note [2], he warns that *'there cannot be a satisfactory metric of p; that is to say, there cannot be a metric of logical probability which is based on purely logical considerations'* [3].

Thus, throughout his first two notes on degree of corroboration, Popper regarded his formulae only in a polemical context, as mock-rival formulae, as it were, to combat inductive logic.

However, his third note, published in 1958, represents an interesting change [4]. In this note Popper *did* elaborate a metric for degrees of corroboration of statistical theories given statistically interpreted evidence, a 'logical or absolute metric' [5] based upon purely logical considerations, which he found 'entirely adequate' [6].

This result, of course, was more than Popper had originally planned. It was an unintended side result which seemed to turn his negative, critical, mock-rival programme into a positive rival programme. It seemed to Popper that Carnap would never be able to have degrees of rationality of beliefs 'measured, like degrees of temperature, on a one-dimensional scale' [7]. But he thought that in *his* new positive programme – at least in the special but important case where the theories are statistical theories and the evidence interpreted statistical reports – 'all these difficulties

---

[1] *The Logic of Scientific Discovery*, 1934, § 82.

[2] 'A second note on degree of confirmation', *The British Journal of the Philosophy of Science*, 7, 1956–7; reprinted in *The Logic of Scientific Discovery*, 1959, pp. 402–6.

[3] *The Logic of Scientific Discovery*, 1959, p. 404; Popper's italics.

[4] 'A third note on degree of corroboration or confirmation', *The British Journal for the Philosophy of Science*, 8, 1957–8; reprinted in *The Logic of Scientific Discovery*, 1959, pp. 406–15.

[5] *The Logic of Scientific Discovery*, 1959, p. 417.

[6] *Ibid.*

[7] *Ibid.*, p. 408.

disappear'[1], and *his* method 'allows us to obtain *numerical results* – that is numerical degrees of corroboration – in all cases envisaged either by Laplace or by those modern logicians who introduce artificial language systems, in the vain hope of obtaining in this way an *a priori* metric of their predicates . . .'[2].

This left Popper with something of a problem. As he himself put it in the postscript to his three notes in 1959: 'It might well be asked at the end of all this whether I have not, inadvertently, changed my creed. For it may seem that there is nothing to prevent us from calling $C(h, e)$ "the inductive probability of h, given e" or – if this is felt to be misleading, in view of the fact that C does not obey the laws of the probability calculus – "the degree of the rationality of our belief in h, given e".'[3]

The answer, of course, depends on Popper's interpretation of his degree of corroboration. If he had interpreted it as a tautologous measure of growth and if he had condemned any synthetic interpretation as 'inductivist', then at least he would have given a clear answer. But *Popper seems to regard this an open problem.* In one sentence he says that if a theory has a high degree of corroboration, then 'we tentatively "accept" this theory – but only in the sense that we select it as worthy to be subjected to further criticism, and to the severest tests we can design'[4]. This remark suggests that he has the tautologous interpretation in mind with only methodological implications: high corroboration means high testworthiness but not high trustworthiness. But the next, concluding sentence adds a rider: 'On the positive side, we may be entitled to add that the surviving theory is the best theory – and the best tested theory – of which we know.'[5] But what is the 'best theory' *apart* from being 'best tested'? The one which is most 'trustworthy'? There is no answer[6].

---

[1] *Ibid.*

[2] *Ibid.*, p. 412, footnote *3.

[3] *Ibid.*, p. 418.

[4] *Ibid.*, p. 419.

[5] *Ibid.*

[6] Incidentally, it is exactly in the third note on degree of corroboration and in this postscript to it that Popper agrees that his degree of corrobo-

Of course, even if he had finally decided to interpret his 'degree of corroboration' as an estimate of verisimilitude, he could still maintain that a *fallible* estimate of 'reliability' does not make him an inductivist. But he seems to be undecided and he stresses only the – no doubt, important – difference between the inductivist and Popperian *interpretation* of e in such formulae: in the Popperian interpretation '$C(h, e)$ can be interpreted as degree of corroboration only if *e is a report on the severest tests we have been able to design*' [1]. But this leaves wide open the problem of the philosophical significance of his $C(h, e)$, especially, when it offers a *metric* for statistical h's.

But whether Popper regarded his $C(h, e)$ – in his new, positive non-polemical interpretation – as a measure of evidential support in the 'tautologous' or in the 'synthetic' sense, it seems to conflict with my thesis that 'degrees of corroboration' can be compared *only* where the one theory supersedes the other [2]. Popper's metric seems to assign precise numerical values to *all* statistical hypotheses, given statistically interpreted test-evidence.

The simple solution of the seeming conflict is that Popper's metric measures only one narrow aspect of corroboration of statistical theories.

(1) First, one has only to remember that in Popper's formulae

---

ration may be interpreted as 'a measure of the rationality of our beliefs'. But this statement is certainly a slip; it goes counter to the general spirit of his philosophy, according to which belief, whether inductive or non-inductive, whether irrational or 'rational', has no place in the theory of rationality. *The theory of rationality must be about rational action, not about 'rational belief'*. (There is a similar slip in Watkins' paper 'Hume, Carnap and Popper', where he says that at least some cases in which it would be 'perverse' to believe that the more corroborated theory has less verisimilitude (*this volume*, p. 281). But why is it perverse? Cp. Boltzmann's position, quoted *above*, p. 398, footnote 1.

[1] *Ibid.*, p. 418. Kyburg, in his survey (see *above*, p. 408) missed this point: his claim that Popper's intuition largely coincides with Carnap's or Kemeny's is no less absurd than if somebody alleged that two scientists largely agree on a controversial matter because they produce similar formulae, despite the fact that the symbols in the two formulae, *when interpreted*, have completely different meanings.

[2] Cp. *above*, p. 395.

the measures of corroborability of any genuinely universal theory are the same, and therefore a theory which has much less empirical content than another, may, on this account, still achieve the same numerical degree of corroboration [1]. But then Popper's numerical appraisal of the corroboration of statistical theories pays no 'due regard to the degree of testability of the theory' [2] – and thus it is unsatisfactory. If we do want to pay due regard to the degree of testability of the theory, we may possibly opt for a 'vectorial' appraisal, consisting of Popper's content *and* of his 'degree of corroboration'; but then the linear ordering, let alone the metric, disappears.

(2)   Popper's *metric* fails also on a second, independent ground. To recapitulate, the formula he offers is

$$C(h, e) = \frac{p(e, h) - p(e)}{p(e, h) + p(e)}.$$

This formula, he claims, yields a metric if h is to be a genuinely universal statistical theory of the form $P(a, b) = r$ where P is his propensity (or any sort of objective, physical probability), a ranges over events (outcomes of an experiment), and b denotes the experimental set-up, stochastic mechanism, or 'population'. His e stands for a 'statistically interpreted report of h', or, briefly a 'statistical abstract of h', that is, a statement of the following form: 'In a sample [of a's] which has the size n and which satisfies the condition b (or which is taken at random from the population b), a is satisfied in $n(r + \delta)$ instances' [3]. We must plan the experiment in such a way that it should be possible that the outcome will make $|p(e, h) - p(e)|$ large (this is Popper's requirement of severity).

But I argued earlier that there is no such thing as the *absolute* probability of a hypothesis (other than zero): we may only calculate *relative* probabilities of particular hypotheses given some theory [4].

---

[1]   Cp. *above*, pp. 410 f.

[2]   *The Logic of Scientific Discovery*, 1934, § 82.

[3]   *The Logic of Scientific Discovery*, 1959, p. 410. For the purpose of this discussion I do not question this theory of interpretation of statistical evidence.

[4]   Cp. *above*, p. 407.

If so, the 'absolute probability' of e is zero, and $C(h, e)$ is 1. In Popper's account, however, $p(e) = 2 \, \delta$, not zero [1]. But what Popper calls 'absolute probability of e' is, in fact, the relative probability of e given the theory h^* that all statistical abstracts of h of the same width are equiprobable. Thus Popper's expression 'absolute probability' is misleading: his formula should read:

$$C(h, e) = \frac{p(e, h) - p(e, h^*)}{p(e, h) + p(e, h^*)}.$$

(Similarly, Popper misleadingly calls $1 - 2\delta$ a measure of the content or of the precision of e. For let e be: 'In 1000 random choices from a population b the outcome is a 500 ± 30 times'. Statements like (1) 'the population was b_1 (not b)'; (2) 'The outcome was a_1 (not a)'; (3) 'the choice was not random'; (4) 'in 1000 random choices from b the outcome was a 328 times', are all potential falsifiers of e and their total measure is 1; but if one restricts one's attention to the set of 'strictly statistical potential falsifiers' of the kind (4), as Popper seems to do in *this* note, one may correctly assign to this smaller set the measure $1 - 2\delta$. But then one should call it rather a 'measure of the strictly statistical content' of e).

Popper's formula is, in fact, a special case of the general formula

$$C(h, e, h') = \frac{p(e, h) - p(e, h')}{p(e, h) + p(e, h')},$$

where h' is a touchstone theory and e must be some severe test-evidence of h relative to h', that is, it should be possible for $|p(e, h) - p(e, h')|$ to assume a value near 1. *But I shall argue that this generalized version of Popper's formula is of some interest only if h' is a genuine rival theory with scientific interest, and not merely a Laplacean reconstruction of a state of ignorance.*

Moreover, all that $C(h, e, h')$ can tell us is that h explains e better than h', or *vice versa*. But in order to obtain this much information we do not need this formula, but only need consider $p(e, h)$ and $p(e, h')$: we shall prefer that one of h or h' which has more explanatory power for some given severe test-evidence e. This,

---

[1] *The Logic of Scientific Discovery*, 1959, pp. 410–1, and especially footnote *4 on p. 413.

essentially, is Fisher's likelihood ratio method combined with a Popperian design of experiments. This method is not intended to provide us with an absolute metric for all h's given e, but only to select the best hypothesis from a well-defined class of competing hypotheses [1]. We shall appreciate statistical theories more if they have defeated several *real* rivals of scientific interest: but the cumulative effect of these victories cannot yield a linear ordering of *all* statistical hypotheses, let alone a metric on some absolute scale.

It must be realised that any absolute, universal metric for corroboration hinges on the arbitrary selection of *one* distinguished touchstone theory for h. In Popper's third note an equidistribution over the set of the samples of h seems to play the role of this distinguished touchstone theory; in Kemeny's and Oppenheim's work, for instance, $\bar{h}$ plays a roughly similar role [2].

As soon as we consider different touchstone theories (of genuine scientific interest), the absolute universal metric disappears and is replaced by a mere partial ordering, which establishes a comparative-qualitative appraisal of competing theories. And this is exactly the crucial difference between inductive logic and modern statistical techniques. *The programme of inductive logic or confirmation theory set out to construct a universal logical confirmation function with one absolute metric, which, in turn, is based on one distinguished touchstone theory. This one touchstone theory usually takes the form of a Laplacean proto-distribution over the sentences of a universal formal language. But this atheoretical (or, if you wish, monotheoretical) approach is useless, and the programme of an absolute, universal confirmation function is utopian. Modern statistical techniques try at best to compare the evidential support of scientifically rival theories.* It is unfortunate that Popper, whose 1934 ideas anticipated much of the development of modern statistics, in 1958–9 proposed a universal, absolute logical metric for statistical theories – an idea completely alien to the general spirit of his philosophy.

---

[1] Cp. e.g. Barnard's elucidations in Savage and others: *The Foundations of Statistical Inference*, 1962, pp. 82 and 84.

[2] Cp. their 'Degrees of factual support', *Philosophy of Science*, **19**, 1952, Theorem 18.

Example. Let us calculate the degree of corroboration of the hypothesis *h* that the propensity of the heights of children (of a given age) in Indian families sharply to decrease as the number of children in the family increases, is near to 1.

Let us take as touchstone theory the hypothesis h^* that there is no such correlation and that the heights are probabilistically constant whatever the size of the family. Let us further assume that in fact the height of children is inversely proportional to the size of (Indian) families in all existing cases. Then for any large sample $p(e, h)$ will be near 1 and $p(e, h^*)$ will be near zero: any large sample will then be a severe test of *h* relative to h^*. If we acknowledged h^* as an *absolute* touchstone theory, we would have to say that *h* was very highly corroborated: $C(h, e) \approx 1$.

But suppose that a rival theory h' is proposed according to which the height of the children is – with propensity 1 – directly proportional to the average daily calory consumption. How can we plan a severe test of *h* relative to h'? On our previous *e* we could have $p(e, h) = p(e, h')$. But if so, what was crucial evidence relative to the touchstone theory h^*, becomes irrelevant relative to the touchstone theory h'. We have to take this time as test-evidence a set of events that will make $|p(e', h) - p(e', h')|$ high. Such test-evidence will be provided by a set of well-fed large families, because if *h* is true and h' false, or *vice versa*, $|p(e', h) - p(e', h')|$ may be near 1. To perform this experiment may take a generation, since we shall have to bring up well-fed large Indian families, which, on our original assumption, do not at present exist. But after having performed the experiment we may get $C(h, e', h') \approx -1$, so that *h* is decisively undermined in the light of h' [1].

Our example shows that severity of tests and degree of corroboration of hypotheses depend on the touchstone theory. The same test may be severe relative to one touchstone theory but irrelevant relative to another; the degree of corroboration of a hypothesis may be high when it defeats one touchstone theory and low when it is defeated by another. It also shows that large amounts of extant evidence may be irrelevant in the light of some rival theories; but a small amount of planned severe evidence may be crucial. Finally it shows how hopeless are efforts to produce *absolute* numerical values of degree of corroboration of *h* by *e*.

All this is a commonplace for the Popperian philosopher, a commonplace for the working statistician; but it must sound preposterous for the atheoretical inductive logician.

---

[1] This is how severe test-evidence may resolve 'lack of identifiability' cp. Kendall–Stuart: *The Advanced Theory of Statistics*, vol. 2, 1967, p. 42).